A Legacy Remembered

Other Books by Sophie M. Crane
Coauthored with Paul S. Crane

Tennessee Taproots (1976)

Tennessee's Troubled Roots (1979)

Tennessee Taproots (Second Edition, 1996)

A Legacy
Remembered

A Century of
Medical Missions

Sophie Montgomery Crane

PROVIDENCE HOUSE PUBLISHERS
Franklin, Tennessee

Printed in the United States of America

02   01   00   99   98   1   2   3   4   5

Library of Congress Catalog Card Number: 98-65983

ISBN: 1-57736-091-5

Cover by Bozeman Design

Photo credit: China map, page 23, *Earthen Vessels and Transcendent Power*, G. Thompson Brown. (Orbis Books: Maryknoll, N.Y.), 1997. Used by permission.

PROVIDENCE HOUSE PUBLISHERS
238 Seaboard Lane • Franklin, Tennessee 37067
800-321-5692

TO
Paul Shields Crane, M.D.

Contents

Foreword

The practice of medicine has played an essential role in every major missionary enterprise of the Presbyterian Church in the United States (PCUS). Early pioneers soon discovered that the astonishing results of surgical operations and drugs opened the door of alien cultures to the hearing of the Gospel. For Southern Presbyterians, medical missions became one of its most successful overseas ventures.

It is hard to think of anyone who is better qualified to tell this story than Sophie Montgomery Crane. She was born to PCUS missionary parents in Nanjing, China. The attending physician was from the mission Drum Tower Hospital. She is a member of a remarkable missionary family with one sister who served in the Congo and another sister and brother who served in Taiwan. She had training in medical technology before going with her husband, Dr. Paul S. Crane, to serve in Korea in 1947. Their vision of a first rate teaching hospital resulted in the establishment of the Presbyterian Medical Center in Chonju, known in Korean as the "Jesus Hospital." Here she and her husband served for twenty-two years. In 1985 she accompanied Paul, then Director of Health Ministries for the PCUS Division of International Mission, on a worldwide tour of Presbyterian medical facilities which took them to twenty countries in Africa and Asia and seventeen hospitals. She has written articles on medical missions for American Presbyterians: Journal of Presbyterian History and edited a directory covering 120 years of PCUS missionary personnel. Through her lifelong acquaintance with the missionary medical community and interviews which she conducted in preparation for this book, she has come to know personally many of the fascinating people of whom she writes.

She tells the story of how medical pioneers established hospitals, clinics, leprosy centers, medical schools and public health facilities on three continents. Initial antagonism changed to overwhelming acceptance. But there were never enough doctors. Financial support was always short. Building supplies and equipment had to be transported over the oceans and up the Grand Canal and the Congo River. There were personal tragedies, health breakdowns, cultural barriers, and government interference. The story unfolds against the backdrop of civil disturbances, revolutions, tribal insurrection, the chaotic movements toward national independence, two world wars and the Great Depression. Yet hundreds of thousands of patients were treated, the blind recovered their sight, the lame walked, lepers were cleansed, and poor had the good news preached to them.

On reading the story, one is struck with the variety of the results which were achieved:

- The initiation of a scientific medical practice with its own terminology, textbooks, and techniques.

- The compassionate treatment of poor and destitute patients afflicted with all the ills of humanity.

- The lifting up of the role of women by providing career opportunities in medicine and nursing.

- Pioneering efforts in preventative medicine and public health services beyond the confines of the medical institution.

- The training of national health workers who would take over the enterprise when it was time for the missionary to leave.

- Witness to the Christian faith through Christian doctors, nurses, hospital chaplains and Bible women.

One surprise was the contribution made by missionary physicians to medical research. The account tells of effective research done in schistosomiasis, sleeping sickness, leprosy, kala-azar, intestinal parasites, and kwashiorkor.

The acid test of the medical program was how its administration was transferred from that of the foreign doctors to national health workers. This was done in a variety of ways, through trial and error, and in spite of human tendencies to hold on to authority too long. But it was done. Today, with the exception of China where former mission institutions have been nationalized, all the medical institutions which years ago were founded and nurtured by the missionary doctors continue under church related national boards of control.

The significance of this superbly written and carefully documented text is enhanced by the fact that the story is still continuing. Institutions described in this book are alive and well and continue to perform a vital contribution to the people of that land. The Presbyterian Church continues to appoint medical personnel. Short-term workers with special expertise serve for short periods of time. Local church committees continue to support medical projects in other lands. All those who wish to participate in this ongoing story will profit from reading this inspiring account of how the work began, the contributions made, and the obstacles overcome.

The story is of interest to a far wider readership than simply that of Southern Presbyterians. Here is a case study of how medical missions evolved down through the years, changing and adapting to new circumstances and challenges. Medical institutions led the way in ecumenical cooperation. Institutions which began with the "Presbyterian" label are now broadly related to the larger Christian movement in that land.

But above all else this is the inspiring story of how brilliantly trained physicians and surgeons, nurses, and technicians gave up the opportunity for medical practice in the United States to respond to the needs of the world. They went because "the love of Jesus Christ had left them no choice" (2 Cor. 5:14 NEV).

G. Thompson Brown

Preface

History rarely comes in neat packages. However, a neat package can be found in the hundred-year history of the overseas medical work of the Southern Presbyterian Church—officially, the Presbyterian Church in the United States (PCUS). This story begins in 1881, with the appointment of the first medical doctor, and ends in 1983, when the Southern (PCUS) and Northern (UPUSA) Presbyterian churches, which had been divided since the Civil War, merged to form the Presbyterian Church (U.S.A.). The purpose of this work is to portray one denomination's medical mission effort. The writing of this book was triggered by travel in 1985 to Presbyterian medical missions in ten countries in Asia and ten more in Africa. I accompanied my husband, Paul S. Crane, M.D., on his orientation trip when he was appointed director of overseas health ministries for the Division of International Missions (Atlanta Stream) of the newly united Presbyterian Church (U.S.A.).

Despite my long association with the PCUS and its medical work, I found myself poorly informed about the largely untold story of its overseas medical projects. I came to believe that not only would others find the story an interesting one but that it should be preserved in the denomination's annals. Information about missionary medicine is to be found primarily in biographies and autobiographies of some of its more colorful missionaries. The information in this work is drawn from some of the same sources, but much of it came from oral interviews with over seventy-five persons involved in the PCUS mission medical enterprise. Their stories are fascinating and often profoundly moving.

My perspective is not objective. I was delivered by a PCUS missionary doctor (Allan C. Hutcheson, M.D.) to PCUS missionary parents (James Nelson and Aurie Lancaster Montgomery) in Nanking, China, and I grew up in a remote Chinese city where a nearby mission hospital and its personnel contributed significantly to the physical, mental, and social well-being of a childhood that I remember as happy and secure. My husband also grew up in a PCUS missionary home, in Korea. The two of us spent twenty-two years (1947–69) in PCUS medical work in Korea, where we experienced the satisfactions and frustrations of this specialized form of missionary service.

The first chapter provides a broad introduction to the PCUS overseas medical mission. The balance of the book visits each of the medical projects in nine countries. The remarkable advances in the practice of medicine and the sometimes violent political upheavals in each country make this a particularly eventful century. How the gospel of Jesus Christ was proclaimed through the ministry of healing makes an absorbing story.

Efforts to make this account as complete and accurate as possible were enhanced by input from a host of persons whose names are listed in the Appendix. I am not only indebted to each one but feel an obligation to preserve the record they shared with me. I regret that a number have not lived to see their stories in print. Copies of the interviews are on file in the Department of History of the Presbyterian Church (U.S.A.) in Montreat, North Carolina, where they may serve as a resource in the study of medical missions. Frederick J. Heuser, director of the Department of History of the Presbyterian Church (U.S.A.), has encouraged me in this project. The staff of the Montreat (North Carolina) branch of the department were unfailing in helping me use their rich resources. I am especially grateful to Priscilla Taylor, a professional editor, whose extraordinary skills immeasurably improved the presentation of the material. Cliff Fiedler, a computer genius, shepherded me through the mysteries of modern technology. Finally, Paul Crane, my husband for over half a century, is largely responsible for seeing the work through to completion. His insights, corrections, suggestions, and enthusiastic belief in the value of recording this history have been an incalculable contribution.

A Legacy
Remembered

Prologue

The Presbyterian Church in the United States (PCUS) was a late-comer in the field of Protestant overseas missions, which is generally recognized as having begun in 1793 when William Carey, of the newly organized Baptist Missionary Society, set sail from England for India.[1] Formed in 1861 at the outbreak of the Civil War this new church (commonly known as the Southern Presbyterian Church) proclaimed its commitment to the missionary cause and, in 1867, in a stunning act of faith in the aftermath of war, appointed its first missionary, the Reverend Elias B. Inslee, to China. In 1983 the PCUS united with the United Presbyterian Church to form the Presbyterian Church (USA).

The PCUS was a latecomer to *medical* missions as well. Not until 1881 did the PCUS appoint its first physicians: Robert Baxter Fishburne, M.D., to China, and Rev. J. Walton Graybill, M.D., to Mexico. Dr. Peter Parker, a Presbyterian who began work in Canton in 1834, is recognized as the first American medical missionary in China, and as early as 1872 mission hospitals were operating in eight major Chinese cities. This history tells the story of the medical work of the PCUS from 1881 to 1983.

The PCUS developed major medical missions in nine countries. For more than half of its history the medical work was concentrated in four of them: China (beginning in 1881), Korea (1894), Congo/Zaire (1906), and Mexico (1921). After World War II (1945) the PCUS began medical work in Taiwan, Japan, and Brazil, and in the 1970s, in Haiti and Bangladesh (see Table P-1).[2]

There is no evidence that the PCUS launched its overseas medical program with any "sounding of trumpets." Rather the first physicians

3

Table P-1
PCUS Overseas Medical Program, 1881–1983

Country	Mission Founded	Medical Program Began—Ended	Personnel* Mission	Personnel* Medical
China	1867	1881—1952	343	77
Korea	1892	1894	287	80
Zaire	1889	1906	472	98
Mexico	1874	1921—1972	145	21
Brazil	1869	1883	409	20
Japan	1885	1950	211	8
Taiwan	1949	1953	92	13
Haiti	1973	1973	14	8
Bangladesh	1974	1974	23	13

* Regular service missionaries ("career," "life," "term").

Statistics compiled from records of the Department of History, PC(USA), Montreat, North Carolina and the Division of International Mission, Atlanta, Georgia.

seemed to have gone primarily to provide medical care for the missionary force on the field. In the last decade of the nineteenth century when the PCUS medical program had its real beginning, however, missionary medicine was perceived to be a "powerful tool of evangelism, especially in areas resistant to the preaching of the Gospel."[3] The missionary physician was described as a "wedge," "bait," "magnet," and the "heavy artillery of the missionary army."[4]

Later, medical work came to be "recognized as much more than simply a tool for missions, but as a vital part of the overall mission's ministry. The care for physical ailments became a living demonstration of God's love and concern for hurting people . . . medical service became a necessary expression (of God's love) in a needy world."[5] The training of local people for medical leadership in their own countries was a logical extension of this expression of compassion. Moreover, if the medical work was to be a legitimate part of Christian witness, it was important to practice the highest quality of medicine possible.

A recent evolution in missionary medical practice is a change in emphasis from treating sick people to addressing the root causes of disease through preventive and primary health-care programs. While not abandoning the curative and educational aspects, mission programs developed pilot projects to demonstrate how modern public health measures can improve the health of the population in a developing country.

David E. Van Reken, M.D., in a monograph about medical missions, describes three "phases" of medical missions: the *doing* phase, the *teaching* phase, and the *enabling* phase. When the overseas medical program of the PCUS merged with that of the UPUSA in the reunion of 1983, the emphasis was on the *enabling* aspects of the work.[6]

Medical Professionals

Medical missionaries were Christians who chose overseas medical work as an expression of their commitment to Christ. How this commitment was expressed varied with the individual; some verbally evangelized as they dispensed medical care, while others believed that the act of compassionate, high-quality care was in itself their most effective witness. Common to all was a dedication to the spreading of the gospel of Christ through medicine.

Over the century being discussed here, the PCUS "regular service" mission force totaled 1,965, of which 15 percent (316) were PCUS medical professionals: 120 physicians (12 women), 149 nurses, 10 dentists, 14 medical technologists, 13 administrators, and 10 "others" (nutritionist, pharmacist, physiotherapist, social worker) (see Table P-2).[7]

The designation "regular service" missionary applies to those known as "career," "life," or "term" missionary. Two additional categories were the "short-term" missionary (serving usually for one to three years) and the medical volunteer (serving for a few weeks or months).

In the 1960s, after jet travel had become commonplace, the sending of "short-term" missionaries became popular. The forty-four medical short-termers consisted of twenty-three physicians (five women), eleven nurses, three technicians, and seven "others." Between 1962 and 1983 the Medical Benevolence Foundation (MBF), a fund-raising organization dedicated to supporting PCUS medical projects, implemented a program under which "medical volunteers" made an estimated 3,000 working visits to overseas medical installations.[8]

Table P-2							
PCUS Medical Personnel by Profession (Regular Service)							
Country	MD	RN	DDS	MT	ADM	Other*	Total
China	48	27	2	77			
Korea.	34	36	2	3	4	1	80
Zaire	25	55	6	7	3	2	98
Mexico	6	12	3	21			
Brazil	3	17	20				
Japan	2	4	1	1	8		
Taiwan	2	5	2	1	3	13	
Haiti	3	4	1	8			
Bangladesh	5	5	3	13			
Sub-totals	127	165	10	15	13	8	338

Minus** 8 10 18

Totals** 119 155 10 15 13 8 320

* MD=Physician; RN=Registered Nurse; DDS=Dentist; MT=Medical Technologist; ADM=Hospital Administrator; Other= Physiotherapist, Occupational Therapist, Social Worker.

** Total adjusted; 18 persons (8 MD, 10 RN) served in more than one country.

Statistics compiled from records of the Department of History, PC(USA), Montreat, North Carolina and the Division of International Mission, Atlanta, Georgia.

In 1897 Samuel H. Chester, executive secretary of foreign missions for the PCUS, made these observations about the medical work: "So much depends on the work being done in the best way, that only those should be sent as medical missionaries who have had the best training our schools afford, supplemented by some hospital experience." He added that although facilities must be adequate, "It is not the policy of the committee, nor of our missions, to invest Foreign Mission funds in the building of large hospitals."[9] The size of most institutions remained relatively small until after World War II.

From the start the mission recognized that it was important for the missionaries to acquire facility in the local language and "regular service" personnel were expected to spend their first year (sometimes years) in the formal study of the language. In time language schools were established in most countries; missionaries appointed to the Congo spent a year in Belgium in the study of French. However, it can be observed that some medical personnel operated with minimum language ability. In some instances political upheaval or personal circumstances interrupted the pursuit of language study; in others the temptation to apply one's skills to pressing needs proved overwhelming. Medical professionals were both blessed and cursed in possessing expertise that was in great demand and could be put to immediate use; unless they were diligent, they could be permanently handicapped by poor communication abilities.

When couples applied for the mission field, both husband and wife were appointed as regular service missionaries. The wife's primary assignment was that of homemaker, which in many instances included the teaching of the children, and she had some flexibility in assuming other responsibilities. Some wives were themselves medical professionals and enjoyed applying their expertise to the work. Congo/Zaire had at least a dozen of these medical couples. Many of the other wives also chose to become actively involved in medical work.

Physicians

Dr. Chester's stipulation that PCUS missionary physicians should be well qualified seems to have been followed. As might be expected, PCUS physicians were primarily from the southern part of the United States, and fourteen of them went to the Medical College of Virginia (Richmond); ten to the Johns Hopkins Medical School (Baltimore); seven to Tulane University (New Orleans); six to Washington University (St. Louis); five each to Vanderbilt University (Nashville) and the South Carolina Medical School (Charleston); four each to Baylor (Houston), the University of Pennsylvania (Philadelphia), and the University of Virginia (Charlottesville). Many graduated with distinction. Ten percent were women. Nineteen regular service and eleven of the short-term doctors attained specialty board certification.

Nurses

Twenty-two years passed between the time the first physician was appointed and the time the first registered nurse (Flora S. Alderman) was appointed, in 1903 to China. Although the art of nursing in the form of "nurturing the young, protecting the helpless, and tending the sick and injured" is at least as old as recorded history, the date regarded as the birth of modern nursing is July 9, 1860, when Florence

Nightingale opened the Nightingale Training School at St. Thomas Hospital in London.[10] The first nursing school in the United States to be based on the Nightingale system was founded in 1873 at Bellevue Hospital in New York City.[11] The nursing profession expanded and became organized between 1900 and 1919. During the same period Presbyterian nurses sought overseas missionary appointments.

The contribution of missionary nurses to the mission medical program cannot be overstated. In addition to supervising nursing care in the hospitals, they operated dispensaries and well-baby clinics, handled supplies, and, when the physician was unavailable, regularly found themselves thrust into an assortment of challenging situations. They were especially concerned with the care of sick missionaries and their children. A prime accomplishment was the establishment of nursing schools. Many of the registered nurses were married and, like working women everywhere, had to decide how to handle family responsibilities along with their professional ones.

Missionary nurses may have had higher professional standing than did their counterparts in the United States. Most of the missionary nurses' work was supervisory or administrative, and they were respected by coworkers and the local people. Some who served in Congo/Zaire came to be called Super Nurses.

Dentists

Dental programs were established in three countries: Korea (where the first dentist went in 1922), Congo/Zaire, and Taiwan.

Paramedics

The first certified medical technologists were appointed to China in the 1930s and to the other countries after World War II. Hospital administrators and other paramedical personnel proliferated after 1950.

Funding of Medical Missions

Before World War II

Pre–World War II funding followed the policies advocated by "The Forward Movement," a movement initiated in 1902 in order to increase support for the missionary enterprise by encouraging churches, societies, and individuals to assume financial responsibility for specific parts of the mission's work.[12] Medical needs, because they were tangible, vivid, and concrete, were particularly appealing to church people. Some missionary physicians gave talks illustrated with dramatic photographs from the field that are remembered to this day. An articulate spokesman could bring tears to the eyes of the audience and seduce them into opening their pocketbooks.

A partial list of names of those memorialized by the building of hospitals in remote parts of China, Korea, or Congo/Zaire reads like a PCUS honor roll: Mary Erwin Rogers, Sara Walkup, Marion Sprunt, Francis Bridges Atkinson. C. W. French, B. M. Palmer, and Edna Kellersberger. Ellen Lavine Graham and A. J. A. Alexander are memorialized by two hospitals each, in China and in Korea; W. R. McKowen by two more, in Korea and in Congo/Zaire. Dr. Goldsby King is honored by three hospitals, in China, Zaire, and Brazil.

Women's missionary societies throughout the church generated interest and funds. For example, the women of Wilmington Presbytery (in North Carolina) built and supported the Jiangyin (Kiangyin) Hospital in China, where a "son of the church," George C. Worth, M.D., was the physician. The Women of the Church organization supported a White Cross program that supplied mission hospitals with linens, pajamas, rolled bandages, layettes, and other expendable goods.

The Laymen's Missionary Movement, endorsed in 1907 by the General Assembly (the governing body of the PCUS), held conventions at which thousands gathered and pledged support for specific projects. At the 1908 Birmingham convention, for example, funds for building the Suqien (Sutsien) Hospital in China were raised.

Young people, too, rallied to the challenge. Yencheng Hospital (China) was built with funds raised on Children's Day 1914. Sunday school children collected the money for "God's Steamer," the S S *Lapsley*, in the Congo. The young people of Wilmington Presbytery sponsored cots in the Jiangyin Hospital in China. The Flora Macdonald College and the Davidson College villages at the R. M. Wilson Leprosy Colony (Korea) were built by funds raised by students at those colleges.

The PCUS mission program experienced a banner year in 1925, when the number of missionaries under appointment reached 553, of whom 75 were medical personnel. However, the Great Depression, together with World War II, devastated the PCUS mission work, and the whole enterprise suffered a decline and retrenchment. Church contributions fell by one-half. No new medical work was begun and existing institutions were sorely pressed.

Post–World War II

The end of World War II brought a period of enthusiastic renewal and advance. The church's Program of Progress campaign for new capital development raised more than two million dollars and contributed to the establishment of new projects as well as to rehabilitation of the old. The medical program began new projects in Japan, Taiwan, and Brazil. In 1965 missionary strength reached an all-time high of 567, of which 82 were medical personnel.[13]

At the same time, medical expenses and inflation soared. The General Assembly's policy of equalizing the mission budget for all causes placed an impossible burden on the medical work; no longer could an individual or organization send money to a specific project. Many church members who objected to this policy chose to donate to agencies not related to the PCUS.

In response to the financial squeeze, the Medical Benevolence Foundation (MBF) was established in 1962. It was designed to enlist the support (over and above their regular church contributions) of PCUS members in the United States who wished to help specific medical projects abroad. The idea for the MBF was conceived by a frustrated physician (Paul S. Crane of Korea) while on furlough in 1962 and, with the strong support of L. Nelson Bell, M.D. (board member and former missionary to China), adopted by the Board of World Missions. In the 1970s, under the dynamic leadership of its director, Keith McCafferty, MBF came to be a major source of support for the medical program of the church. It collected and distributed used medical equipment and supplies for overseas use and recruited medical personnel to serve as short-term volunteers. MBF also provided a channel for the receipt of grants from foundations and government agencies that would not give money directly to a denominational church body. Major contributions through MBF for construction and equipment came from the U.S. Agency for International Development (U.S.AID) through its American Schools and Hospitals Abroad program (ASHA) and the Protestant Central Agency for Development Aid/Evangelische zentralstelle fur Entwicklungshilfe E. V. (EZE) of Bonn, West Germany.

The Women of the Church, in addition to the White Cross program, made significant contributions to the medical program through their annual "Birthday Offering." The size of these offerings attests to the abiding interest of church women in the medical aspect of missions (see Table P-3).[14]

In the 1970s the equalization policy was modified to allow designated giving to PCUS-approved projects. The 1981 budget for international missions projected receipt of $3,728,000 from the basic budget and $4,000,000 from "special askings." Medical projects also received support through the Second Mile Missionary Support Program (missionary salary support), the Special Opportunities Support (SOS), Hunger and Overseas Relief Offerings, and individual presbyteries.[15]

The financial support for the PCUS medical programs always hung by a slender thread because the needs and opportunities far exceeded the resources provided by the PCUS community. It often appeared to the medical missionaries that they were left "swinging in the wind."

Table P-3
Donations to PCUS Medical Work
Women of the Church's Annual Birthday Offering

Year	Amount Donated	Project
1955	$208,577	Yodogawa Christian Hospital, Osaka, Japan
1957	$107,615	Tuberculosis work in Korea, primarily in Kwangju
1963	$ 75,000	Sanatorio La Luz, Morelia, Mexico, and Hospital de la Amistad, Ometepec, Mexico
1965	$400,000	Presbyterian Medical Center/Jesus Hospital, Chonju, Korea
1969	$434,534	Good Shepherd Hospital (IMCK), Tshikaji, Zaire
1976	$155,880	Bangladesh Christian Health Care Team
1983	$555,681	White Cross Shipping Fund

Statistics from Patricia Houck Sprinkle, *The Birthday Book: First Fifty Years* (Atlanta, Georgia: Board of Women's Work), 1972, and from the Board of Women's Work, Presbyterian Church, U.S., Atlanta, Georgia.

The Practice of Medicine

Background

The PCUS overseas medical program began just as medicine in America was entering the scientific era that made it possible to actually determine the causes of illnesses and devise remedies that cure, prevent, and in some cases, eliminate diseases (e.g., smallpox). In their book *Two Centuries of American Medicine: 1776–1976*, James Bordley III and A. McGehee Harvey describe how, during America's first century, the "role of the physician was that of the Good Samaritan. His success depended upon his sympathy, his humanity and his art. Lacking a scientific base, his therapy . . . was, for the most part, ineffective." In the second century with the reorientation of medicine on a solid scientific basis, "the medical profession within a few decades had become . . . surprisingly productive."[16]

Before trained medical personnel were appointed to the field, lay PCUS missionaries responded to the suffering and pain they encountered with what has been described as "a form of pillbox ministry, gravely administering draughts, lancing excrescences and proceeding by trial and error."[17] Western medicine, at this point, demonstrated little obvious superiority over the local traditional healer. However, compassion and concern for the sick, in imitation of Christ's ministry, always formed an integral and effective part of mission strategy.

The first PCUS medical missionaries were products of the new era in medicine. The "pillbox missionary" and the "Good Samaritan physician" quickly faded away. The China Mission, at its 1898 annual meeting, formally recognized that it was no longer possible for untrained persons to dispense medical help in a responsible manner: "The Mission declines to make appropriations to be used by any except Doctors of Medicine, male or female, in purchasing medicines to be disposed to the Chinese." However, Miss Eliza French, Mrs. Hampden C. DuBose, and Mrs. P. Frank Price, all of whom were actively engaged in ministry to the sick, were to be exempted from this rule.[18]

A brief review of some of the achievements in medicine, particularly in the second half of the nineteenth century, illustrates both how primitive Western medicine was and how far it has come (see Table P-4).

The Competition

Medical missions did not move into a vacuum. In every country, Western scientific medicine confronted traditional systems of medical care that were deeply embedded in the culture. Attitudes toward illness, deformity, and treatment remained linked to these ancient systems.

Asia

Asia has a system of medicine with a history of at least three thousand years.[19] A complex system of concepts rooted in Chinese philosophy and culture stresses harmony and balance between two great contrasting forces: the positive and the negative, light and dark, male and female, hot and cold, good and evil, *yang* and *yin*. Any imbalance between these opposing forces causes disease. The function of the practitioner is to help restore these forces to their proper balance. Therapy includes (1) the use of medicines compiled from herbs, animal (including human) parts, and minerals plus a heavy dependence on narcotics, and (2) the use of *acupuncture* (the insertion of needles into specific points of the skin) and *moxibustion* (the heating or burning of specific points with a small container of burning herbs). Empirical administration of therapy by intelligent practitioners no doubt compared favorably with Western practice prior to the advent of scientific medicine.

In addition to this orthodox system of medicine, there exists a system of "people's" remedies which, while influenced by the

---

Table P-4

Achievements in Medical Science

Year	Achievement
1798	Vaccination for smallpox discovered by Jenner
1846	General anesthesia applied to surgery
1847	Illness linked to cleanliness (aseptic childbirth)
1865	Antiseptic surgery (carbolic spray used to reduce germs)
1873–98	Pathogens identified for leprosy, malaria, tuberculosis, cholera, tetanus; mosquito linked to yellow fever and malaria
1890	Asepsis (surgery in a bacteria-free environment)
1895	X ray put to use in medicine
1936	Sulfanilamide introduced
1940	Penicillin introduced

Compiled from Grundmann Christoffer, "The Role of Medical Missions in the Missionary Enterprise: A Historical and Missiological Study," *Mission Studies (Journal of the International Association for Mission Studies)*, vol. II-2 (1985), 39–48, and from the *Encyclopedia Britannica*, vol. 15 (1969), 99–106.

orthodox system, incorporates an array of folk-healing methods. Practitioners include soothsayers, geomancers, fortune-tellers, herbalists, Buddhist and Taoist priests, drug peddlers, shamans, charlatans, traditional doctors, and, sometimes, Christian ministers.

Surgery was not highly developed in Asia, although tradition has it that some 1,500 years ago surgery, including some brain surgery such as trephining the skull, was performed. The initial appeal of the mission medical program was based largely on the successes of the practice of modern surgery.

Most Asians still accept traditional medicine. It can be assumed that patients who appear at a mission hospital have first consulted a traditional physician. In China, Japan, and Korea, the practitioner of traditional medicine receives the same medical license and enjoys the same privileges as the graduate of modern medical schools. Western-trained physicians and nurses often adhere to some of these traditions and practices.

Africa

In Africa the missionary physician faced an entirely different problem. The close relationship of healing and religion in African culture has elicited considerable study in recent years. Vernon A. Anderson, missionary to Congo/Zaire (1920–60) whose avocation was anthropology, wrote his Ph.D. dissertation on "Witchcraft in Africa, A Missionary Problem." In it he points out that members of "primitive cultures" ask "who" rather than "what" is the causal factor when an illness or a catastrophe strikes. A witch doctor is a diviner who finds the "who"—an antisocial creature or a "witch"—by the practice of either good ("white") magic or harmful ("black") magic. Dr. Anderson observed that witch doctors never cast a spell on someone they do not know; there is always a previous, and usually malignant, relationship.[20]

This concept of a "who" as the cause of illness underlies the practice of voodoo and is found today in Haiti as well as in Congo/Zaire. The concept of the "who" is also a major component of "people's medicine" in Asia and is implicit in the practice of some faith healers in Western societies.

These attitudes change slowly. It is interesting to note that the missionary doctors in Congo/Zaire were called *Munganga* or *Ngangabuka*, the same title used for the traditional healer/witch doctor.

Hospitalization

Hospitalization, the housing of sick persons in a separate institution for treatment and care, was not part of the culture in either Asia or Africa; the ill were cared for at home by family members. The mission institution had to deal with the persistent intrusion of relatives who might, on occasion, share the bed, bring inappropriate food, or decide to supplement medication with drugs supplied by the traditional healer. Many mission hospitals built viewing windows for the operating room so that family members could observe what was happening.

Missionary Physicians

Missionary physicians, with a few notable exceptions, have been criticized for failing to understand and respect traditional medicine. Three reasons for their resistance to traditional healers can be identified.

First, as a result of the newly established scientific base for medicine, Western medical professionals were intolerant of any system that did not meet certain scientific standards. Missionaries strove, with difficulty, to maintain high standards of medical practice. This mind-set was not conducive to an appreciation of other approaches to healing.[21]

Second, missionary doctors encountered many tragic examples of patients who had suffered at the hands of traditional practitioners. The lack of standardization in compiling drugs, as well as in training practitioners, compounded the problem.

Third, extremely busy schedules left the missionaries with little time or inclination to delve into traditional medical practices. Most did not have the language skills with which to communicate with traditional healers, many of whom felt threatened by the foreign competition.

Experienced medical missionaries often came to appreciate the fact that in the field of psychosomatic problems the traditional healer's success rate was sometimes equal, if not superior, to Western medicine. The traditional healer was better able to deal with mental pathology than the neophyte from an alien culture.

The Practice

Before World War II medical practice in the PCUS mission was similar to that in the United States, where it was common for hard-working, hard-driving physicians to establish and run their own hospitals. The institution revolved around the personality and initiative of one or two dominant personalities. The missionaries, however, were further burdened by responsibilities for construction, supply, administration, and evangelization. Missionary physicians also often dealt with far-advanced or exotic cases not encountered in the West. In general, they had the knowledge but not always the resources necessary to provide the needed treatment.[22] Most physicians were overworked and many suffered burnout. Suicide claimed the lives of two medical professionals—Samuel Houston Miller, M.D., in China (1915–16) and Effie Lucille Dale, R.N., in Congo/Zaire (1936–37).

After World War II medical work moved toward a team approach, with multispecialties and strong training programs consolidated into medical centers. The medical missionaries kept abreast of medical advances through study programs on furloughs. Many of the physicians obtained board certification with wide specialty representation (general and thoracic surgery, internal medicine, pediatrics, ophthalmology, orthopedics, obstetrics/gynecology, public health, family practice). Most of the missionary nurses had B.S. degrees in nursing; some had master's degrees; one earned her Ph.D. The hospital staffs expanded to include chaplains, technicians, social workers, and maintenance personnel. Hospital administrators brought their special expertise. Short-term missionaries and medical volunteers added depth and quality. The training of local people became a top priority, with many receiving scholarships for advanced study abroad; those who returned to their native land quickly assumed positions of responsibility and leadership.

During the 1960s a series of "mutual agreements" between the PCUS and local churches resulted in new patterns for mission work, based on church-to-church partnerships rather than on mission control. The implications of this partnership model for church-owned institutions, including the medical institutions, varied from country to country. In some places the institutions were turned over to the national church, in others, to independent boards with strong ecumenical church representation.[23]

Components of Mission Medicine

Medical mission work has traditionally concentrated on the treatment of disease, the training of local people, and community health. Research into root causes of disease also engaged the energies of some of the medical professionals.

Treatment of Disease

The early missionary physicians, who were trained as generalists, cared for every kind of illness. With the advent of anesthesia and aseptic technique, surgery was not only effective but also well accepted, and many missionary doctors became extraordinarily proficient surgeons. The excision of pathologically advanced, medically neglected, and therefore enormous cysts, malignant tumors, goiters, and hernias was dramatic (and photographically useful for illustrating missionary talks). Cesarean sections, treatment of burns, cleft palates, and trauma were common surgical problems. Diseases included malaria, dysenteries, typhoid, typhus, rabies, cholera, smallpox, diphtheria, leprosy, tuberculosis, and parasitic infestations.

Missionary physicians in Zaire saw crocodile, hippopotamus, and snake bites, yaws, and sleeping sickness; those in China, opium addiction, rabies, kala-azar (a parasitic disease), schistosomiasis (a parasitic disease), and victims of banditry and of famine; those in Korea, cancer of the stomach, parasitic liver disease (from clonorchis and amoeba), and tuberculosis of lungs, bones, and joints. In Mexico, James R. Boyce, M.D., collected a quart jar of bullets extracted from patients who came from "feuding country" in the southern mountains of that country.

World War II brought monumental advances to medicine. A partial list includes the introduction of antibiotics, drugs for tuberculosis and leprosy, vaccines for polio and measles, the eradication of smallpox, better diagnostic tests in the laboratory and in radiology, and the advanced use of technology resulting in specialization of professionals and paramedical personnel. Medical expenses soared, and mission medical institutions were financially hard-pressed as they competed with multiple demands for limited church dollars. The mission medical staff had to try to practice a high quality of medicine in the face of inadequate supplies, primitive facilities, volatile political conditions, and ever-increasing regulations from local governments.

Training of Local People

Training, perhaps the most significant contribution of medical missions, was developed on many levels—from the teaching of mothers to give their children a nutritious diet to the training of highly skilled specialists. Development of training programs varied from time to time and from country to country.

The PCUS, while not a builder of medical schools, participated in union (interdenominational) institutions, for example, by appointments to the boards and faculties of Cheeloo University Medical School in China and of Severance Union Medical School (Yonsei University) in Korea. In Zaire plans to implement the dream for a union medical school were permanently abandoned in 1960 following independence.

The training of physicians on the intern/residency level contributed immeasurably to upgrading the profession. An important by-product of the training of medical professionals was the strengthening of the local churches through an educated and affluent laity.

The introduction of nursing as a respected profession for women helped to revolutionize the status of women abroad with far-reaching results. Accredited nursing schools, some of which had junior college or university standing, were established in many of the countries where the PCUS worked.

The training of medical technologists made it possible to offer a new level of scientific medicine. Training programs for nurse's aides, midwives, and paramedical personnel also were developed. Men as well as women took part in these programs. Especially in the early years, the unlicensed, but well-trained, assistant was an invaluable aide to the missionary physician.

Community Health/Primary Health Care

Although community health was emphasized in later years, the early missionaries made significant contributions to the general welfare of their communities by operating well-baby clinics, giving prenatal care, and teaching hygiene and nutrition. In the early 1970s the development of primary health care, preventive medicine, and village health projects became a priority in the PCUS medical work. Personnel and financial resources were channeled into this area, reflecting the growing international concern articulated in the campaign "Health for All by the Year 2000" promoted in 1978 at the WHO/UNICEF Conference held at Alma Ata, Kazakh Republic of the U.S.S.R.

Specific contributions to local public health problems included the following:

1. In Zaire, Dr. Eugene R. Kellersberger's contribution to the treatment, control, and elimination of trypanosomiasis (sleeping sickness), caused by the bite of the tsetse fly, is internationally recognized.[24]
2. In both Zaire and in Korea, the PCUS leprosy work was also renowned. Dr. Kellersberger left the Zaire mission in 1940 to become executive secretary of the American Leprosy Missions.
3. In China, kala-azar (a parasitic disease transmitted by the bite of the sand fly) was endemic in the North Jiangsu area. The TKP General Hospital in Huaiyin, under Drs. James B. Woods Sr. and L. Nelson Bell, carried on research as well as treatment that contributed to the control of this fatal-if-untreated disease.[25]
4. In China, Dr. James B. Woods Jr. developed a clinic to treat schistosomiasis (a parasitic disease caused by a water-transmitted blood fluke), which was prevalent in the Zhenjiang/Chinkiang area. He was able to demonstrate that a very inexpensive drug (tartar emetic) could be used in place of other expensive standard agents.[26]
5. In Korea in the 1960s, the national program to eradicate intestinal parasites (initiated by Dr. Paul S. Crane) marked a turning point in the level of energy and vitality of the Korean people.
6. In Zaire innovative programs (led by Drs. John K. Miller and Richard C. Brown) contributed to an international understanding of how to deal with problems of diarrhea (through oral rehydration) and of kwashiorkor (with peanuts). The missionaries also developed programs to encourage local leaders to accept responsibility for their community's health.
7. As a result of the priority given to public health measures, new work, begun in Haiti in 1973 and in Bangladesh in 1974, focused on preventive and community health.

Research

Along with treatment of disease came questions, and the need to look for answers through research: *Why* is stomach cancer so prevalent in Korea, compared with the United States? *Why* is arteriosclerosis (hardening of the arteries) so rare among Asians? *Why* so much liver disease in Asia? *Why* is Buerger's disease (thromboangitis obliterans—thrombosis of arteries and veins) so widespread in Korea?

Conclusion

The century of PCUS overseas medical mission developed in tandem with the revolutionary changes that were taking place both in the political realm and in the practice of scientific medicine in the West. The youthful enthusiasm that in the 1880s proposed "The Evangelization of the World in This Generation"[27] found its counterpart in medicine's new-found ability to prevent, as well as treat, many of the age-old plagues of the human race. Through its medical mission program, PCUS attempted to demonstrate compassionate concern for the pain and suffering of a lost world as an essential element in the presentation of the good news of the gospel of Jesus Christ.

Notes

1. Ruth A. Tucker, *From Jerusalem to Irian Jaya* (Grand Rapids, Mich.: Zondervan Publishing House, 1983), 116.
2. Individual medical professionals served for short periods in countries where the PCUS did not establish medical projects: in Ecuador, Nigeria, Nicaragua, Peru, Rwandi, and Vietnam.
3. David E. Van Reken, M.D., *Mission and Ministry: Christian Medical Practice in Today's Changing World Cultures* (Wheaton, Ill.: A Billy Graham Center Monograph, 1987), 9.
4. A. F. Walls, "The Heavy Artillery of the Missionary Army: The Domestic Importance of the Nineteenth-Century Medical Missionary," *The Church & Healing*, W. J. Sheils, editor (Oxford: Basil Blackwell, 1982), 290.
5. Van Reken, *Mission and Ministry*, 9.
6. Ibid., 5–6.
7. Sophie M. Crane, *Missionary Directory* (Atlanta, Ga.: Division of International Mission, PCUSA, 1987).
8. Keith McCaffety, executive director of MBF, letter to the author, Oct. 27, 1986.
9. Samuel H. Chester, Report to the Executive Committee of Foreign Missions by the Secretary on his visit to China, Korea, Japan, 1887.
10. *Encyclopedia Britannica*, vol. 16, 1969, 791.
11. *Encyclopedia Americana*, vol. 20, 1983, 557–62.
12. G. Thompson Brown, "Overseas Mission Program and Policies of the PCUS: 1861–1983: A Brief Chronology" (Atlanta, Ga.: Division of International Mission, General Assembly Board of the Presbyterian Church, typescript, 1985), 6.

13. Ibid., 14.

14. Patricia H. Sprinkle, *The Birthday Book: First Fifty Years* (Atlanta, Ga.: Board of Women's Work, PCUS, 1972), 4–5.

15. Brown, "Overseas Mission Program and Policies," 19.

16. James Bordley III and A. McGehee Harvey, *Two Centuries of American Medicine: 1776–1976* (Philadelphia: W. B. Saunders, 1976), preface.

17. A. F. Walls, "The Heavy Artillery of the Missionary Army," 287.

18. James E. Bear, *The Mid-China and the North Kiangsu Missions*, vol. II, typescript (Richmond, Va.: Union Theological Seminary Library), 518.

19. These comments on oriental medicine were compiled primarily from two books: Paul S. Crane, M.D., *Korean Patterns* (Seoul, Korea: The Royal Asiatic Society, 1978), 103–10, and Yuet-Wah Cheung, *Missionary Medicine in China: A Study of Two Protestant Missions in China Before 1937* (Lanham, N.Y.: University Press of America, 1988), 65–82.

20. Vernon A. Anderson, Ph.D., "Witchcraft in Africa, A Missionary Problem" (Louisville, Ky.: Presbyterian Theological Seminary, monograph, 1942). Dr. Anderson makes the point that witchcraft once flourished in Europe and in colonial America, where the majority of "witches" were female.

21. Many inferior medical schools in the United States were closed during the first decade of the twentieth century; the licensing of medical personnel by examination was an effort to discourage "quacks" and protect the public.

22. X-ray equipment was not introduced on the mission field until the 1920s. The first medical technologists were appointed in the 1930s.

23. Brown, "Overseas Mission Program and Policies," 14.

24. Winifred K. Vass, *Doctor Not Afraid: E. R. Kellersberger, M.D.* (Austin, Tex.: Nortex Press, 1986), 133.

25. John C. Pollack, *A Foreign Devil in China* (Minneapolis, Minn.: World Wide Publications, 1988), 151–55

26. Alexander S. Moffett, M.D., letter to the author, May 1991.

27. Tucker, *From Jerusalem to Irian Jaya*, 261–86. A slogan of the Student Volunteer Movement, an organization founded in 1886, which for some fifty years inspired many young people to become missionaries.

PART I
China

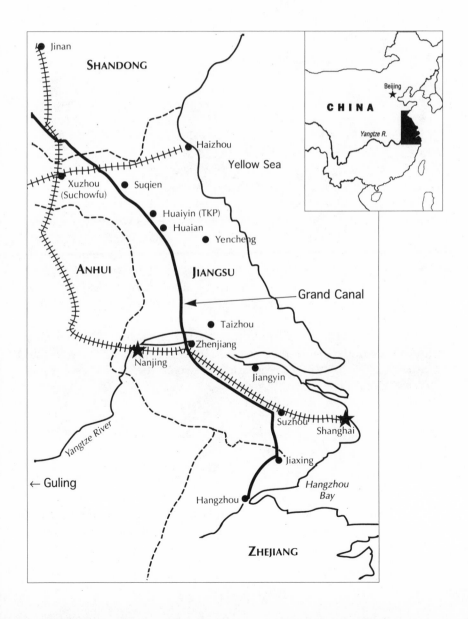

Chapter One

China
(1881–1952)

The medical mission of the PCUS in China began in 1881, with the appointment of Richard Baxter Fishburne, M.D., and ended in 1951 when Joseph L. Wilkerson, M.D., left the People's Republic of China. Of the total PCUS mission force of 343 that served in China between 1881 and 1952, some 22 percent were medical personnel: 48 physicians, 27 nurses and 2 medical technologists.

For PCUS missionaries the entire period of service in China was chaotic; for the Chinese people the seven decades were devastating. Wars, banditry, revolution, famine, poverty, and epidemics took their toll; cultural and social values were challenged by exposure to Western civilization. And yet, in the words of Yale historian Jonathan Spence, "Despite the terrible sufferings of so many Chinese people during the long years of fragmentation and reform, the idea of the nation had remained alive."[1]

The story of the PCUS medical mission in China falls naturally into four periods: (1) pioneer period (1881–1900), (2) early twentieth century (1900–20), (3) the decades between the two world wars (1920–41), and (4) the post–World War II years (1946–52).

Anyone writing about China faces the problem of the spelling of place names. This work applies the "pinyin" romanization, with the name as commonly used by the missionaries in parenthesis.

The Pioneer Period (1881–1900)

The pioneer period began with Chinese hostility, suspicion, and opposition to the West and ended with the Boxer Rebellion of 1900, in

Richard Baxter Fishburne (1881–83) with his language teacher. Dr. Fishburne was the first physician appointed by the PCUS to serve in its overseas mission. The confrontation of two cultures is illustrated in this picture by the informal versus the formal posture—the crossed legs and feet on the floor, the bare head and the hat, the umbrella and the fan, and the difference in dress. Photograph courtesy of Mrs. A. R. Seccombe.

which some 134 missionaries, 52 missionary children, and many Chinese Christians were killed. Although under serious threat, the PCUS missionaries suffered no fatalities.[2]

The PCUS mission was located in Jiangsu (Kiangsu) and Zhejiang (Chekiang) provinces in the fertile, heavily populated, and historically prosperous Yangzi (Yangtze) River delta area. Most of the PCUS stations were in cities located on the Grand Canal, China's remarkable 1,100–mile man-made inland waterway that once was the major link between the capital in Beijing (Peking) with Hangzhou (Hangchow) in the south.

To expedite its work, the PCUS in 1889 divided its enterprise in China into two missions. The Mid-China Mission worked in the area south of the Yangzi River, and the North Jiangsu Mission, except for the river port of Zhenjiang (Chinkiang), worked north of the river.

The Mid-China Mission was located in one of China's wealthiest areas—a fertile, productive countryside dotted with large cosmopolitan cities. All but one of the Mid-China stations was on a railroad (the Yangzi River port of Jiangyin (Kiangyin) was within twenty-five miles of a railhead). Many other Protestant denominations also operated in the area, so that ecumenical projects developed, especially in education.

In contrast, although the North Jiangsu Mission area had historically enjoyed prosperity because of the commercial activity along the
Grand Canal, once the railroads passed it by, the Grand Canal deteriorated and fell into comparative disuse. The word *Subei*, meaning
"north of the river," became a pejorative term associated with poverty
and backwardness.[3] Very little industry developed, and the largely
rural population frequently suffered from floods, banditry, and
famine. Somewhat more cosmopolitan (after the building of railroads)
were the cities of Zhenjiang (Chinkiang) and Xuzhou (Hsuchow). The
PCUS was virtually the only mission body in the area and had little
contact with other foreign groups. As late as 1940 the North Jiangsu
missionaries were considered pioneers.

The early missionaries responded to the plight of the sick and
suffering as best they could. The first mention of any PCUS medical
work appeared in the 1879 annual report of the Executive Committee
of Foreign Missions to the Eighteenth General Assembly: four
hundred persons received medical aid in Suzhou (Soochow) from
Mrs. Pauline DuBose, wife of Rev. Hampden C. DuBose (1872–1910).
In a report on "Medical Missions in China" in 1882, Rev. John W.
Davis of Suzhou states, "More or less medical work is done by clerical
missionaries at all mission stations."[4] For example, Miss Helen
Kirkland, an evangelistic missionary, wrote in 1881, "Medicine takes
me into many houses but I use nothing but the simplest remedies,
quinine, rhubarb, carbolic acid, santonin and all Dr. Jaynes Medicines
(worm medicines), which we find excellent."[5]

A letter written in 1883 by Dr. Fishburne gives insight into the
level of medical practice in which "antiseptic surgery" was hailed as
a great surgical advance. He tells of going with a Dr. Boone
(Methodist missionary) to see the first dressing of a limb that had
been amputated two days before: "The operation was a beautiful one
(i.e., to us butchers), it being done strictly according to the Lister antiseptic method."[6]

Because Dr. Fishburne returned to the United States after only two
years, the PCUS medical program in China began to establish continuity only with the arrival of Edgar Woods Jr., M.D. Following his
appointment in 1887 to the turn of the century, eleven physicians—
three of them women—arrived and scattered to their stations (see
Table 1-1).

Table 1-1

The Pioneers Physicians

Richard Baxter Fishburne	1881–83	2 years
Edgar Woods Jr.	1887–99	12 years
Annie R. Houston Patterson	1891–1939	48 years
Wade Hampton Venable	1893–1929	36 years
James Baker Woods Sr.	1893–1941	48 years
James Richard Wilkinson	1894–1920	26 years
George Clarkson Worth	1895–1936	41 years
Nettie Donaldson Grier	1896–1940	44 years
Rev. Lynford L. Moore	1897–1902	5 years
John Wilson Bradley	1899–1929	30 years
Jane Varenia Lee	1899–1936	37 years
Charles S. Terrill	1899–1900	1 year

As a group these physicians were well trained by the standards of the time. Most had college degrees before entering medical school, plus from one to three years' postgraduate training. Four were graduates of the University of Virginia School of Medicine. Annie Houston (Patterson) graduated from the Women's College of Baltimore and Nettie Donaldson Grier from the Women's Medical College, New York.

Annie Houston Patterson, M.D. (1891–1939) with her first child. Dr. Houston was the first woman missionary physician appointed by PCUS and the third physician assigned to China. Photograph courtesy of Mrs. P. M. Churchman.

*Dr. James B. and Mrs. Bessie
S. Woods, a pioneer couple
who completed forty-eight
years of service in China
(1893–1941). She was nineteen years old when they first
went. Photograph courtesy of
Virginia Somerville.*

It is startling to remember how young these "pioneer" missionaries were. Annie Houston Patterson, at twenty-four, was the
youngest. James B. Woods was twenty-seven (and his wife, Bessie,
only nineteen) when they left for China. Nine of the eleven were in
their twenties; James Wilkinson was thirty-three and Jane Varenia Lee
was thirty-six. Many of these young people had young families.

The remarkable fact about the group is their length of service. Four
of the eleven served over forty years, three over thirty years, and one
for twenty-six years. Three, Drs. Grier, Patterson, and James Woods,
had terms of service that spanned the history of PCUS medical work
in China except for the brief post–World War II interlude.

Three of the eleven dropped out or went into other work: Rev.
Lynford L. Moore, M.D., more a minister than a physician, resigned
after five years because of poor health and returned to the United
States. Jane Varenia Lee, with some eleven years in teaching prior to
earning a medical degree, switched to full-time educational work
and served for twenty-two years as principal of the Luola
Murchison Sprunt Academy (for girls) in Jiangyin. Charles S. Terrill
became acutely ill and was sent back to the United States in less than
one year.

Medical work began as clinics in a room or a simple Chinese
building and evolved into hospital-based programs. Only one

hospital, the Elizabeth Blake Memorial Hospital in Suzhou, was built before the turn of the century.

The use of opium was widespread. According to one account, about one-tenth of male adults were said to be addicted; according to another, in a rural village with 500 men, only 10 did not use opium.[7] The Reverend DuBose's opposition to the opium trade gained him international recognition and made him "the most widely known missionary [of the PCUS] and one of the most picturesque figures of the missionary body in this land."[8] He helped found the National Anti-Opium League of China, which, in 1900, pressured the British Parliament to condemn the opium trade, and took part in a missionary conference in Shanghai that sent a cable to The Hague on the subject. The "Imperial Edict for the Abolition of the Opium Trade in China" of 1906 was practically a verbatim copy of a "memorial" written by the Reverend DuBose.[9]

Early–Twentieth Century (1900–1920)

China, following the fall of the Qing (Ching) Dynasty and the establishment of the Republic (October 10, 1910), entered a period of extraordinary political upheaval. Although foreign investments flooded in, investment from the United States ($49.3 million in 1914) accounted for only 3.1 percent of the total foreign investment and was concentrated in mission properties (including hospitals and schools) and Shanghai real estate.[10]

During this period the PCUS built ten hospitals in China, three in the Mid-China Mission area and seven in North Jiangsu. In addition, through an interdenominational effort, the Cheeloo University School of Medicine at Jinan (Tsinan) was founded to train Chinese medical personnel.

Between 1900 and 1920 the PCUS appointed seventeen physicians and thirteen nurses. The arrival of the first registered nurse in 1904 was a significant advance.

Western scientific medicine, which experienced growing acceptance from the Chinese public, received official recognition after missionary physicians helped control the outbreak of the North Manchurian Plague (bubonic) of 1910. [11] Mission hospitals were inundated by patients, and available resources were stretched to the limit.

The Decades between the Two World Wars (1920–1941)

After World War I the PCUS missions experienced considerable success in the midst of continued social unrest. A peak year in financial support and in mission personnel was 1925.[12] Old plants were expanded and renovated, two new hospitals were built, and the goal of two physicians and one nurse for each hospital was partially achieved with the appointment between 1920 and 1927 of eight doctors and seven full-time nurses.

Then, in 1927, PCUS missionaries were forced to evacuate their stations for a time, when the Nationalist (Kuomindang) Party under Chiang Kai-shek attempted to unify a country fragmented under the warlords and threatened by the newly emerging Communist Party, which concentrated its efforts in the rural areas. Next, the situation became further complicated by the Japanese invasion, which began with the bombing of Shanghai in 1931 and the seizure of Manchuria in 1932, and aggressively advanced in 1937 with the occupation of east China (including the area served by the PCUS). The PCUS missions were able, with difficulty, to carry on under Japanese rule until the bombing of Pearl Harbor in 1941.

At the same time, support available from the United States was seriously curtailed by the worldwide depression. Support was further affected by the publication, in 1932, of the critical *Rethinking Missions: Laymen's Foreign Missions Inquiry Report after 100 Years*, which reflected the so-called "liberal" trend in the major denominations.[13] Particularly galling to the medical missionaries was the chapter on "Medical Work of Missions," which gave a warped and unfair presentation of the work being done. A study of the "Fact Finding Reports"[14] on which the report was based revealed that the conclusions reached indeed did not reflect the facts. The PCUS Executive Committee of Foreign Missions issued a "Statement Regarding the Report of the Laymen's Foreign Missions Inquiry" in which they stated that neither "our Missions or our missionaries [were] among the special subjects of this Inquiry and Report."[15]

Between 1927 and 1941, the mission lost fifteen physicians and seven nurses. During the same period only eight doctors, two full-time and one part-time nurse, and two medical technologists were appointed. However, although the mission staff was skeletal, trained Chinese medical personnel were able to join the staffs, and the medical work continued to be a major force in the mission program. Patients came in great numbers, taxing the physical capacity of the facilities and the personnel.

Hospitals were expected to be as self-supporting as possible. Mission support came primarily in the form of salaries of the missionary staff and in capital funds for buildings. White Cross supplies (linens, gauze, bandages, etc.), supplied regularly by the Women of the Church, continued unabated and were a critical contribution.

Surgery remained the primary attraction for patients. Cases were often brought in late stages so that tumors and cysts were sometimes of extraordinary size. Wounds from war or banditry were common; goring by water buffalo was not uncommon. Malaria (including plasmodium falciparum or "malignant malaria") was endemic in the wet delta region. Kala-azar was epidemic north of the Yangzi River, while schistosomiasis was common in the south. Tuberculosis, smallpox, tetanus (especially in newborns), rabies ("not a nice way to die," comments Dr. Felix Welton), cholera, typhoid, boils and skin infections, bacillary and amoebic dysenteries, and parasitic infestations were commonly seen. Typhus was likely to break out when there were famines. Leprosy was treated on an outpatient basis except at Cheeloo, where a leprosy hospital was built.

The mission hospitals acquired their first X-ray machines in the 1920s, and only two (certified) medical technologists were sent by PCUS to China (Elinor Myers Woods in 1931 and Ruth Worth in 1932). Perhaps these facts speak to the level of sophistication of the medical practice at this time.

A letter written in October 1926 by Dr. Philip B. Price to prospective recruits gives a good description of some of the realities of medical practice on the mission field:[16]

The language problem. Some doctors and nurses, because of busy lives, failed to acquire fluency in the language. "We were startled to find many white-haired veterans still reserving a little time each day for study with a native scholar."

Gap between reality and preconceived ideals. Buildings were antiquated and inappropriate; equipment was barely adequate for sheer necessities; assistants were keener on prestige than on routine work and self-giving service; patients expected the foreign doctor to cure, in a single visit, their complicated and long-standing ailments. "I find that missionary life is more romantic in the abstract than in the concrete."

The need for a variety of skills. In addition to confronting all sorts of medical or surgical conditions, the missionary doctor had to deal with problems of real estate, building, finance, administration, bookkeeping, organization, and teaching.

Medical isolation. At a time when the medical profession was experiencing dramatic changes, missionary physicians found it difficult to keep pace with progress in the medical world.

Interpersonal relationships. "Your biggest and most protracted surprise will be the human element." Older colleagues may not be enthusiastic about proposed changes, local doctors want the missionary doctor to carry all the responsibility, nurses frequently leave to set up practice as "Western-trained" doctors or midwives, relatives of patients may insist on occupying the adjoining bed and many filch linens, food, and supplies. "Missionaries, for the most part, are a group of independent, strong-minded, democratic people; each member of your mission rather likes to have his finger in your pie, and you may put your finger in each of their pies. And you will find that you yourself are surprisingly full of faults and failings, that you rub people the wrong way, and that you are not quite as Christ-like as you had thought."

The problem of evangelizing. "Of course your main reason for coming to the foreign field is to win souls . . . I have found more missionary doctors and nurses than one likes to admit, who simply don't do any evangelistic work at all . . . "

One last bit of advice. "Come married—if you can. It takes away the loneliness, and adds humanness; it divides the hardships and multiplies the joy."

During the 1930s the gradual military intrusion of the Japanese into the PCUS mission area became increasingly oppressive. The Japanese army destroyed one hospital, Jiangyin (Kiangyin), during their takeover in 1938; other hospitals were evacuated for a period. Travel and supplies had to cross battle lines; relations with the

Japanese officials were always delicate, depending on the personal whim of the ranking army officer; an enormous increase in the refugee population added to the burden of the mission's medical institutions. Costs of local supplies and rising inflation further complicated the operation.

By 1940 war between Japan and the United States had become increasingly likely. Tensions were high, and China was a tinderbox. The North Jiangsu Mission at an annual meeting prayed for "courage, gaiety, and a quiet mind."[17] Mission personnel were encouraged to leave or, if on furlough, to stay in the United States. Those who were in China at the time of Pearl Harbor were repatriated to the United States in prisoner-of-war exchanges in July 1942 and July 1943.

The Post–World War II Years (1946–1952)

The sudden end of World War II in mid-August 1945 came as a surprise in China. On August 1, 1945, U.S. General Albert Wedemeyer wrote the Joint Chiefs of Staff from Chonqing: "If peace comes suddenly, it is reasonable to expect widespread confusion and disorder. The Chinese have no plans for rehabilitation, prevention of epidemics, restoration of utilities, establishment of balanced economy and redisposition of refugees."[18]

In December 1945 the PCUS sent an advance team to survey the situation in the former mission areas, which had suffered severely in the nine years of Japanese occupation. Six of the ten former PCUS hospitals remained standing, though in very poor condition, lacking equipment and supplies. Cheeloo University Medical School, which had been relocated to West China for the duration of the war, prepared to reopen in the Jinan (Tsinan) location.

A single PCUS mission replaced the Mid-China and North Jiangsu missions, and the missionaries, with great enthusiasm and anticipation, prepared to return to the stations and resume operations. A number of new appointees were assigned to the Language Institute in Beijing (Peking).

In 1947 unresolved relations between the Nationalists and Communists intensified and broke into civil war. When the Red Armies took Beijing in November 1948, the high hopes of the missionaries were crushed. They assembled in Shanghai where, as one put it,

"multi-mission meetings" grappled with what to do. Missionaries
nearing retirement and those with children returned to the United
States; some went to Taiwan (at the invitation of the Canadian
Presbyterian Mission and the North Synod of the Presbyterian Church
in Taiwan); others were assigned to missions in Japan, Congo/Zaire,
Mexico, and Brazil. A consensus, based on the experience of people of
other missions, concluded that people with specialties (not preachers)
could continue work under the Communists.[19]

Medical personnel who volunteered to stay included Joseph and
Estelle Wilkerson at Jiaxing (Estelle left for the United States in
August 1949 after the birth of their first child in Shanghai.), Margaret
Wood at Huaiyin (Tsingkiangpu/TKP), Charlotte Dunlap and Ruth
Worth at Zhenjiang, Henry Nelson at Taizhou, and Lalla Iverson at
the Cheeloo University School of Medicine in Jinan.

At first it was possible to carry on the work to some degree. Then,
in December 1948, came the crucial "Battle of the Hwai Hai" just
outside Xuzhou (a North Jiangsu Mission station) involving half a
million combatants.[20] On April 24, 1949, the Red Armies crossed the
Yangzi and took Nanjing. Chiang Kai-shek and the remnants of his
government and army left for Taiwan, and the Communists claimed
victory. On October 1, 1949, Mao Zedong declared the founding of the
People's Republic of China.

Pressure against Americans increased after the start of the Korean
War in June 1950, and in July 1951, with Joe Wilkerson's departure,
the last of the PCUS medical personnel left mainland China.

Notes

1. Jonathan D. Spence, *The Search for Modern China* (New York/London:
W. W. Norton 1990), 273.
2. G. Thompson Brown, *Christianity in the People's Republic of China*
(Atlanta, Ga.: John Knox Press, 1983), 37.
3. Emily Honig, "Invisible Inequalities: The Status of Subei People in
Contemporary Shanghai," *China Quarterly*, June 1990, 273.
4. *The Missionary*, 1882, 200.
5. Ibid., 1881, 36.
6. Richard Baxter Fishburne, M.D., letter, 1882 or 1883.
7. Eva Jane Prince, *China Journal, 1889–1900: An American Missionary
Family During the Boxer Rebellion* (New York: Charles Scribner, 1989), 174.

8. P. Frank Price, *Our China Investment* (Nashville, Tenn.: Executive Committee of Foreign Missions, c. 1926), 170.

9. Ernest T. Thompson, *Presbyterians in the South*, vol. III, (Atlanta, Ga.: John Knox Press, 1973), 130–31.

10. Spence, *Search for Modern China*, 271, 282.

11. Cheung, Yuet-wah, *Missionary Medicine in China: A Study of Two Canadian Protestant Missions in China Before 1937* (New York: University Press of America, 1988), 2.

12. G. Thompson Brown, "Overseas Mission Program and Policies of the Presbyterian Church in the United States, 1861–1983: A Brief Chronology" (Atlanta, Ga.: Division of International Mission, General Assembly Board of the Presbyterian Church, typescript, 1985,), 10.

13. William E. Hocking, Chairman of the Commission of Appraisal, *Rethinking Missions: Laymen's Inquiry after 100 Years* (New York & London: Harper, 1932).

14. Orville A. Petty, ed., *Laymen's Missions Inquiry: Fact Finding Reports, Supplementary Series, Part II, vol. 5* (New York: Harper & Brothers, 1933), 425–501.

15. "Statement Regarding the Report of the Laymen's Foreign Missions Inquiry" (Nashville, Tenn.: Executive Committee of Foreign Missions of the Presbyterian Church in the U.S., pamphlet, 1933).

16. Philip B. Price, M.D., letter (partially quoted), 1936.

17. Annual Report (Nashville, Tenn.: Executive Committee of Foreign Missions of the PCUS, 1935), 19.

18. Spence, *Search for Modern China*, 484.

19. Annual Report, 1949, 12, 14.

20. Seymour Topping, *Journey between Two Chinas* (New York: Harper & Row, 1972), 24–48.

Chapter Two

Mid-China Mission

The Mid-China Mission built three hospitals: in Suzhou (Soochow), Jiangyin (Kiangyin), and Jiaxing (Kashing); and assigned staff to three interdenominational institutions: the Drum Tower Hospital in Nanjing, the Guling (Kuling) Hospital in Lushan, and the Cheeloo University Medical School in Jinan (Tsinan). The three PCUS Mid-China hospitals developed three different modes of operation:[1]

1. Elizabeth Blake Hospital/Suzhou operated under the PCUS mission's direct control, with a missionary (Dr. Mason Young) in charge.
2. Jiangyin Hospital operated under the control of a "Joint Committee" of eleven Chinese and six missionaries.
3. Jiaxing Hospital was operated by the Synod of East China under a board of directors made up of Chinese and missionaries.

The work of the hospitals is described in this chapter; the medical school is discussed in chapter 4.

ELIZABETH BLAKE HOSPITAL
Suzhou (Soochow)

Suzhou was celebrated in Chinese lore for the beauty of its canals and gardens; it was one of the first interior cities opened to foreigners by treaty agreement and became one of China's largest and more developed cities. PCUS mission work began in Suzhou in 1872; other Protestant denominations also worked in the same area.

The Elizabeth Blake Hospital of Suzhou had two distinguishing features: (1) Upon its completion in 1899 it became the *first* overseas

Elizabeth Blake Hospital, Suzhou, in 1897 was the first hospital built by the PCUS worldwide. Courtesy of Presbyterian Church (USA), Department of History (Montreat, North Carolina).

hospital to be built by the PCUS, and (2) its psychiatric unit was one of only two in all of China to provide inpatient services for the mentally ill.

The Elizabeth Blake Hospital enjoyed the leadership of two strong personalities: James Richard Wilkinson, M.D. (1894 until his resignation in 1920) and Mason Pressly Young, M.D. (1915 until the bombing of Pearl Harbor). Efforts were made to provide the hospital with two missionary physicians, but because of furloughs and other contingencies, this ideal was rarely reached.

The first two registered nurses to be appointed by the PCUS anywhere (Flora S. Alderman in 1904 and Agnes Violet Innes in 1905) were assigned to this hospital in China; both died within months of their arrival.[2] A number of nurses subsequently served there for short periods. Lucy Grier, whose seven years (1933–40) proved to be the longest time served by any nurse in Suzhou, was the daughter of Dr. Nettie D. Grier of Xuzhou. She not only had a good command of the language but was well trained, with a master's in public health from Columbia University Teachers College (1933).

James R. Wilkinson, M.D. (1894–1920)

Dr. James Wilkinson, a graduate of the South Carolina State Medical College (1885) with ten years of medical practice experience, arrived in Suzhou in 1895 to find that care of the sick was already an important mission activity. He was able to begin work immediately, without experiencing the opposition and hostility from the local people that most of the other pioneer physicians endured.

The mission bought a large tract of land outside the city wall to the north, and, with the enthusiastic assistance and support of Rev. John W. Davis, hospital construction began.[3] Professor J. R. Blake, who had taught Davis at Davidson College, gave the money for construction ($30,000) in memory of his mother, Elizabeth. Compared with the usual start-up grant of around $10,000 received by most of the mission's hospitals, this funding was munificent. In 1912 an additional $10,000 was given (by E. B. Chester of Brownsville, Tennessee) for the Women's Hospital and Nurses' Training School.[4] The buildings had both electricity and running water, and the plantings of trees and shrubs gave the grounds a parklike appearance.

Dr. Wilkinson built up a large medical plant with a strong educational as well as evangelistic outreach. By 1911 he was treating many

Nursing school students at the Elizabeth Blake Hospital, Suzhou. Courtesy of Presbyterian Church (USA), Department of History (Montreat, North Carolina).

mentally disturbed patients and soon thereafter built the 100-bed psychiatric unit. A small medical school offered a seven-year course that combined classwork with practical work in the hospital. The school had six students in 1901 and its first graduate in May 1905. The student body numbered thirty-two in 1911—the year that an interdenominational medical school was established in Nanjing.

Mason P. Young, M.D. (1915–1941)

Dr. Mason Young, a graduate of Jefferson Medical College, Philadelphia (M.D., 1913), with two years' advanced training at the Episcopal Hospital in Philadelphia, further developed the Elizabeth Blake Hospital. He expanded the psychiatric work begun by Dr. Wilkinson and oversaw the construction of additional buildings. The staff was increased, and good records were kept. Suzhou had two other hospitals that practiced Western medicine, and Dr. Young cultivated mutually beneficial relations with other medical professionals in Suzhou.

The hospital's 1933 annual report illustrates the activities of a busy, well-run institution. The year was unusual in that there was no war or political disturbances of any kind; all patients were civilians. There were also no epidemics, and no cases of cholera or meningitis were seen. The 160-bed hospital (100 beds psychiatric) had a staff of four PCUS missionaries (physicians Mason Young and Felix Welton, Lucy Grier, R.N., and Ruby Satterfield, treasurer). On the Chinese staff were six physicians, three interns, twelve nurses, forty-three student nurses, two laboratory technicians, a pharmacist, an accountant, an evangelist, and seventy-six employees. A new building for the outpatient department was completed and a third story added to the nurses' home. Financially the year was a good one and finished without a deficit.

The two most common diseases were pulmonary tuberculosis (eight deaths), and malaria (three deaths). Deaths also occurred from typhoid fever, pneumonia, beriberi, measles, and diphtheria. Ten transfusions were given during the year.

The psychiatric department reported 35 neurology and 165 mental patients discharged during the year. Patients came from eighteen provinces; the ratio of men to women was three to one. Most were from the upper social class. Dementia praecox, manic depressive, and syphilitic groups made up 65 percent of the total number; 78 percent were discharged as cured or greatly improved. Over 700 thermogenic (fever producing) injections were given using malaria and sulfosin intramuscularly and typhoid vaccine intravenously. The most favorable results were obtained in the syphilitic group.

During the Japanese invasion of 1937–38 the Elizabeth Blake Hospital was badly vandalized. Dr. Young, on his return in 1938, did not attempt to restore inpatient services. He worked instead in four refugee clinics under a joint Red Cross Committee until forced to leave for the United States in 1941.

The Elizabeth Blake Hospital was further destroyed during World War II. Some of the hospital buildings were burned; others were completely looted and left as bare shells without floors.

Jiangyin Hospital
Jiangyin (Kiangyin)

Jiangyin was a walled city located some 100 miles from Shanghai on the south bank of the Yangzi River. Forts, which had been the scene of fierce battles over the centuries, stood guard over the narrowing of the river.

Mission work, begun in 1895, initially met with hostility and persecution. During the first year a riot erupted when an infant's corpse, planted on the mission property by a malicious person, was "discovered." Missionaries were accused of killing children in order to use their organs for medicine. The property was thoroughly vandalized and the missionaries barely escaped with their lives. However, the plot was ferreted out, the culprit identified, and the missionaries exonerated.[5]

George C. Worth, M.D. (1897–1936)

By 1897 property for a mission station was purchased and George Clarkson Worth, M.D., was assigned to begin a medical program. Dr. Worth exemplified the outstanding quality of the Presbyterian medical missionaries. The grandson of North Carolina Governor Jonathan Worth (1865–68), George Worth grew up in Wilmington, North Carolina, was educated at the University of North Carolina, received his medical degree from the University of Virginia (M.D., 1892), and did three years' postgraduate work at Charity Hospital, New York City (1892–95). He married Emma Chadbourne in 1895 just before leaving for China. The Worths were "self-supporting" mission-aries, accepting no salary from the PCUS.

Dr. and Mrs. Worth's home church, the First Presbyterian Church of Wilmington, took a warm personal interest in the Worths, whom they described as "our" missionaries in China. The Presbyterians in Wilmington developed a special relationship with Jiangyin station, providing capital funds for the buildings and support for the mission-aries. Presbyterian women in Wilmington adopted the hospital as their project, raised funds for the initial building, and provided continued support. The young people raised money for the cots and "were taught to pray daily for the patient in our cot."[6]

Construction of the hospital began in 1904. Shortly after its comple-tion, one of the buildings caught fire. The people of Jiangyin quickly rallied, demonstrating a dramatic change in attitude toward the mission from the one that had provoked the riot just ten years before.

The excellent relationship between the mission and the commu-nity, in fact, became an outstanding feature of the PCUS mission's work in Jiangyin. The hospital, like all the other mission institutions in Jiangyin, operated under the control of a Joint Committee of Chinese and missionaries.

In 1924 a group of the "gentry," influential men of the town, raised money for an X-ray machine for the hospital and built a wing for the treatment of wounded soldiers. During civil strife, Dr. Worth and other missionaries were called on to serve as arbiters and, on one occasion in 1925, with bullets flying, carried the flag of truce between two warring armies. The city paved the street leading to the mission property in appreciation for the part the missionaries took in the peace negotiations after that battle. A stone tablet giving an account of the service rendered by the missionaries was put up in the pavilion at the terminus of this street.[7]

In response to the cholera epidemic that devastated the area in 1932, the Jiangyin hospital staff treated some 400 cases of cholera and vacci-nated hundreds more. Dr. Worth estimated that 4,100 pints of saline solution weighing around two tons were administered to victims of the disease. A stupendous amount of work went into the preparation, as well as administration, of these solutions, which were made from steril-ized, filtered rain water. Dr. Worth wrote, "Doctors, orderlies, nurses were all weary but cheerful . . . Do you wonder that I am proud to be a fellow worker with such folks, and a fellow Christian with them?"[8]

Woman's ward at the Jiangyin (Kiangyin) Hospital. Photograph courtesy of Ruth Ward.

One of Dr. Worth's primary aims was to develop Chinese leadership in the medical field. He trained a staff of qualified Chinese physicians and encouraged the Chinese to assume responsibility and authority as soon as they were able.[9] As early as 1912 a Dr. Wang, trained by Dr. Wilkinson at Suzhou, ran the hospital during Dr. Worth's furlough year. Dr. Worth later turned the administration of the hospital over to Dr. Y. L. Chen and concentrated his own energies in obstetrics and gynecology.

Dr. Worth served as the only missionary doctor at Jiangyin during most of his forty-one years of service. Drs. Francis R. Crawford and Charles H. Voss served with him for short periods of time. Emma Worth died in 1926; Dr. Worth died at the age of sixty-nine in 1936 in Shanghai. Both were buried in Jiangyin.

Ida McKay Albaugh, R.N., (1908–19) started the nursing school in Jiangyin and was instrumental in founding the Chinese Nursing Association, which, among other things, set standards, administered examinations for R.N. certification, and gave accreditation to Chinese nursing schools.

Dr. Worth's daughter, Ruth, was one of two certified medical technologists who served the PCUS in China. Because of the depression in 1932, the church could not afford to send her, and so her father provided support for Ruth Worth's first term of service. She directed the laboratories, trained technicians by the apprentice method, and engaged in research on malaria.

Alexander S. Moffett, M.D. (1936–1940)

Alexander S. Moffett, a graduate of Vanderbilt University Medical School (M.D., 1932), was assigned to Jiangyin in 1935 just before Dr. Worth's death and served until forced to evacuate in 1940. Dr. Moffett, a member of a large missionary family with more than a dozen aunts, uncles, and cousins serving in China, grew up in Jiangyin and described it as "a nice place in which to grow up."[10]

Dr. Moffett was impressed with the level of the Chinese leadership. In addition to Dr. Chen, superintendent, he remembers Dr. Ma, a skillful surgeon and delightful coworker, and the head nurse who was renowned for her work in the nursing profession and as a midwife; several interns were in training.

Dr. Moffett considered his main contributions to be the institution of medical recordkeeping and coding of diagnoses, and the making of intravenous solutions from distilled water, which eliminated the chills caused by filtered rain water. The records were kept in English; the staff liked learning medical English, and Dr. Moffett never achieved his goal of keeping the records in Chinese. To distill water, Dr. Moffett had a local tinsmith make a still similar to a bootlegger's still.

In 1938 the Japanese invaded the area and burned the Jiangyin mission compound including the hospital buildings. For a while the Chinese staff ran a small twenty-bed hospital in a nursing school building that had escaped the burning, but this operation was discontinued after a guerrilla attack in which staff members were beaten.

During the brief 1946–49 postwar period, an effort was made to revive the medical work in Jiangyin with a Chinese physician in charge. According to an overly optimistic report in 1950, "The work in the hospital . . . is coming back to the place it previously held in this whole section."[11]

JIAXING HOSPITAL
Jiaxing (Kashing)

Jiaxing is an important city on the railroad about halfway between Shanghai and Hangzhou. The 225-bed hospital established by the PCUS in Jiaxing became "one of the largest and most important medical centers in Central China," where training as well as treatment was a high priority.[12]

Early History to 1927

Wade Hampton Venable, M.D., the pioneer, graduated from the University of Virginia (M.D., 1889) and had some five years of postgraduate training in a number of hospitals. While on shipboard during the eighteen-day voyage to China, he fell in love with a fellow passenger who was also en route to China as a PCUS missionary; his marriage to Eliza Talbot took place on September 26, 1893, one day after the SS *City of Peking* docked in Shanghai.

In 1895 the Venables were assigned to begin work in the fiercely antiforeign walled city of Jiaxing. Dr. Venable and Rev. W. H. Hudson rented a small house outside the north gate and established a preaching hall and dispensary. Crowds of people came for treatment in the clinic, a room ten-by-ten feet with a dirt floor. By spring the wives were able to join their husbands, and land was purchased for what was to become a distinguished medical institution.

The first hospital buildings were modified Chinese houses. In 1908 Mrs. A. J. A. Alexander of Spring Station, Kentucky, gave funds for the construction of "a commodious and well equipped modern hospital."[13] In 1917 the "Ladies Foreign Missionary Society" of New Orleans raised $15,000 for a four-story women's building named in memory of Rev. Benjamin Morgan Palmer, the distinguished minister of the First Presbyterian Church of the city. The "Ladies" continued to support the Jiaxing Hospital and, again in 1925, raised money for an extension to the Palmer Building. An elevator and flush toilets were unique features of this new building.[14]

Dr. Venable, in addition to his hospital duties, taught the Bible, translated Archinard's *Bacteriology* into the Chinese language, and served (1915–17) as president of the China Medical Missionary Association. In 1917 poor health forced him to retire from the Jiaxing Hospital.

Allen C. Hutcheson, M.D., a surgeon, joined Dr. Venable in 1908 and served at the Jiaxing Hospital until asked in 1917 to take charge of the surgical department of the Nanjing University (Drum Tower) Hospital.

Francis R. Crawford, M.D., a surgeon, became director of the Jiaxing Hospital in 1917 upon the departure of Drs. Venable and Hutcheson. A graduate of the Johns Hopkins School of Medicine (M.D., 1911) with postgraduate training both in the United States and in Germany, Dr. Crawford led the hospital into a productive period.

Jiaxing Hospital's premier nurse, Elizabeth Corriher, R.N., was a true pioneer of the nursing profession. She had the distinction in 1906 of having taken the first examination for nurses to be given in the state of Virginia.[15] Elizabeth Corriher established a strong nursing program at Jiaxing Hospital and founded the Nurses' Training School, which was accredited in 1918 by the Chinese Nurses' Association.

For a brief period, between 1921 and 1927, Jiaxing Hospital attained the mission's goal of having two missionary physicians and two nurses. Edwin W. (M.D.) and Bessie K. (R.N.) Buckingham were a doctor/nurse couple; the contribution made by Rubye Mae Diehl, R.N., was enhanced by her postgraduate training in X ray, laboratory, and anesthesia.

1927 to 1941

The presence of medical missionaries at the Kashing Hospital was greatly reduced following the evacuation of 1927. The mission continued to provide support and cooperation, but no more missionary medical personnel were assigned to Jiaxing except for Dr. Crawford (to 1932). For two years (1927–29) the hospital was rented to a Chinese group under the leadership of the Chinese superintendent (Chen Tsai-En, M.D.)[16] In 1929 the management was turned over to the Synod of East China under a board made up of Chinese and missionaries.[17]

The Jiaxing Hospital was badly damaged during the 1937–38 Japanese war. Both Chinese and Japanese soldiers occupied the buildings and the north end of the Palmer Memorial Building was demolished by bombs. The other buildings were thoroughly looted and ruined.

In 1939, under Japanese occupation, the hospital buildings were repaired, and E. M. Lippa, M.D., a Jewish refugee from Austria, was engaged as director. Refugees, welfare children, and orphanages were the major concerns.[18]

Post–World War II (1946–1951)

During World War II the city of Jiaxing became the location of a large Japanese military training facility. The Japanese used the hospital complex as an officers' billet, and it was terribly abused. Jiaxing continued as an important military base under both the Nationalists (after 1945) and the Communists (after 1949).

In the spring of 1946, Dr. Mason P. Young and his wife were among the first group of PCUS missionaries to return to postwar China. Rather than return to Suzhou where the Elizabeth Blake Hospital had been virtually destroyed, Dr. Young accepted assignment to Jiaxing to develop a teaching hospital for the mid-China area.

The buildings were basically intact though in deplorable condition. The Youngs began renovation ("shoveled out truckloads of garbage") and collected supplies and equipment. The hospital board was reactivated, and the hospital reopened with a U.S.-trained Chinese pediatrician (Dr. Hsiang Teh-Chuan) as superintendent. The hospital was soon "full and running over."[19]

When the Communist takeover became imminent, the Jiaxing Hospital Board asked that the neophyte medical missionaries, Dr. Joseph L. and Mrs. Estelle I. Wilkerson, be assigned to the Jiaxing Hospital. The Wilkersons, having been persuaded that medical people would be allowed by the Communists to practice undisturbed, agreed to the assignment.

Joseph Wilkerson, M.D., thirty-five years old, had completed medical school (University of Virginia, M.D., 1942), three years of postgraduate work, two years in the U.S. Navy, and one and a half years of Chinese language study (in Yale and Beijing). Estelle Wilkerson, R.N., had a B.S. in nursing education from the University of Virginia. They were married in January 1948 just before leaving for China. Both were eager to begin their missionary vocation and put their expertise to use where the need was so great. Their experience under Communist rule turned out to be an extraordinary ordeal.[20]

After the departure in early 1949 of Dr. and Mrs. Mason Young (for retirement) and of Rev. and Mrs. George A. Hudson (for work in Taiwan), the Wilkersons (and a Catholic priest) became the only American missionaries left in Jiaxing. Estelle Wilkerson became pregnant. She worked in the hospital for a period until a nurses' strike, instigated by the Communists, disrupted the nursing service. In August (1949) she went to Shanghai for X rays, went into labor, and delivered their first child. Dr. Wilkerson was unable to get a travel permit to see his wife and baby before they left for the United States. From August 1949 to July 1951, although not physically abused, Dr. Wilkerson, lacking Chinese language expertise and the support of an experienced missionary, was very alone as he endured life at the hands of the Communists.

The hospital continued to operate after the Communist takeover although the Chinese physicians did not stay. Until late in 1950 Dr. Wilkerson treated patients in the clinic and did some surgery. Twice he was asked to operate on Communists: a female spy with appendicitis and a colonel who was in a jeep accident. The latter operation was done in the hospital on the military base. Then an epidemic of acute schistosomiasis broke out among the Communists. Schistosomiasis, caused by a water-transmitted blood fluke, was endemic in the area whose local people had developed a degree of immunity. Eighty hospital beds were kept filled with susceptible northerners. Many believe that the severity of the epidemic among the Communist military may have caused them to call off their planned invasion of Taiwan.[21]

The Communists required the hospital to purchase all its supplies and medicines on the local market. Dr. Wilkerson was forbidden to use any of the hospital's large quantity of medical supplies, which included a newly arrived, complete U.S. Army field hospital in unopened boxes. Instead he was required to inventory these supplies, much of which, he speculates, ended up with the Chinese forces fighting in Korea.

The hospital was required to send a representative to public executions and other events. On one occasion the Christians of Jiaxing were told they had to criticize the missionaries at a public event. The Christian leaders met and selected for opprobrium a female missionary who had long since died, calling her an "imperialist warmonger" and other epithets. One of the Chinese leaders explained, "In Heaven she will know and understand . . . it can't hurt her."

For seven months beginning in late 1950 Dr. Wilkerson was virtually confined to a room in his home. Accompanied by a guard, he was allowed to attend church, but was required to sit on the back row and not speak to anyone. He was allowed to receive a few letters from his wife. A Chinese cook fed him as best he could on a diet consisting primarily of peanuts, sweet potatoes, and rice. Dr. Wilkerson gained weight but suffered from avitaminosis and began to lose sensation in his fingers.

In July 1951 missionaries in Hong Kong learned of Dr. Wilkerson's plight. They were able to send him money (three million *reninpiao* in Chinese currency) through the bank, with which he paid off the cook, light bills, and taxes. He was required to advertise in the paper that he was leaving so that debts could be settled. Finally he was granted an exit permit and went by train via Shanghai to Hong Kong and by ship to the United States. In 1953 the Wilkersons were assigned to Taiwan, where they served until their retirement in 1980.

UNION WORK

The Mid-China Mission furnished personnel to three union (interdenominational) institutions: Cheeloo University Medical School (discussed in chapter 4), the Drum Tower Hospital in Nanjing, and the hospital at Guling (Lushan). In addition Mary N. Woodbridge, M.D., practiced medicine at a rescue mission in Shanghai.

The Nanjing University Medical College and Drum Tower Hospital, Nanjing

The Drum Tower Hospital received its name from its location next to Nanjing's ancient drum tower, whose huge drums signaled the opening and closing of the city gates and warned of fires and the approach of hostile forces. The hospital, founded in 1892 by W. E. Macklin, M.D., of the Disciples of Christ in China, became in 1909 the hospital for the Nanjing University Medical College. Randolph T. Shields, M.D., a leading spirit in the founding of the medical college, served as its dean and taught anatomy, embryology, and histology; he also practiced obstetrics in the hospital.

In 1917 Nanjing University Medical College united with the Cheeloo University Medical School and moved to Jinan. The Drum Tower Hospital continued as an interdenominational institution.[22] When Dr. Shields moved with the medical school to Jinan, the Mid-China Mission assigned Allen C. Hutcheson, M.D., from Jiaxing to Nanjing. In 1920 Dr. Hutcheson, a fellow of the American College of Surgeons (1920) and editor of the *China Medical Journal* (1913–15), became the superintendent.[23]

In 1927 all missionary personnel, under imminent threat to their lives, were forced to evacuate Nanjing on very short notice. Dr. Hutcheson was among those who did not return to China.[24]

Guling (Kuling) Hospital, Lushan

Wade Hampton Venable, M.D., suffered a physical breakdown in 1917 and was transferred in 1919 from Jiaxing to Guling in the beautiful Lushan mountains of central China. This mountain retreat, where many foreigners and Chinese fled each summer to escape the Yangzi River "oven," is credited with saving the lives of many missionary children who were at risk in the hot, humid, mosquito-infected delta country. Rev. P. Frank Price in his book, *Our China Investment*, lists forty missionary children who died in China before 1927.[25] The year-round 140-bed hospital was primarily a tuberculosis sanatorium but offered other services as well.

Shanghai

Mary Elizabeth Newell Woodbridge, M.D., did not serve in a PCUS mission hospital but applied her training and talents through other means. A graduate of Northwestern (M.D., 1901), she went to China in 1904 with the Women's Union Missionary Society of America. In 1915 she married Rev. Samuel I. Woodbridge, a PCUS missionary whose wife had died some years earlier. Mary Elizabeth Woodbridge practiced medicine from 1915 to 1929 at the "Door of Hope," a rescue mission for Chinese girls in Shanghai.

Notes

1. Annual Report, (Minutes of the PCUS General Assembly, 1932) 29.
2. The cause of the deaths not determined.
3. The decision to build outside the city wall was influenced by the presence of a Methodist hospital in the center of the city.
4. Samuel H. Chester, "Our Own Medical Missions," *Mission Survey*, August 1916, 590–98.
5. Lacy Little, *Rivershade: Historical Sketch of Kiangyin Station, China*, c. 1925, 8–11.
6. Eliza Wright Murphy, "The Story of Kiangyin Hospital," pamphlet printed by the Wilmington Presbyterial Auxiliary, 1926.
7. Little, *Rivershade*, 50, 54–58.
8. George C. Worth, M.D., letter to the Ladies of the Wilmington Presbyterial Auxiliary, September 30, 1932.
9. Ruth Worth, M.T., interview, 1984.
10. Alexander S. Moffett, M.D., interview, 1990.
11. Annual Report, 1950, 81.
12. P. Frank Price, *Our China Investment*, (Nashville, Tenn.: Executive Committee of Foreign Missions, c. 1926), 43.
13. Annual Report, 1916, 591. The Alexander family generously supported the mission program in China and in Korea. In 1902 Dr. A. J. A. Alexander was appointed a missionary to Korea but, upon the death of his father, returned to the United States after only a few weeks.

14. "History," Ladies Foreign Missionary Society, First Presbyterian Church, New Orleans, La., typescript.

15. Price, *Our China Investment*, 80.

16. Album celebrating the fortieth year of the founding of Kashing Hospital, in Chinese, 1935.

17. Annual Report, 1929, 40.

18. Ibid.,1932, 29.

19. Ibid., 1948, 60.

20. Joseph L., M.D., and Estelle Wilkinson, R.N., interviews, 1984 and 1991.

21. Henry Nelson, M.D., interview, 1994.

22. Support for the Drum Tower Hospital was provided by the Presbyterian Boards (North and South), the Methodist Board (North), and the Disciples of Christ.

23. Price, *Our China Investment*, 80.

24. Zhang Quanfu, M.D., letter, 1986. The government of the People's Republic of China took over the Drum Tower Hospital in 1951; by 1986 it had become the largest hospital in Nanjing, with 600 beds, a staff of over 1,000 persons, 20 departments, and 2,500 outpatients per day.

25. Price, *Our China Investment*, 176–79.

Chapter Three

North Jiangsu Mission

The North Jiangsu Mission area stretched from the Yangzi River north to the border of Shandong Province, a distance of about 300 miles, and from the Yellow Sea to an indefinite point in the west. Working out of Zhenjiang (Chinkiang) where the Grand Canal crossed the Yangzi River, PCUS missionaries established stations in four walled cities north along the Grand Canal: Huaiyin (Tsingkiangpu/TKP) in 1887, Suqien (Sutsien) in 1894, Xuzhou (Hsuchow) in 1896, and Huaian (Hwaian) in 1897. Stations were next established to the east and parallel to the Grand Canal: the port city of Haizhou (Haichow) in 1905, Yencheng in 1913, and Taizhou (Taichow) in 1915. Programs at these eight stations were the principal providers of modern medicine in a very large, heavily populated region.

Most of the hospitals followed the classic one-doctor/one-nurse model. An exception was the TKP General Hospital at Huaiyin, which developed into a multispecialty institution with teaching and research components—the largest (380 beds) PCUS mission hospital in the world prior to World War II.[1] Xuzhou had two hospitals and was assigned two missionary physicians; the Women's Hospital and the Men's Hospital operated separately until after the missionaries left.

TSINGKIANGPU (TKP) GENERAL HOSPITAL
Huaiyin (Tsingkiangpu)

Early History

Three Woods brothers were among the pioneers who began the work at Huaiyin (TKP). Rev. Henry Woods (1884–1929), a distinguished

51

scholar and linguist, led the way in 1887 and was joined by Drs. Edgar Jr. and James Baker in 1888 and 1894. In 1980 Hanover Presbytery (Virginia) celebrated the 400 cumulative years of service to the PCUS overseas mission program contributed by nineteen members of this family.

The Huaiyin (TKP) area to which Drs. Edgar and James Woods were assigned was a tough one. In this conservative, rural area plagued by banditry and famine, the Chinese were extremely hostile and suspicious. They circulated terrible tales of how the Western doctors were cutting out eyes and hearts, drinking blood, and so on. Purchase of land was difficult, accomplished only in 1896 after settlement in a *yamen* (legal) case. An ever-increasing volume of patients were cared for in primitive buildings and with inadequate equipment. Supervision of famine relief in the "great" famines of 1907, 1910, and 1912 was an added burden to the staff but created goodwill in the community.

After twelve years (in 1899) Dr. Edgar Woods was forced to resign because of his wife's poor health. Dr. James Woods's term of service (forty-eight years) was the longest served worldwide by any PCUS medical missionary.

Described as a modest man, Dr. James Woods was intelligent (graduating with high honors in 1890 from the University of Virginia), spiritual (never asked for anything saying, "God knows what we need"), and fun loving. Known as an excellent teacher, he was invited to join the faculty of the Nanjing University Medical College but chose to stick with his assignment in the remote up-country. He encouraged the missionaries to develop healthy mental and physical habits along with handling their heavy work schedules; he promoted summer vacations to the mountains (and talked "like a Dutch uncle" to those who didn't want to take a vacation); and he supported the plan to have monthly "social" evenings in which no business was discussed.[2]

During the Boxer Rebellion, Dr. James Woods and Rev. James Graham remained in Huaiyin (TKP) after others evacuated because word had come that the Griers from Xuzhou were arriving with a sick child. The town was in an uproar and Dr. Woods tells of trying to play chess while a mob howled outside the house. Early in the evening came a knock at the door and the Griers, disguised in Chinese clothing, slipped in. Dr. Woods walked the floor all night to prevent baby Isobel from crying and alerting the mob. In the early morning the Griers and the two men climbed a back wall and escaped to safety in a small boat that had been prepared for them.

The Love and Mercy Hospital

In 1912 (twenty-seven years after Dr. Edgar Woods's arrival), the mission acquired a large tract of land across the Grand Canal from the city, and in 1914 a proper hospital was completed. The "Love and Mercy Hospital" cost $9,500, had eighty beds, was built of brick along modern lines, had a corrugated iron roof, and was located on grounds that were spacious and had ample sunshine and fresh air. Assisting Dr. James Woods were two Chinese doctors who had been trained in mission schools. Mrs. Woods described the opening ceremonies:

> The microscope and sterilizer excited more interest than anything else, unless it was the "lift"; some of the gentlemen were considered almost recklessly brave when they consented to make the trip from one floor to the other . . . I wish you could have seen their excitement over the extended view they got from the third-story windows. They had never been so high up nor seen so far in all their lives . . . The little-foot ladies, who had never had occasion to climb a staircase before, had to sit down and slide down the steps as they did not dare try to walk down them.[3]

In 1916 L. Nelson Bell, M.D., a recent graduate of the Medical College of Virginia, answered an emergency request to provide relief for Dr. Woods. It is to the credit of both that Dr. Woods and Dr. Bell, a winsome but strong personality (described by a fellow missionary as "this human dynamo who has hit our station"),[4] were able to work together in harmony. Despite differences in age and temperament, these two men provided dynamic leadership to the TKP General Hospital. Both were dedicated to providing the highest possible quality of professional care along with the proclamation of the gospel of Jesus Christ.

The primary nurse at the TKP Hospital was Cassie Lee Oliver (Talbot), R.N., and her twenty years of service coincided with the hospital's most productive period of growth. Both Mrs. (Bessie) Woods and Mrs. (Virginia) Bell took an active part in the work of the hospital; Mrs. Woods as supervisor of laundry and supplies and Mrs. Bell as

Tsingkiangpu General Hospital, Huaiyin, 380-bed multispecialty hospital, the largest PCUS hospital worldwide prior to World War II. Photograph courtesy of Virginia Somerville.

supervisor of the women's clinic. Mrs. Woods took special delight in the annual donation of White Cross linens from the women of the Synod of Virginia; she dyed the pastel baby clothes a bright red in keeping with the Chinese custom of dressing their babies in bright colors.

The hospital flourished. Electricity was installed in 1921–22. A tuberculosis facility was built in 1923 and the "Houston Unit" in 1924.[5] The Nursing School was established and accredited in 1926.

The TKP Hospital also supported a clinic at Huaian (Hwaian) where William Malcolm, M.D., served in 1912 just long enough to build a residence and small dispensary. From 1913 to 1940 Ellen Baskervill Yates, R.N., operated the clinic, which the TKP physicians visited on a regular basis. In the earliest days the ten-mile trip down the Grand Canal was made by a small motor launch. After a road was built, travel was possible by motorcycle or by car (the so-called Baby Austin could barely negotiate the narrow Huaian streets). Ellen Yates's clinic became an important link to modern medical care for the citizens of this city of over 100,000 persons.

1927 Evacuation and Developments in the 1930s

In 1927 the missionary personnel in Huaiyin (TKP) were forced to evacuate. The Chinese staff remained and kept the hospital open and intact. The largest single loss was the destruction of the X-ray machine.[6]

A selection of facts gleaned from the TKP General Hospital's annual reports (1929–40) reveal the scope of work done at Huaiyin (TKP).[7] The staff treated diphtheria (epidemics were common), three kinds of malaria (the "malignant" malaria, not usually found north of the Yangzi River, began to appear as refugees from the south moved into the area), 1,800 sick soldiers in one year, 100 cases of leprosy in the outpatient clinic, opium addiction, and kala-azar. Blood transfusions were becoming accepted by 1934. Sulpha drugs were mentioned in the

1940 report ("no one scientific discovery of recent years has proven itself as suited to the needs of our work as have these new drugs"). Cooperation with the police department in public health measures included inoculations for smallpox, the teaching of midwives, and public health education. Weekly visits to the jail for religious services and a clinic were parts of the hospital's program; Dr. Bell reported seeing the head of an executed prisoner hanging over the city gate with the bandage he had applied still in place.[8]

The financing of a hospital, a difficult problem in any land, was further complicated in China by the poverty of patients, the high cost of imported drugs and supplies, inflation, and increasing cost of local products. The goal was to make the hospital as self-supporting as possible, and mission appropriations, other than missionary salaries and capital investments, were small; overseas gifts and relief funds were critical.

Benjamin Clayton, a philanthropist from Houston, Texas, made it possible for the hospital, despite the depression of the 1930s, to expand its program in innovative ways. Three of these initiatives were unique to the TKP Hospital.

Accredited Intern/Residency Program

The accredited intern/residency program for young American doctors began in 1929. The four who participated were Norman G. Patterson (Medical College of Virginia, M.D., 1929), P. Kenneth Gieser (Northwestern University, M.D., 1934), Kirk T. Mosley (Tulane University, M.D., 1939), and T. Chalmers "Chal" Vinson (University of Texas, M.D., 1940); all four applied for full-time missionary service.

In 1984, Dr. Mosley, then clinical professor in family practice and community medicine at the University of Oklahoma College of Medicine, wrote, "The internship was a great experience. Dr. Woods was an excellent clinician and teacher. The number and variety of diseases were great. . . . Dr. Bell was a skillful surgeon and the surgical wards were always full."[9]

The Treatment of Kala-azar

This parasitic disease was first seen in the Jinan, Xuzhou, and Suqien hospitals. It gradually swept southward reaching epidemic proportions in the Huaiyin (TKP) area by 1929. The disease was fatal unless treated, but the drugs were highly toxic and the treatment required careful supervision.

Staff at the TKP General Hospital in 1934. Left to right: Drs. I. P. Wu (medicine), J. B. Woods Sr. (medicine), P. K. Gieser (intern), L. N. Bell (surgery), C. T. Ts'ao (ophthalmology), and I. S. Koh (medicine). Photograph courtesy of Virginia Somerville.

The adjoining boys' school property became available and was made into a fifty-bed kala-azar unit. Many cases were treated on an outpatient basis, and a research program was set up to test the use of new drugs. Patients with kala-azar numbered 3,283 in 1932, 4,048 in 1939, and 4,717 in 1940.

Certified Medical Technologist

The appointment in 1931 of a certified medical technologist, Elinor Myers (who became Mrs. J. Russell Woods in 1934) raised the professional standards of the hospital, upgraded the laboratories, and contributed to the research on drugs used for kala-azar. She also helped Dr. Bell prepare reports of his cases as part of the requirements for admittance to the American College of Surgeons.

Under Japanese Occupation (1937–1945)

During the occupation of the area by Japan in 1937, Huaiyin (TKP) was severely bombed (forty-seven air raids and nine bombings), but the hospital, with its American flag flying, was not hit. After the

Japanese took control, the missionaries managed to establish and maintain a relatively workable relationship with the Japanese officials. To quote:

> We have sought to scrupulously maintain our status as citizens of a third power and Christian missionaries, and have continued without interruption our work of healing the sick and preaching the gospel . . . we have found that [the Japanese] have treated us and this hospital fairly.[10]

As threat of war between Japan and the United States increased, the missionary staff was sharply reduced. Dr. James B. Woods Sr., who reached the official retirement age in 1937, continued his service at the TKP Hospital by special request until November 1940. The Nelson Bells went on furlough in May 1941. Missionary personnel at the hospital were Cassie Lee Oliver Talbot, R.N., Dr. Chal Vinson, and Rev. James Nelson Montgomery from nearby Huaian, who became superintendent. In August 1941 the nine Americans then in Huaiyin (TKP) were incarcerated for sixteen days on the second floor of one of the missionary residences. They were told this action was in retaliation for the freezing of Japanese assets by the United States. This incident was a foretaste of what lay ahead after December 7, 1941.[11]

In September 1941 Dr. and Mrs. Vinson received exit permits and went, with other new missionaries, to the Philippines to continue study of the Chinese language in what was considered a safer environment; unfortunately they ended up spending the war years interned in Japanese prisoner-of-war camps there. After Pearl Harbor, the missionaries in Huaiyin were confined to the hospital complex until they were repatriated in the July 1942 prisoner-of-war exchange.

During World War II the hospital continued functioning, with Chinese doctors and staff and under tight Japanese control.[12] At the end of the war the institution was still in operation but rundown, dirty, and lacking supplies and equipment.

Post–World War II (1946–1951)

In October 1946 Margaret Wood, R.N., was assigned to Huaiyin (TKP) to act as interpreter for the United Nations Rehabilitation and Relief Administration (UNRRA) team that was in the process of rehabilitating the hospital. (Her earlier experience in the Suqien Hospital is described in the next section of this chapter.) The UNRRA team stayed in Huaiyin (TKP) until the arrival, in 1947, of mission personnel: Cassie Lee Talbot, R.N., Margaret Wood, R.N., and Chal Vinson, M.D.

In 1948 Margaret Wood elected to continue at Huaiyin (TKP) after Cassie Lee Talbot and the Vinsons (with one small child and another on the way) returned to the United States. In December the Nationalists, who were in full retreat following the great Battle of the Hwai Hai (discussed earlier), swept through Huaiyin. They ordered Margaret Wood to evacuate to Zhenjiang and provided space for her and two small suitcases on one of their trucks. The Nationalists then burned the hospital to prevent its being taken by the Communists. Many of the staff made their way to Zhenjiang carrying medical supplies with which they were able to open a clinic for refugees from the north.[13]

Both hospitals in which Margaret Wood served (Suqien and Huaiyin/TKP) were burned. She said, "It was hard to see anything successful during those years [1946–51], but the presence and power of the Spirit and faith and courage of the Chinese Christians was always an inspiration and comfort."[14]

SUQIEN HOSPITAL
Suqien (Sutsien)

In 1894 the PCUS opened a station at Suqien, a walled city of some 100,000 persons located where the Grand Canal crossed the old Yellow River bed halfway between Huaiyin (TKP) and Xuzhou. Suqien was not a friendly town, and the only place the missionaries found to live was in a mud-walled inn next to the city wall in the red-light district of town. Anyone walking along the embankment inside the wall could throw stones into the courtyard. This the Chinese delighted in doing whenever they saw one of the "foreign devils."

The three primary physicians in Suqien were Annie Houston Patterson, John W. Bradley, and Norman G. Patterson. Margaret P. Wood, R.N., was left in charge of the hospital between 1937 and 1941.

Annie Houston Patterson, M.D. (1894–1922)

Rev. Brown Craig Patterson and his wife, Annie Houston Patterson, M.D., were among the pioneers in Suqien. Dr. Patterson, the only physician within a sixty-mile radius, immediately began treating the sick. Her letters tell of a parade of skin diseases and boils, carbuncles and ulcers, malaria, typhus, leprosy and opium addiction. The following incident is thought by the missionaries in Suqien to have been the turning point in Chinese acceptance of the mission:

> [One day] a family brought their son to be cured. [Dr. Patterson] looked at his terribly distended abdomen and realized he was dying from intestinal worms. She also recognized that she was being tested and would be run out of town if he died. She knew she had to treat him to be accepted by the crowd. She had them put the boy on a mat in the middle of the courtyard so everyone could see, those on the city wall as well as those in the yard. She then gave him small doses of medicine at intervals. She tried to explain what the trouble was and then she watched and prayed. As the boy began to expel the worms the crowd became very excited and much friendlier. When the boy was able to get up and go home the whole mood of the crowd changed to one of appreciation of the foreigner.[15]

After seven years Dr. Patterson was joined by John W. Bradley, M.D. Although listed in the mission records as an "evangelistic missionary," she continued her dispensary and assisted Dr. Bradley in the hospital. Along with raising a family of five children, this remarkable woman is reported to have treated as many as 10,000 persons a year in her clinics. She also wrote a Chinese catechism that received wide circulation.[16]

John W. Bradley, M.D. (1901–1929)

Twenty-six-year-old John Wilson Bradley, M.D., a graduate of the South Carolina State Medical College at Charleston in 1896, arrived in China in 1899. His fiancee, Mamie McCollum, joined him in 1901, and they were married in Shanghai before going to Suqien. In 1903 the Bradley family, including a year-old son, was en route by houseboat to Suqien from a vacation in the mountains when Mamie Bradley contracted cholera and died within a few hours. In 1906 Dr. Bradley married Agnes Tinsley Junkin, who had arrived in China in 1904.

Suqien Hospital was built in 1912 with $10,000 raised at the 1908 Laymen's Convention in Birmingham, Alabama. Construction was hampered by general unrest resulting from famine and the downfall of the Qing Dynasty. At one point, kilns, constructed for the production of brick for the hospital, were vandalized.

60 A LEGACY REMEMBERED

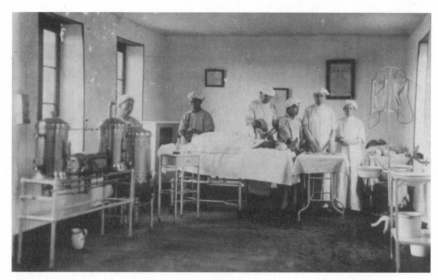

Operating room in the Suqien Hospital. Photograph courtesy of G. Thompson Brown.

Dr. Bradley served in Suqien from 1901 until his death in 1929 and was known for his service to famine sufferers and victims of banditry. He was fortunate in having the help of Dr. Annie Patterson. Others who served in Suqien for short periods were Charles H. Voss, M.D., and Carrie Knox Williams, R.N.

Norman G. Patterson, M.D. (1929–1937)

Norman Guthrie Patterson, M.D., was assigned to Suqien after Dr. Bradley's death in 1929. The son of Craig and Annie Patterson, Norman Patterson was born and grew up in Suqien and was the first of the American medical school graduates to take part in the rotating internship program at the TKP General Hospital. While at TKP, Norman Patterson happily accepted the weekly assignment to visit the Huaian clinic because of the presence there of Athalie Hallum, a lovely young teacher of missionary children. They were married in 1930.

The Suqien Hospital was the smallest of the North Jiangsu hospitals and not well equipped. Norman Patterson carried on an active surgical practice until 1937 when he returned to the United States for furlough and further surgical training; he was unable to return because of the war.

In 1936 Norman Patterson recruited Margaret Poague Wood, R.N., a graduate of the University of Pennsylvania Nursing School (R.N.,

1934). While attending classes at the Assembly's Training School in Richmond, Virginia, she met Norman Patterson, who, despite the depression, was able to secure funds for her appointment to Suqien. After one year in language school in Beijing, she went to Suqien and served there until Pearl Harbor.

Margaret P. Wood, R.N. (1936–1941)

As already mentioned, Margaret Wood was in charge of the hospital from the time of Norman Patterson's departure in 1937 until April 1941, and she describes the conditions as akin to constant wartime conditions. On one occasion, in fact, with the help of the senior male nurse, Margaret Wood amputated the leg of a seriously injured man; he healed without complication. Her main work, however, consisted of relief activities for refugees and the management of patients with kala-azar. Getting supplies from Shanghai across Japanese lines was a major problem.[17]

The Japanese burned the Suqien Hospital during World War II.

XUZHOU HOSPITALS
Xuzhou (Hsuchow)

In 1897 when the PCUS opened work in Xuzhou, this was its most remote station in North Jiangsu. The journey, some 300 miles north of the Yangzi River, took up to four hard, tedious weeks. Later, Xuzhou became a railroad hub where the north-south Nanjing to Beijing line crosses the east-west Xian to Lainyungang (Haizhou) line. Once Xuzhou could be reached from Shanghai by train in twenty-four hours, it developed into a city of considerable industrial and commercial activity.

Medical Missionaries at Xuzhou

The primary physicians in Xuzhou were Henrietta D. Grier at the Women's Hospital and Archibald A. McFadyen at the Men's Hospital. Others who served at Xuzhou include Rev. Lynford L. Moore, M.D. (1897–1902) and L. Gladys Smithwick, M.D. (1929–36), both of whom resigned for health reasons. Gladys Smithwick later became the first PCUS woman physician in Zaire, serving there from 1949 to 1964.

Henrietta D. Grier, M.D. ("Aunt Nettie"), was one of the earliest missionaries assigned to Xuzhou. Known to the Chinese as "Guh

Dai-foo" (Dr. Guh), she was the kind of person around whom legends grow. She arrived in China as a missionary of the Northern Presbyterian Church (UPUSA) and became a missionary of the Southern Church (PCUS) in 1896 after her marriage to Rev. Mark Brown Grier.

The first years in Xuzhou, as in other parts of the North Jiangsu area, were difficult. The Griers were misunderstood, maligned, feared, and persecuted by bitterly hostile local people. With energy and goodwill, Aunt Nettie helped to break down the barriers by her care, primarily, of women and children. Trained in surgery as well as medicine, she made a specialty of cataract surgery and built a multitude of friends among those who had been blind and could now see. At the time of the Boxer Rebellion in 1900, a telegraph operator, at the risk of his own life, warned the Griers of the imperial edict to "kill the foreigners," thus giving them time to escape with their baby by boat to Huaiyin (TKP) and then to Japan.[18]

Archibald Alexander McFadyen, M.D., a graduate of the North Carolina Medical College (M.D., 1903), arrived in Xuzhou in 1904 to assume responsibility for the men's work of the hospital. He and Dr. Grier built and operated separate institutions but covered for each other when needed.

Dr. McFadyen's fiancee, Catherine Williams, followed him to China, and their marriage took place in Shanghai in 1906. She developed kala-azar and died in 1914. Two years later Helen Murr Howard, R.N., became the second Mrs. McFadyen. In addition to raising a family, Helen McFadyen took charge of the male and female nurses in the Men's Hospital.

The Hospitals

In 1915, the Mary Erwin Rogers Memorial Hospital for Women was erected in Xuzhou in memory of his wife by J. M. Rogers of Winston Salem, North Carolina. The following year a Men's Hospital was built, funded in part by Mrs. J. Lee Sloan of Davidson, North Carolina, in memory of her parents, Charles L. C. and Anna W. Dupuy. In 1924 a children's ward was built with $10,000 given in memory of their son, Bennie, by Mr. and Mrs. Neil S. Blue of Rockford, North Carolina.

Combined, the Women's and the Men's Hospitals of Xuzhou (150 beds) formed a strong institution with a nursing school and an outreach program into rural areas. Many of the Chinese staff were graduates of the Cheeloo University College of Medicine. For many

Laboratory at the Xuzhou Men's Hospital. Photograph courtesy of G. Thompson Brown.

years Dr. McFadyen served on the board of directors of the medical school. The treatment of patients with kala-azar became an ever-increasing problem as that disease slowly spread southward. Xuzhou Hospital worked closely with the Cheeloo College of Medicine in testing treatment for the disease.

Dr. McFadyen often accompanied evangelistic missionaries on their trips into remote rural areas. He wrote in 1924 of an 1,800–year-old temple in an outlying town, which the mission purchased for $180:

> The temple is in good repair and, when cleaned up, is well worth $1,000. After a few changes and a lot of whitewash we hope to convert it into a chapel with a small clinic behind, and we hope that a girls' school may be opened in connection with it.[19]

The Xuzhou hospitals continued operation under strong Chinese leadership during the three major crises that swept the area: the 1927 evacuation, the Japanese invasion, and World War II. Two-thirds of the city was destroyed when the Japanese entered the city in 1938.

Once, after the Japanese occupation in 1938, Dr. Grier and two missionary ministers went to plead for the release of four pastors imprisoned by the Japanese military. When Dr. Grier dropped to her knees and began to kow-tow (beat her head on the floor), the Japanese officer relented and released the prisoners.

The Reverend Grier died in 1917 soon after the hospital, whose construction he was overseeing, was completed. His death did not bring an end to Aunt Nettie's missionary career in Xuzhou; she retired in 1940 after forty-three years' service. Dr. and Mrs. McFadyen returned to the United States in July 1942 in the Japanese prisoner-of-war exchange. After Dr. McFadyen's death in 1946, Helen McFadyen returned to Xuzhou to serve briefly during the post–World War II period.

Post–World War II (1946–1948)

In December 1948 during the Battle of the Hwai Hai that brought the Communists into power, the Xuzhou hospitals took care of wounded from both sides. Rev. Frank A. Brown Sr. wrote in his diary:

> December 8 . . . It is a comfort to walk down the long wards, so clean and quiet, with the staff working to cure some of the misery amid this cruel war. They are upholding the great tradition of the past 52 years since this hospital was founded. They show the effect of the long years of training by the McFadyens and by Dr. Grier. As you walk at night among these 20 hospital buildings on this compound, and recall their history, you feel that you are on holy ground. Faith built them all—faith of the sending church, faith of the missionaries, faith of the Christian Chinese who are now carrying on.[20]

In 1981 PCUS executives visiting Xuzhou found the former mission hospital full of patients and bursting with activity, in startling contrast to another equally large government institution. The spirit of compassionate, high-quality service apparently had persisted through the intervening years.

ELLEN LAVINE GRAHAM HOSPITAL
Haizhou (Haichow)

Haizhou, a port city on the Yellow Sea, is located at the terminus of the Xian/Lainyungang railroad (completed in 1929). Unlike other North Jiangsu stations, it occupied hilly ground and had a relatively pleasant climate.

Hospital Established

Lorenzo S. Morgan, M.D., and Ruth Bennett, M.D., graduated in the same class (1904) at the Johns Hopkins University School of Medicine, married, and arrived in China in January 1905. After working and studying the language in Huaiyin (TKP), they were assigned in 1908 to open the medical work in Haizhou.

The Morgans began with a small clinic in rented rooms. As elsewhere, the local people were initially fearful of the strangers with yellow hair and blue eyes. "They thought that these foreigners . . . would catch the Chinese peoples to dig out their eyes and heart for their meals."[21] At first, no one came to the clinic. Gradually, however, as the sick were cured, patients came in great numbers. Dr. Lorenzo Morgan's help was enlisted in 1918 to stamp out an epidemic of pneumonic plague in Shansi Province.

In 1914 the Ellen Lavine Graham Hospital, a ninety-bed facility, was built outside the west gate of the city. Funds for the hospital were given by Mr. and Mrs. C. E. Graham of Greenville, South Carolina, in memory of their daughter, who had died shortly after graduation from Columbia University, New York.[22]

PCUS missionaries who served in the Haizhou hospital include Mary S. Bisset, R.N. (1919–27); Caspar L. Woodbridge, M.D. (1923–27), son of pioneer China missionaries and, like the Morgans, a graduate of the Johns Hopkins School of Medicine (M.D., 1921); Ruth Bracken, R.N. (1929–34), who served for two years in Xuzhou prior to 1927; and John H. Reed, M.D., a graduate of the Medical College of Virginia (M.D., 1928), who served from 1932 until World War II intervened.

The Haizhou region was bandit country. In 1931 Rev. John W. Vinson was captured and killed while on a preaching mission in a rural area. It is interesting to note that Rev. John Vinson was the only PCUS missionary to be murdered while serving the PCUS overseas.

Fighting between government soldiers and bandits was common, and the hospital was often full of the wounded. A "military department" was set up where soldiers had wards and a courtyard of their own as "they do not mix well with the common people, being of an overbearing disposition."[23]

During the 1927 evacuation, the hospital continued to operate despite the fact that Haizhou was occupied by five different armies. Haizhou was heavily bombed during the 1937–38 Japanese invasion. The port facilities at Haizhou were important to the Japanese during

World War II, and the hospital continued in operation under Japanese supervision during that time.

Post–World War II (1946–1948)

In 1946 Rev. W. C. McLauchlin, in the absence of a missionary physician, renovated the Haizhou hospital with the help of the Chinese staff. "Mr. Mac" went to Shanghai and returned with an LST (Landing Ship Tank) loaded with a magnificent supply of medical equipment and goods, which he had talked UNRRA officials into giving and shipping to him.

Lalla Iverson, M.D., a board-certified pathologist who became head of the Department of Pathology at Cheeloo University College of Medicine, remembers how some of the nonmedical missionaries, who had no understanding of the specialized expertise of a pathologist, tried to have her assigned to the Haizhou hospital on the theory that she would be more valuable to the mission in general practice there.

In 1948 Haizhou fell under Communist rule, and the government of the People's Republic of China assumed control of the hospital.[24]

SARA WALKUP HOSPITAL
Taizhou (Taichow)

Taizhou, the "Honorable City," was the last mission station that the PCUS opened in China. A walled city located in the flat delta country north of the Yangzi River and east of the Grand Canal, Taizhou was relatively prosperous and very proud of its history as the home of peace and plenty. Transportation to Taizhou was by canal boat.

Robert Black Price, M.D. (1916–1941)

The Taizhou hospital was the classic one-doctor/one-nurse operation. Robert Black Price, M.D., a graduate of Vanderbilt University Medical School (M.D., 1906), was assigned in 1916 to the newly opened Taizhou station where, assisted by Eleanor Bridgman, R.N., and Hazel Lee Matthes, R.N., he served until World War II intervened. The Chinese in Taizhou remember Dr. Price as the unfortunate doctor who had six daughters, all but one born in Taizhou.

Dr. Price found Taizhou much like the Mississippi delta region in which he had grown up. "Like our delta friends, the Taichow [people] are also prosperous (for China), and like other prosperous people, they are somewhat self-satisfied and very willing to let the world wag on in the same old way, which they think has proved a pretty good way for them."[25] Apparently the famine and banditry common in other areas of North Jiangsu were not serious problems in Taizhou.

Dr. Price built the fifty-bed Sara Walkup Hospital in 1922, with funds provided in memory of his mother by William Henry Belk of the Belk Department Stores of North Carolina. A three-story T-shaped building was added in 1930, and a one-story building housed tuberculosis patients. The hospital, known by the Chinese as the "Good News" (or "Gospel") Hospital," was fairly well equipped for its time, having a small X ray, an electric generator, and a water pump in addition to the operating room, laboratory, and pharmacy.

In 1927 the hospital in Taizhou changed flags six times but continued operating. In 1938 the hospital did not close when the Japanese occupied the area, and the missionary presence continued through 1941. The hospital operated under Japanese management throughout World War II.

Post–World War II (1946–1951)

Following the war, largely through the efforts of Miss Marguerite Mizell, an evangelistic missionary, the "old" and "new" hospital buildings were renovated and equipped with supplies donated by relief agencies.[26] The Chinese staff consisted of Dr. Miriam Lee,[27] a part-time internist, several residents, a medical technician, a pharmacist, and the former head nurse (Chen Zhi).

Henry (M.D.) and Katie (R.N.) Nelson (with two-year-old Sperry) arrived in August 1948 after completing six months of language study in Beijing. The political climate by that time had become most uncertain, with the steady advance southward of the Red Armies. Dr. Nelson, the son of Methodist missionaries, was born in Huzhou and graduated from Vanderbilt University (M.D., 1945). He applied for and received his Jiangsu medical license and was made director of the hospital; six months before leaving, he turned over the directorship to Dr. Miriam Lee. He also set up a hospital board made up of Chinese members.[28]

The seventy-bed hospital received support from several sources: patients' fees covered staff salaries and medicines; a mission subsidy, amounting to approximately 10 percent of the operating budget, continued until the missionaries departed; church women in the

United States sent White Cross linens; and UNRRA donated supplies and equipment.

When the Communist takeover became imminent, Katie Nelson was seven months pregnant. She and others were evacuated. Henry Nelson and Rev. and Mrs. R. P. Richardson (Pete and Agnes) decided to stay in Taizhou and attempt to carry on under Communist rule. The Richardsons enjoyed support from many elements of the Chinese community because of their warm personalities and their long years of service in Taizhou (1923–40). Their presence contributed to a relatively satisfactory, though temporary, period of service and was in sharp contrast to the situation in Jiaxing where, after the Communist takeover, Dr. Joe Wilkerson was stationed alone without the support of an experienced missionary.

In early January 1949 the Communists entered Taizhou quietly because the city fathers met them at the gates and invited them in. The Communists announced they would take over half of the hospital for a provincial hospital but would allow the mission to continue in the "old" building. In the frantic three days and two nights before the takeover was completed, Dr. Nelson was able to move the operating and sterilizing equipment, X-ray machines, dark room, and many supplies to the "old" building. He also built a brick wall separating the two facilities. Water and electricity were shared.

Patients continued to come to the hospital, and Dr. Nelson was able to work in relative freedom. His donation of blood to a wounded Communist made a tremendous impression on the community.

After the Chinese entered the Korean War in October 1950, the situation became tense for Americans, and in January 1951 Dr. Nelson and the Richardsons were given permission to leave. They went, without incident, to Shanghai and by train to Hong Kong. The Nelsons continued service with PCUS as medical missionaries in Zaire until 1984 and returned to China in 1986 to work with the Amity Foundation in the former PCUS hospital in Zhenjiang.

YENCHENG HOSPITAL
Yencheng

Yencheng, a walled city located east of the Grand Canal and the most isolated of the North Jiangsu stations, was established in 1913. Early missionaries compared the area to Holland: a flat delta with canals, irrigation, windmills, and relative prosperity. In 1913 it was without famine and without beggars.

The establishment of a hospital at Yencheng grew out of the mission's concern for families stationed three days away from a physician. Dr. Robert M. Stephenson, who was assigned to Yencheng in 1913, left China after the death of his wife in childbirth.

Dr. William Malcolm, a fifty-two-year-old Canadian physician with service in Huaiyin (TKP) and Huaian, was asked to go to Yencheng. He served there for one year before returning to his practice in the United States. Dr. Julius Winch Hewett, an Englishman, had been a missionary for twenty years with the China Inland Mission before responding to a special request from PCUS to establish the medical program in Yencheng.

Funds for the Yencheng Hospital were raised by the children of the PCUS on Children's Day 1914; construction began in 1916. The hospital was small, and during a flood, the grounds were covered with up to five feet of water.

Dr. Hewett served in Yencheng for ten years until 1927. During the 1927 upheaval, soldiers occupied and thoroughly vandalized the Yencheng Hospital.

Patients at the Yengcheng Gospel Hospital. Photograph courtesy of G. Thompson Brown.

In 1931, Felix B. Welton, M.D., age thirty-two and a 1927 graduate of the Medical College of Virginia, became the next physician assigned to Yencheng. Dr. Welton described the situation as follows:

> No mission medical work had been carried on for some time and, though there was a hospital, it was quite primitive and lacking in supplies; beds consisted of saw horses with planks or bamboo beds ... [I remember] making up an ointment with benzoin, vaseline, and "flowers of sulphur" [among the few items in the pharmacy] to treat scabies at the jail.[29]

These were the depression years; support and supplies were limited. After two years' service and the death of their first child, the Weltons transferred to the Elizabeth Blake Hospital in Suzhou, where he served as the surgeon.

In 1934 Kirk T. Mosley, M.D., who had finished the TKP intern/residency, applied for missionary appointment and was assigned to reopen Yencheng Hospital. Under his leadership the work grew by "leaps and bounds." In one year the number of inpatients doubled (from 200 to 400) and the number of outpatients increased from 3,000 to 5,000.[30]

The Japanese invasion of 1937–38 ended PCUS medical work in Yencheng; the buildings were destroyed during World War II.

GOLDSBY KING MEMORIAL HOSPITAL
Zhenjiang (Chinkiang)

Zhenjiang, a river port located at the junction of the Grand Canal with the Yangzi River and on the Shanghai/Nanjing railroad, was one of China's early "treaty ports." It was a difficult town in which to operate a mission. A four-block British concession established in the 1860s generated animosity. Although Zhenjiang was one of the earliest of the PCUS mission stations, medical work was not begun until 1922. A small Methodist hospital operated outside town.

Pre–World War II (1923–1940)

The Goldsby King Memorial Hospital was, in one sense, an American hospital transplanted from the United States to Zhenjiang. When Dr. Goldsby King died in Selma, Alabama, in 1920, his wife and

Hospital compound of the Goldsby King Memorial Hospital, Zhenjiang, in 1934. Left to right: doctor's residence, main building, and out-patient building. After 1949 these buildings became the No. 1 People's Hospital of Zhenjiang. Courtesy of 1934 annual report of the hospital.

daughters sold his practice and used the proceeds to build the hospital in China in his memory. The equipment and surgical apparatus, all of which were of the finest quality, were shipped to China to furnish the new 120-bed hospital.[31]

Henry W. Newman, M.D., a Southern Baptist missionary, transferred to the PCUS mission in 1923 to begin construction of the hospital. Dr. Newman left in 1925 and was replaced by Dr. James B. Woods Jr.

James B. Woods Jr., M.D., the son of the pioneers, James B. Sr. and Bessie S. Woods, was born in Huaiyin (TKP), educated at the Medical College of Virginia (M.D., 1932) and had a good command of the Chinese language. He, with Charlotte Dunlap, R.N., provided the medical leadership in Zhenjiang until the missionaries left in 1940 and 1941.

Chinese physicians on the staff consisted of two graduates of the Cheeloo College of Medicine and two interns (one from Cheeloo and the other from a government medical school). An accredited nursing school was established.

Schistosomiasis, a parasitic disease caused by a blood fluke, was endemic south of the Yangzi River. The disease is contracted in water when the larvae of the blood fluke penetrate human skin (or mucous membrane). Dr. James Woods Jr. developed a clinic where many people were effectively treated, and, as has been noted, he was able to demonstrate that a very inexpensive drug (tartar emetic) could be used in place of the otherwise unaffordable agents. On one occasion the sailors aboard a British gunboat that was anchored in the Yangzi River were allowed to take a swim in the river. When a large number of them became ill with a strange disease, Dr. Woods quickly recognized the early stages of schistosomiasis and was able to offer them effective treatment.[32]

The work was complicated by inadequate support as a result of the depression in the United States and by the political instability in China. Between 1925 and 1940 the hospital closed and reopened three times.

In summarizing his experience as a medical missionary, Dr. James Woods Jr. said that the most surprising thing to him about the mission's medical program was the change in attitude of the Chinese over time, from extreme hostility to acceptance of Western medicine. By the 1920s patients were flocking to the mission hospitals. The emphasis on training attracted many highly intelligent young people to the training programs. "I found missionary medical work the most satisfying of anything I ever did."[33]

During World War II the hospital remained open under Japanese control.

Post–World War II (1946–1951)

The PCUS medical team assigned to Zhenjiang after the war was made up of three experienced missionaries: Alexander S. Moffett, M.D., with five years in Jiangyin; Charlotte A. Dunlap, R.N., with eighteen years in Zhenjiang; and Ruth Worth, M.T., with eight years in Jiangyin. The Chinese staff consisted of three full-time and two part-time physicians and seven interns. Dr. Moffett's comments, summarized here, give a vivid picture of the life and the concerns.[34]

The missionaries found themselves deeply involved in the distribution of relief supplies, which poured into China through UNRRA, Church World Service, and the American Red Cross. Zhenjiang became a distribution point for medical supplies going to Protestant and Catholic hospitals and clinics in the area; one room in the Moffett home was often cluttered with these supplies. The missionaries made every effort to ensure equitable distribution.

For a short time the outlook for the medical work was very encouraging. The hospital, renovated with the help of UNRRA, was busy, the nursing school reopened, laboratory technicians were trained in a two-year apprentice program, inpatient recordkeeping was upgraded, and relations with local professionals were good. Dr. Moffett, a fellow of the American College of Surgeons, chose to specialize in pediatric surgery when he found that the Chinese surgeon was the same age and had approximately the same years of surgical experience. Dr. Moffett taught classes in pediatric surgery and in anesthesia at the Jiangsu Provincial Medical School in Zhenjiang. A number of well-trained Chinese doctors were in practice in Zhenjiang, and they formed a Medical Society that met regularly. Dr. Moffett addressed the society at one of its meetings.

The mission hospital had a small portable X ray that used surplus U.S. Navy film, all very old and requiring at least double exposure time. One of the interns received training in basic X-ray technique, and patients came from all over the surrounding area. It was a happy day indeed when the hospital acquired a new U.S. Army surplus 30 MA X-ray machine from UNRRA.

An epidemic of laryngeal diphtheria brought patients from throughout the area, many in late stages of the disease. When all of the hospital's twelve tracheostomy tubes were put to use, Dr. Moffett had a local silversmith copy the design and make a silver tracheostomy tube.

The Chinese doctors were under a great deal of pressure from the threat of lawsuits. Dr. Ma, formerly the surgeon at Jiangyin Hospital, had a flourishing practice in Zhenjiang but had given up surgery because of this threat. American doctors, even though some never acquired a Chinese medical license, were not under the same pressure. The Zhenjiang Hospital, however, was threatened by a suit from a patient unhappy with the results of an operation performed by one of the residents.

A visit from Dr. Moffett's uncle, Dr. J. Leighton Stuart, the American ambassador to China, was a pleasant interlude. The community pooled its resources to put on a festive meal that featured Spam as the entree. The Moffett children, ages six, ten, and twelve, greatly enjoyed an expedition to Nanjing to visit the ambassador. The visit included a movie, a shopping spree at the PX, and a return trip to Zhenjiang via U.S. Navy motorboat.

By 1948 the Communist advance made it necessary for Dr. Moffett to evacuate his family. Charlotte Dunlap and Ruth Worth stayed on, hoping to be able to work under Communist rule.

Staff of the Goldsby King Memorial Hospital in 1949 after the Communist occupation. Back row: Ruth Worth, M.T., Margaret Wood, R.N., and Charlotte Dunlap, R.N. Photograph courtesy of Margaret Wood.

One of the physicians turned out to be a Communist who had been planted in the hospital. The Chinese staff were probably aware of this problem, but the missionaries were not. By Christmas 1950 Charlotte Dunlap and Ruth Worth voluntarily ceased going to the hospital and applied for exit permits. They were not incarcerated but stayed in their home for five months until exit permits were granted. They took the train to Shanghai, then to Canton, and walked across the bridge to freedom in Hong Kong.[35]

In 1985 Zheng Zhi-Qing, M.D., the retired director of the then Number 1 People's Hospital of Zhenjiang, told American visitors with great pride that "this hospital" was formerly the "Goldsby King Memorial Hospital." How surprising it was to find that anyone in the People's Republic would know, or care, that such was the case!

Notes

1. John Pollack, *A Foreign Devil in China: The Story of Dr. L. Nelson Bell* (Minneapolis, Minn.: World Wide Publications, 1988), 161.

2. Elizabeth Woods DeCamp, R.N., interview, Feb. 1990.

3. Mrs. James B. Woods, "The Merciful and Pitiful Hospital at Tsing Kiang Pu," *Missionary Survey*, April 1916, 296.

4. Pollack, *Foreign Devil in China*, 72.

5. L. Nelson Bell, M.D., "What One Church Is Doing to Equip Our Work in Tsingkiangpu," *Missionary Survey*, August 1923, 604. The Houston Unit (a women's hospital and administration building) was funded for $20,000 by the First Presbyterian Church of Houston, Texas.

6. Tsingkiangpu General Hospital Annual Report, 1929, 5.

7. Ibid., 1929, 1932, 1938, 1939, 1940.

8. Virginia Bell Somerville, R.N., interview, Jan. 1990.

9. Kirk T. Moseley, M.D., letter, Nov. 1984.

10. TKP Annual Report, 1939, 2.

11. James N. Montgomery, letters to L. Nelson Bell, M.D., Aug. 31, Sept. 17, Sept. 27, Oct. 5, 1941. The nine Americans were Rev. and Mrs. J. N. Montgomery and ten-year-old Robert, Rev. and Mrs. A. A. Talbot (Cassie Lee, R.N.), Dr. and Mrs. Chal Vinson, and Misses Jessie D. Hall and Mary W. McCowan.

12. Drs. C. T. Ts'ao (Eye and Medicine), C. S. Ch'ien (Surgery), I. P. Wu (Medicine), I. S. Koh (Medicine), and Eli Liu (Surgical Assistant).

13. After 1948 the Communist authorities used the remaining buildings of the Huaiyin (TKP) hospital in a variety of ways, including an army technical school, a hospital of traditional medicine, and housing for squatters.

14. Margaret P. Wood, R.N., interview, May 1990.

15. Margaret Patterson Mack, copies of her mother's letters, 1991.

16. The designation of "evangelistic missionary," based, no doubt, on the Reverend Patterson's assignment to evangelistic work, did not recognize Dr. Annie's medical credentials and reflects the status of women in the mission at that time. Women missionaries were not granted voting privileges in the mission until the 1920s.

17. Margaret Wood, interview.

18. P. Frank Price, *Our China Investment*, (Nashville, Tenn.: Executive Committee of Foreign Missions, c. 1926), 54.

19. A. A. McFadyen, M.D., "The Men's Hospital," *Missionary Survey*, Feb. 1924, 130.

20. Frank A. Brown Sr., "The Last Hundred Days," Shanghai, pamphlet, Feb. 21, 1949.

21. Zhang Quanfu, M.D., "Brief History of The Ellen Lavine Graham Hospital, Haichow, China," typescript, June 20, 1986.

22. Samuel H. Chester, "Our Own Medical Missions," *Mission Survey*, August 1916, 590–98. The Graham's built a second Ellen Lavine Graham Hospital in Kwangju, Korea.

23. Lorenzo S. Morgan, M.D., "The Military Situation in China," *Foreign Missionary*, April 1917, 298.

24. Zhang Quanfu, M.D., reported that in 1986 it was the largest general hospital in Haizhou with 330 beds, a staff of 200, and 800 patients daily in the outpatient department.

25. Robert B. Price, M.D., "Medical Missionary Work in Taichow," *Missionary Survey*, 12.

26. Dr. Robert Price had died in 1946 in the United States.

27. Miriam Lee, M.D., a graduate of the Women's Medical College in Shanghai, did postgraduate study in the United States.

28. Henry Nelson, M.D., interview, Aug. 1984.

29. Felix B. Welton, M.D., interview, Oct. 1984.

30. Annual Report, 1936, 18.

31. Samuel A. Chester, "The Goldsby King Memorial Hospital," *Presbyterian Survey*, Aug. 1924, 512.

32. Alexander S. Moffett, M.D., correspondence, Jan. 1991.

33. James B. Woods Jr., M.D., interview, Aug. 1984.

34. Moffett, Jan. 1990.

35. Ruth Worth, M.T., interview, July 1984.

Chapter Four

Medical
Education

The first two decades of the twentieth century were an exciting time in the field of medical education. The Flexner Report of 1910, which was commissioned by the Carnegie Foundation for the Advancement of Teaching, examined the status of medical education in the United States and Canada in view of the recent enormous advances in science. As a result of this study half of the medical schools in the United States were closed; the remaining schools made a determined effort to raise the level of their teaching.[1] In China, too, there was a strong move in the medical missionary community to provide high-quality education for Chinese medical students.

The China Medical Missionary Association, founded in 1886, gave medical missionaries throughout China a forum in which to develop programs across denominational lines. At its 1890 meeting in Shanghai, Dr. John G. Kerr, a Northern Presbyterian missionary, said, "The education of physicians and surgeons for the people of this great empire is a subject of the utmost importance, and one which may well engage the attention of the medical profession of the world."[2]

Medical teaching in China began with apprentice/assistantship training. Some fine physicians were prepared in this manner, but the need for a better method became acutely apparent. In the first decade of the century a number of so-called medical schools operated in connection with some of the larger mission hospitals, including the PCUS-operated Elizabeth Blake Hospital in Suzhou.

At a series of meetings and conferences between 1907 and 1910, medical missionaries dealt with the need for mission bodies to unite their efforts in order to establish good schools that would produce qualified Chinese medical personnel. The language used in the records of these meetings reflect the seriousness with which the problem was regarded: "earnestly recommend," "emphatic expression of opinion," "overwhelmingly in favor," "strong expression," "immense advantage," "unique opportunity," "strong growing sentiment," "extremely desirable," "urge. . . ."

In the early years of the century a number of interdenominational schools were established. In 1909 the East China Union Medical College in Nanjing was founded; in 1913 it, along with the Drum Tower Hospital with which it was incorporated, became the medical department of the University of Nanjing. This medical school was the largest interdenominational institution in China at that time; it was supported by Presbyterians (North and South), Methodists (North and South), Baptists (North and South), and Disciples of Christ.[3] As has been noted, Randolph T. Shields, M.D., was actively involved in founding this school and from 1909 to 1917 served as its dean as well as its professor of anatomy, embryology, and histology.

The burning issue of the day was whether English or Chinese would be used as the medium of instruction in the medical schools.[4] On the one hand, few medical texts existed in Chinese, and technical nomenclature was limited. Also English-speaking professors from abroad, on a short-term basis, could easily be used to enrich the program because communication would not pose a problem for them. On the other hand, few students were adequately prepared to study in English; if the purpose was to produce practicing physicians primarily for the hinterland, English was of questionable value.

By 1935, through a process of cooperation, concentration, and elimination, the struggling denominational schools had merged into six mission medical schools. Four were coeducational: Cheeloo University College of Medicine (Jinan), Canton Christian College (Guangzhou), Mukden Medical College (a British institution in Manchuria), and West China Union University Medical School (Chengdu). One was for women only—Women's Union Medical College (Shanghai)—and one for men only—St. John's University (Shanghai).Three taught in Mandarin, one in Cantonese, and two in English.

During this same period there were a number of significant secular developments.[5] In 1915 the number of Chinese physicians, many of whom had been educated abroad, was large enough to form the National Medical Association; in 1932, in a fine example of international cooperation, it amalgamated with the Chinese Medical

Missionary Association to form the Chinese Medical Association. These associations were deeply involved with the standardization of Chinese medical nomenclature and the translation of medical texts and journals into Chinese.

The bylaws of the newly formed Chinese Medical Association called for a Chinese president and two vice presidents, one Chinese and one foreigner. The election of Dr. Randolph T. Shields as the first foreign vice president was a tribute to his leadership in medical affairs. In 1944 the China Medical Association was estimated to have a membership of 3,500 physicians.[6]

The Rockefeller Foundation, after its official incorporation in 1913, took very seriously the proposition, "Might we not . . . attempt scientific medicine in China?" The China Medical Board of the Rockefeller Foundation was formed in 1914, and the famous Peking Union Medical College was founded in 1921. Financial assistance was given to other medical projects as well.[7] In addition to the Cheeloo University College of Medicine, the PCUS institutions that received grants from the China Medical Board were the Elizabeth Blake Hospital in Suzhou (in the form of salary subsidy for a missionary physician and nurse) and Jiaxing Hospital (an X-ray machine).

CHEELOO UNIVERSITY COLLEGE OF MEDICINE
Jinan

The involvement of the PCUS in academic medicine in China can be traced through the three physicians who were most actively involved in the Cheeloo University College of Medicine: Randolph T. Shields, Philip B. Price, and Lalla Iverson.[8]

Randolph Tucker Shields, M.D. (1917–1941)

Dr. Shields, a graduate of the University College of Medicine in Richmond, Virginia (M.D., 1901), arrived in China in 1904. Medical education was his primary interest throughout his missionary career, and he was actively involved in the establishment of union medical schools first in Nanjing and then in Jinan. In 1917, following the negotiations that led to the founding of the Cheeloo University College of Medicine, the Shields moved to Jinan, where they spent the balance of their missionary career.

The Cheeloo University College of Medicine, formed by the union of
five medical colleges, was a thoroughly international and interdenominational institution supported by British, American, and Canadian
mission societies.[9] In 1924 the parliament of Canada granted Cheeloo
University a charter authorizing it to confer degrees on its graduates.[10]
As a result, degrees from Cheeloo were prestigious and highly prized.

Full-time medical faculty numbered more than thirty, about
equally divided between Chinese and Westerners. Dr. Shields,
professor of embryology and histology, also practiced obstetrics and
parasitology. He was dean of the College of Medicine from 1926 to
1935. He also took a leadership role in the university and, at various
times, was called upon temporarily to fill positions in the administration: dean of the Department of Arts and Science in 1919, vice
president of the university 1928–30, acting president in 1929 and
again in 1937–38. In 1935–36, while on furlough in the United States,
Dr. Shields conducted a fund-raising campaign to build new hospital
buildings and set up an endowment.

Admission to the Cheeloo College of Medicine required completion of a six-year secondary school (high school) plus two years of
premedical instruction in college. The medical course took five years,
the last of which was an intern year. Tuition in 1930 was $80; room and
board was $100 per year. In 1935 tuition was raised to $100 per year.[11]

Instruction was given mainly in Mandarin. A required course in
English, however, enabled students to read English medical litera-
ture. The study of English by the students, and of Chinese by the
Western faculty, was of prime importance.

Cheeloo University Medical School, Jinan. Photograph from Charles Hodge Corbett,
Shantung Christian University (Cheeloo) *(New York: United Board of Christian
Colleges in China, 1955).*

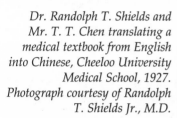

Dr. Randolph T. Shields and Mr. T. T. Chen translating a medical textbook from English into Chinese, Cheeloo University Medical School, 1927. Photograph courtesy of Randolph T. Shields Jr., M.D.

Training was also offered in nursing, pharmacy, laboratory technique, and, reflecting the international flavor of the institution, "massage and electrotherapeutics" (physiotherapy), headed by a graduate of the London School of Massage. The Nurses' Training School had a staff of six Western and ten Chinese graduate nurses and sixty students; the school was conducted according to the rules of the Chinese Nursing Association.

An important contribution of the Cheeloo College of Medicine to medical science in China was the preparation of textbooks in the Chinese language. The Publication Council and the Terminology Committee of the Chinese Medical Association had its headquarters in the medical school, and many members of the medical faculty engaged in translation. By 1935 more than forty medical works had been published, including the *English-Latin-Chinese Medical Lexicon*. Dr. Shields translated three texts: Lewis's *Histology*, Gray's *Anatomy*, and Stitt's *Parasitology*; Dr. Price revised a book on general surgery.[12]

Second in importance to translation was work done in research, particularly in relation to kala-azar, the disease so prevalent around Jinan and in the North Jiangsu area. Many other diseases received careful study and interesting cases were reported in Chinese, British, and American medical journals.[13]

A study of the financial reports between 1926 and 1938 reveal an average annual budget of around $75,000. Contributions made by the PCUS reflect the depression in the United States: in addition to support of the Shields and Price couples, the PCUS funds totaled only $1,100 in 1925–26, $1,333 in 1930–31, $303.56 in 1933–34, $258.57 in 1934–35, and $301.04 in 1936–37. The other eight missionary societies contributed approximately $10,000 annually, plus the support of some twenty doctors and nurses. The Rockefeller Foundation, through its China Medical Board, made generous annual grants totaling well over $500,000. The Rockefeller Foundation also made a separate grant to the Publications Council and contributed to the building of the new hospital.

Philip B. Price, M.D. (1929–1937)

Dr. Phil Price, a second-generation missionary and graduate of the Johns Hopkins University School of Medicine (M.D., 1921), must have been a small boy of eight or nine when Dr. Randolph and Mrs. Ella Page Shields first arrived in China and lived for some years in the home of his parents, Rev. and Mrs. P. Frank Price. Dr. Phil Price and his wife, Octavia Howard Price, R.N., were assigned to Cheeloo in 1929, where Dr. Price became assistant, and then associate, professor of surgery. He also, in 1934–35, became deeply involved in the planning and construction of the new hospital and outpatient facility. Octavia Price became supervisor of the operating rooms.

The University Hospital, which had as its central aim the training of medical students, grew from 109 beds in 1925 to 180 in 1936. Public health outreach, beginning as a volunteer service to nearby villages, became an integral part of the training of medical students. In 1925 a fifty-bed hospital for the treatment of leprosy patients was built on land donated by the provincial government; construction costs and equipment were provided by the Mission to Lepers of London. A series of refresher courses designed for practicing physicians were well attended.

The period from 1917 to 1937 was one of exciting growth and progress, but also of political and cultural turmoil. The annual report for 1925–26 began, "The past year will be remembered by all educationalists in China as one beset with unusual difficulties"; another report stated, "We are glad to report that the session of 1936–37 has been completed with no untoward events to interrupt the academic and clinical work of the College."

The periods of turmoil included student strikes in 1920 and 1929, war conditions in 1926–27 in which the hospital treated large numbers of wounded,[14] the devastating flood of 1935 when the Yellow River burst its dikes and flooded an area of 6,000 square miles, and the invasion by Japan in 1937. Government regulations, including military training for the male students, further complicated the administration.

The school year ending in June 1937 was the last "normal" session to be held at the Cheeloo University College of Medicine. Ninety-eight students enrolled that year, and fourteen (three of whom were women) graduated.

A carefully compiled report of the graduates of the Cheeloo University College of Medicine from 1915 to 1934 shows that of a total of 313 graduates, 86 served in mission hospitals (14 were working in 8 PCUS hospitals). There were 40 School of Pharmacy graduates, 10 laboratory technicians, and 19 physiotherapy graduates. The Nurses' Training School graduated 119 (91 women and 28 men).

In July 1937, the Marco Polo Bridge incident, in which a Japanese garrison battalion engaged Chinese troops, marked the beginning of the Japanese occupation of east China and has been considered by some to be the "first battle of World War II."[15] (Dr. Price had crossed the bridge earlier on the day the incident occurred.) Total disruption of the medical school ensued.

The medical school reopened in September with eighty-seven students but was forced to suspend classes on October 6. Fifty-nine students and most of the Chinese faculty accepted the invitation of the West China Union University to share the use of their facilities in Chengdu, Sichuan. British and American members of the staff, including Drs. Shields and Price, stayed behind to keep the University Hospital functioning under Japanese rule.

Dr. Shields became acting president and took over the eye clinic and the pathology departments; Dr. Price became superintendent of the hospital as well as chief of surgery. The Prices returned to the United States for furlough in December 1937; Dr. and Mrs. Shields were repatriated to the United States in the famous July 1942 prisoner exchange.

Following the end of World War II, Cheeloo University returned to the Jinan campus which had been used by the Japanese as a military hospital and was full of the sick and wounded. The Japanese gradually evacuated the buildings, and for two years, from April 1946 to July 1948, the Cheeloo University, with its College of Medicine, was back in full operation in its home territory.

Lalla Iverson, M.D. (1947–1949)

In 1947 PCUS appointed Dr. Lalla Iverson, who had just earned her certification by the American Board of Pathology, to the Cheeloo College of Medicine, where she was asked to head the Department of Pathology. A graduate of the Johns Hopkins School of Medicine (M.D., 1943 AOA), Dr. Iverson was the first PCUS missionary physician worldwide to have specialty board certification.

These were heady days, as students and faculty gathered with high hopes for the future of China and for their role in reviving Cheeloo as a center for high-quality medical education. Western faculty returned; large grants of money, from Chinese as well as overseas sources, flowed in; and quantities of drugs and equipment were donated by relief agencies to help rehabilitate the institution. However, the struggle between the Nationalist and Communist armies steadily escalated, making it imperative to again move the university to a safer part of the country.

In June 1948, the College of Medicine accepted the invitation that came from Fuzhou (Fuchow) where three mission hospitals, totaling 450 beds, offered adequate clinical training, laboratories, classrooms, and housing for staff and students. A skeleton staff that included

Refugees cling to the engine (1949). Photograph courtesy of Margaret Wood.

seven Westerners remained in Jinan to keep the University Hospital open as long as possible.[16]

The story of the evacuation to Fuzhou, a southern coastal city over 1,000 miles away, has become legendary. Dr. Iverson played a major role in arranging for the use of a former U.S. Navy LST (Landing Ship Tank) for transportation from Qingdao (Tsingtao) to Fuzhou. She was one of a committee of three who went to Shanghai where they not only persuaded the authorities to assign them the ship, but persuaded various relief organizations to donate a considerable amount of equipment, which was loaded aboard. As the PCUS 1949 annual report put it, "Perhaps a more experienced person would not have had the faith and audacity to accomplish so much."[17]

On July 14, three chartered DC-3 planes flew personnel, textbooks, and equipment over Communist lines from Jinan to the port city of Qingdao (Tsingtao), some 250 miles away. On July 27, more than 100 passengers (students, staff, and their families) boarded the SS *Wan Jing* for the journey to Fuzhou, arriving on August 2. In reply to a letter sent by the dean of the medical school, the doughty Scottish captain of the SS *Wan Jing* wrote:

> Your letter of August 5th was received by me on our return to Shanghai from Okinawa. It was indeed a very great pleasure to myself, officers and crew to receive such a kind letter of appreciation from you, on behalf of your staff and students, for the little help we were able to render you all on your recent trip on the "Wan Jing" from Shanghai-Tsingtao-Foochow. It might interest you to know that we, in turn, were greatly impressed by the manner in which you all, in your hour of adversity, uprooted as you were from the home you had known for years and sent on to another part of your great country, possibly totally unknown to you (I most sincerely hope it will treat you kindly) carried on, young and old, to the best of your ability—many of you having to leave loved ones behind. We were also very much struck by the immaculate state in which you left the quarters you had occupied. They are great young people and China will be all the better for their services when they have, in due course, graduated. I have already passed on your message to officers and crew and please convey our best wishes to all the people we have met, and, as we say in Scotland, "Lang may your Lum reek."
>
> (Signed) John B. McCaw,
> Master of the "Wan Jing"[18]

The Cheeloo University College of Medicine had only one year (1948–49) in Fujien, but it was a year memorable for its accomplishments and for the special bonds of friendship that grew out of this period of adversity. A total of eighty-eight students—sixty-one men and twenty-seven women—were enrolled. The core faculty numbered ten to twelve; resident physicians and technicians augmented the staff.[19]

While in Fuzhou, Dr. Iverson organized the Department of Pathology, extended pathology diagnostic services to other provinces in South China, and developed new knowledge in the geographic comparisons of disease. In August 1949, she went to Taiwan for a short vacation and was unable to return to mainland China because of the Communist occupation of Fuzhou. The impenetrable "bamboo curtain" descended to sever the PCUS connection with Cheeloo.

The Communists promptly moved Cheeloo College of Medicine back to Jinan, where it became part of the Shandong University. In 1985 visitors were told that, while Beijing University Medical School (formerly Peking Union Medical College) and Shanghai Medical College were rated first and second in the country, the Shandong College of Medicine ranked as the third best medical school in China.

Notes

1. Abraham Flexner, *Medical Education in the United States and Canada*, commissioned by the Carnegie Foundation for the Advancement of Teaching, 1910.

2. Randolph T. Shields, M.D., "Medical Education in China," *Presbyterian Survey*, August 1936, 465.

3. James E. Bear, *Mission of the Presbyterian Church in China: 1912–1920*, vol. IV, typescript in the library at Union Theological Seminary, Richmond, Va., 383.

4. "Purpose" (for the establishment of the East China Union Medical College), (Shanghai: Minutes of the China Centenary Missionary Conference, 1907), 6.

Purpose
Sec. 1. The aim of this institution shall be to give thorough instruction in
modern medicine and surgery to the Chinese in their own language and
under Christian influences, and thereby: a. To provide mission hospitals
with capable Chinese physicians. b.To furnish Christian communities
with well trained native physicians. c. To train Chinese for positions as

instructors and professors in this and other medical schools. d. To assist in providing this Empire with a Christian medical profession.

Sec. 2. It is also hoped that this institution, while primarily for educational purposes, will take an active share in the investigation of diseases peculiar to China, the study of their causes and determination of methods for their prevention.

5. One idealistic experiment was the founding of the Harvard Medical School in China by a group of Harvard medical students. This school, which operated for only five years (1911–16), illustrates the interest of many leaders in the medical profession in the United States in the Chinese problem. Although the school had Harvard's blessing, it had no organic connection or financial backing from Harvard University. However, "certainly one of the direct fruits of this enterprise . . . was to blaze a new trail for the introduction of the highest standards of scientific medicine to China, a trail leading to the establishment (in 1921) by the Rockefeller Foundation of the famous Peking Union Medical College (PUMC) with its magnificent buildings, equipment and faculty." Jean A. Curran, "The Harvard Medical School of China," *Harvard Medical Alumni Bulletin*, Christmas 1963, 12–19.

6. Szeming Sze, editor, "China's Health Problems," *Chinese Medical Journal*, Chinese Medical Association, Washington, D.C., 1944.

7. Mary E. Ferguson, *China Medical Board and Peking Union Medical College* (New York: China Medical Board of New York, Inc., 1970), 14–15.

8. Information about the Cheeloo University College of Medicine came in large part from the annual reports (Cheeloo University Bulletins) of 1925–26, 1930–31, and 1934–38; a number of articles and speeches by R. T. Shields, M.D., lent by his son, R. T. Shields Jr., M.D.; Octavia H. Price, *Octavia: Her Life As She Remembers It*, typescript; and Lalla Iverson, M.D., interviews.

9. The original institution at Jinan (the Union Medical College of Shandong Christian College) was the first union medical school in China; it was established in 1904 by the American Presbyterian (Northern) and the English Baptist missions. In 1916 the Union Medical College of Peking (after selling its property and buildings to the Rockefeller Foundation) merged with the medical school in Jinan. Later additions included the Nanjing University Medical College (1917), the Hankou Medical College (1919), and the North China Union Medical College for Women (1923). Cheeloo was coeducational from 1923.

10. Cheeloo University, Annual Report, 1930, 4.

11. Cheeloo University *Bulletin of the College of Medicine*, 1930, 10; 1935, 10.

12. Charles Hodge Corbett, *Shantung Christian University (Cheeloo)* (New York: United Board of Christian Colleges in China, 150 Fifth Ave., 1955), 205–06.

13. Ibid., 206–09.

14. Among the wounded were many "White Russians" who were serving as mercenaries; some had been fighting in various armies since 1914.

15. Jonathon D. Spence, *The Search for Modern China* (New York: W.W. Norton, 1990), 445.

16. Corbett, *Shantung Christian University*, 249–57.

17. Annual Report (Nashville, Board of World Missions, 1949), 64.

18. Cheeloo University College of Medicine, *Bulletin* (Foochow: Nov. 1948), 3–4.

19. Ibid., 6–11.

PART II
Korea

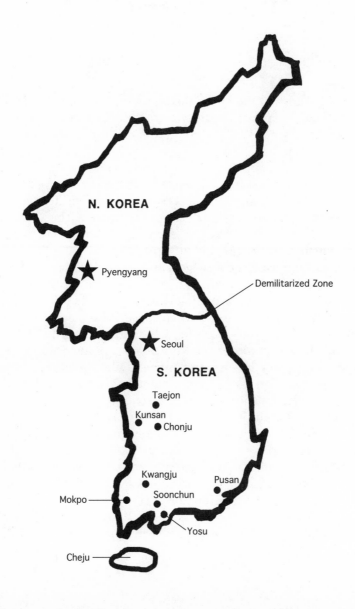

N. KOREA

★ Pyengyang

— Demilitarized Zone

★ Seoul

S. KOREA

Taejon
●

Kunsan
● ● Chonju

Kwangju
●   Pusan
Mokpo —   Soonchun   ●
   ●   ●
          ● Yosu

Cheju —

Chapter Five

Korea
(1894–1940)

The story of the PCUS medical work in Korea naturally divides into two parts. The forty-eight years before and the thirty-seven years after World War II were so different that in this history they are treated separately.[1]

When PCUS appointed its first medical missionary to China in 1881, Korea was a closed country, locked into the self-imposed isolation of a "Hermit Kingdom." The last two decades of the century were wrenching ones for this small but proud country. The Yi Dynasty—one of the longest family dynasties in recorded history—had ruled Korea for more than five centuries and was in a state of decline. "Poverty, discontent, and injustice, coupled with a conservative and unyielding aristocracy [*yangban* class], made Korea a tinderbox for social upheaval."[2] In addition, predatory neighbors (China, Japan, and Russia) vied with one another to gain dominance. A Korean adage described the situation: "When the whales fight, the shrimp are crushed."

In 1876 Japan forced the Koreans to sign their first modern treaty and set up a Japanese legation in the capital city of Seoul. China, with whom Korea had for centuries maintained a "younger brother/older brother" relationship, reacted by sending a "resident" to Korea to counter Japan's influence. A number of Western counties, beginning with the United States in 1882, signed treaties of friendship, commerce, and navigation. Political dissension within the country—between the traditionalists and modernizers—as well as the pressures from abroad contributed to the general turmoil. Into this maelstrom, the PCUS began its mission in Korea in 1892.

In missionary circles, Protestant mission work in Korea is commonly described as having been opened by the "scalpel of the doctor." It happened like this: In 1884 Prince Min Yong-Ik, a relative of the queen, was stabbed in an attack at a feast celebrating the opening of the first post office in Seoul. The post office was sponsored by a progressive faction and opposed by the traditional faction in the court. Horace N. Allen, M.D., a member of the newly opened American legation and a former medical missionary (Northern Presbyterian) in China, prevented the court physicians from pouring hot pitch into Prince Min's wound to halt the bleeding, controlled the hemorrhage, sutured the wound, and cared for the young prince until he recovered. In appreciation, the king not only gave Allen land and a building with which to start a hospital, but granted permission for missionaries to enter Korea as well. As a result, Western medicine in Korea, on the whole, did not face the extreme hostility that it encountered in China.[3]

The first Protestant missionaries posted to Korea, Rev. Horace G. Underwood (Northern Presbyterian) and Rev. and Mrs. Henry G. Appenzeller (Methodist), arrived in Seoul on Easter Sunday, April 5, 1885; others soon followed. Six years later, Underwood, who was known as a "great enthusiast and fertile-minded leader,"[4] returned to the United States on furlough. His presentation of the opportunities in Korea led to the PCUS's decision to open a mission in that country. From the beginning, the Protestant mission effort in Korea was characterized by amicable relations between denominations.

The PCUS mission in Korea began in 1892 with the arrival of seven pioneers. In contrast to China, where the first physician was not appointed until fourteen years after the opening of the mission work, (Alesandro) Damer Drew, M.D., was appointed one year after the mission was established; he arrived in Korea in 1894.

Pioneer Period (1892–1910)

The PCUS pioneers arrived at a critical time in Korea's history. Japan's victory over China in 1895 (fought primarily on Korean soil) and over imperial Russia in 1905 led inexorably to Japan's annexation of Korea in 1910. In such a time of political uncertainty and social turmoil, many Koreans turned to the church and were open to its teachings. Hence, the period was one of great progress for the Christian movement in Korea.

The Presbyterian missions in Korea adopted what is known as the Nevius Plan of Mission, named for its developer, Rev. John L. Nevius, a Northern Presbyterian missionary in China. This comprehensive plan operated on the principles of self-support, self-government, and self-propagation, combined with a highly developed system of Bible schools. Although the mission leadership in China rejected the Nevius plan, the fledgling Presbyterian missions in Korea followed it more completely than anywhere else in the world. This plan helped to train national leaders and is credited with producing the strong Korean church that exists today.[5]

Although medical work was not specifically mentioned in the Nevius Plan, the principle of self-support was observed as far as possible. An early decision was also made to open new mission stations only when they could be staffed by at least two evangelists and one physician.

In 1893 the Presbyterian Council, an organization composed of members of the Northern, Southern, Canadian, and Australian Presbyterian missions, assigned the province of Cholla, in southwest Korea, to the PCUS as its main area for work. No Protestant Christians were known to be in this region, and no Protestant missionaries had ever visited the Chollas.[6]

The word *Cholla* was derived from the names of two principal cities, *Chonju* and *Naju*; in Korean, the alliteration *Chonna* becomes *Cholla*. The Japanese later divided the province for administrative purposes into North and South Cholla. The Chollas had an estimated population of some 1.5 million in the 1890s, rising to around 4 million in the 1930s, and 6 million by 1983.

The Chollas were largely agricultural and considered to be backward, conservative, and poor. The area has the highest mountains in southern Korea (over 5,000 feet) and Korea's largest rice-growing plain. Steep mountains and narrow valleys are the norm, and the seacoast varies from wide mud flats to rocky shores. The high tides of the Yellow Sea, second only to those of the Bay of Fundy in Nova Scotia, make travel to the many islands difficult. People from the Chollas are referred to as being from "Hawaii"; land-based Asians generally consider island people, including Hawaiians (and the Japanese) to be backward and inferior.

The PCUS established five stations: two in North Cholla (Kunsan and Chonju in 1896) and three in South Cholla (Mokpo in 1898, Kwangju in 1904, and Soonchun in 1913). Hospitals were built in each of the five stations.

Korea's mission stations were built on hills and were distinguished by lovely vistas. The Koreans believed that dragons lived under such sites, making them unfit for human habitation.

Japanese Rule (1910–1945)

As with colonial regimes everywhere, the rule of Korea by Japan after 1910 benefited the ruler rather than the ruled and was deeply resented by the Korean people, who treasured their long history as an independent nation.

Japan can be credited with providing some benefits for Korea, such as banking, a judicial system, utilities, communications, and transportation (roads and highways; trains that ran on time). The construction of dikes reclaimed many thousands of acres of land from the sea. A public health system and government-operated hospitals, though poor in quality, were established throughout the country. The standard of living for ordinary Koreans improved.

At the same time, the Japanese controlled Korean society by force; police were everywhere. Political activity was suppressed, and the freedoms of speech, of the press, and of assembly were severely curtailed. The best of the land in Korea, through various means, gradually ended up belonging to Japanese. A common practice was the granting of easy loans to the Koreans; when the borrower could not repay the loan by a stipulated date, the land was forfeited. In the attempt to make the Korean society thoroughly Japanese, the schools were required to teach in the Japanese language, and Koreans were made to assume Japanese names. Korean language, art, dance, and music were discouraged.

In this repressive situation the church provided one of the few places where some small exercise of freedom and leadership was possible. The Korean Bible in the native phonetic script (*hangul*) helped preserve the language, educational opportunities for men and women flourished, and missionaries served as a link for the Koreans to the outside world. Not surprisingly, the Japanese regime deeply distrusted the church and the missionaries. Many Korean Christians were imprisoned and tortured, and endured other hardships.

In 1936 militarists seized power in Japan through the assassination of moderate leaders and set Japan on the course that led directly to World War II. The new regime, among other things, imposed the practice of Shinto, the Japanese state religion, on its colonies, including Korea. The "shrine issue" became the final blow that led to the withdrawal of the PCUS presence.

In October 1936 the mission's schools in Korea were ordered to take part in ceremonies at the Shinto shrines, and the students required to do obeisance to the spirits of the emperor and others enshrined there. After many tense sessions, the Presbyterian missions closed the schools in September 1937 rather than comply with this demand.[7] The Presbyterian hospitals continued to operate until 1940, at which time they, too, closed rather than follow orders to install shrines on their premises.[8]

Harassment of Korean churches and Christians steadily increased. Many leaders were imprisoned and, when it became obvious that Koreans who associated with missionaries were in special peril, most of the missionaries heeded the advice of the American consul and left for the United States in November 1940. The five PCUS missionaries who did not leave were interned under guard in their homes by the Japanese. One, Rev. J. C. Crane, escaped in November 1941, just before Pearl Harbor, thanks to the collusion of his guard, with whom he had established a friendly relationship. The four others returned to the United States in the summer of 1942 on the SS *Gripsholm* in a prisoner-of-war exchange.[9]

PCUS Medical Work Begins

The first group of physicians who went to work in Korea with the pioneers enthusiastically explored the area and helped found the stations. Caring for the health of missionary personnel was a major concern. Dispensaries were established in Kunsan, Chonju, and Mokpo primarily as a way to enhance evangelistic activity.

In contrast to the extreme hostility of the local people experienced by the medical missionaries in China, the missionaries in Korea were overwhelmed by people seeking medical help. However, in contrast to the pioneers in China, most of whom served for long periods of time, none of the five physicians who made up the first group in Korea continued long in mission medical work. A. Damer Drew resigned because of health problems; Mattie Ingold (Tate) and the Owenses (Clement Carrington and Georgiana Whiting) transferred to evangelistic and educational assignments; A. J. A. Alexander returned to the United States after only two months because his father had died while he was en route to Korea. During four months of 1904, no PCUS medical personnel at all were on the field in Korea.

Between 1904 and 1910 the second group of medical personnel revitalized the medical program and established the medical work on a firm basis in four of the five PCUS mission stations. Still, a history of illness and turnover plagued the medical mission in Korea. Of the six physicians and four nurses appointed during this period, only Robert M. Wilson, M.D., and Ethel Kestler, R.N., served their full terms to retirement.

Two of the six physicians belonging to this second group founded institutions that remained in operation until 1940. Thomas H. Daniel built hospitals in Kunsan and Chonju, and Robert M. Wilson not only built the hospital in Kwangju but also established the leprosy colony near Soonchun.

Severance Union Medical College

The establishment in Seoul of the Severance Union Medical College in 1904 and the Severance Nursing School in 1906 was important to all the medical missions in Korea. As noted, this cooperation on mission medical education found expression at about the same time in China in the Nanjing University Medical College, established in 1908.

Oliver R. Avison, M.D., of the Northern Presbyterian mission was the leading spirit of Severance. In the spring of 1900 he outlined his dream of an interdenominational effort in medical education to the meeting of the Ecumenical Conference on Foreign Missions at Carnegie Hall in New York City. This dream sparked a response from Louis H. Severance, a Standard Oil executive who was in the audience. Severance made the initial donation of $10,000 and continued to provide substantial funds for the institution that came to bear his name.[10]

Severance Hospital and Medical School developed into a 250-bed institution. Americans, British, Japanese, Chinese, and Koreans served on its twenty-five-member faculty. The first class of seven young physicians graduated in June 1908 and the first nurse in 1910. Graduates served in many mission institutions.

The PCUS participated in this institution by serving on the board and by providing the support from 1913–36 for Oh Kyung-Son, M.D., professor and first Korean president of the institution. PCUS medical missionaries who served on the faculty for short periods of time were Thomas H. Daniel, M.D. (1916–17); Elizabeth Shepping, R.N. (1918–19); and Roy S. Leadingham, M.D. (1920–21).

PCUS Medical Mission (1910–1940)

Modern medicine was virtually nonexistent in the Cholla region before 1910, except for that provided by the PCUS. The Japanese, after their takeover, established government hospitals in the larger cities, but many people, including Japanese citizens, continued to seek the services of the Western doctor. Although the authorities generally supported the mission's efforts in medicine, Japanese government regulations became administrative concerns. A quote from the 1915 *Missionary Survey* conveys the tension under which the missionaries worked:

> The nurses in Korea and the government have had a round, with the result that all nurses, native and foreign, were summoned before certain appointed Japanese doctors to take an examination before license was granted them. Miss Greer reports that she stood her examination before the Japanese doctors of Kwangju, and that it was a sensible one, much to her joy, and they congratulated her on her papers, and gave her the license. Some of our doctors have received their life permits to practice in Korea. Among these were Dr. Leadingham and Dr. Oh, and all of the doctors have doubtless received their permits by this time. This is a great relief to them, as they were uncertain as to the attitude of the Government to medical Missions.[11]

During the Japanese colonial period, the PCUS medical program was centered primarily in the five hospitals located in the five mission stations. Other important elements of the medical program were the dental work in Kwangju, the leprosy work, and the medical education provided by Severance Union Medical College in Seoul.

The goal of two doctors and two nurses for each mission hospital was never realized; only once, in 1926, was coverage with even one doctor and one nurse at each institution achieved.[12] In the 1920s many missionaries broke down from overwork, dietary deficiencies, and sicknesses of various kinds. The 1930 annual report of the Executive

Committee of Foreign Missions stated that "for many years there was more sickness in our Korea Mission than in any other of the nine Missions of our church."[13] In response to this problem, a summer camp was established at around 4,000 feet in the Chiri Mountains to provide an escape from the humid summer heat and a needed break from the pressures of the work. Missionaries were encouraged to take a summer vacation, develop hobbies, use fresh flour and sugar, and protect themselves against vermin.

The last decade before World War II (1930–40) was an active one for the medical work. The reduction in operating funds because of the depression in the United States, the perennial shortage of medical personnel, and the growing Japanese pressure on the Christian community remained serious problems. However, there were bright spots as well. Korean doctors, some graduates of Severance Union Medical College and others trained on location, were able to staff the hospitals when no missionary physicians were available. Table 5-1 presents some statistics on the work of the five PCUS hospitals in Korea in 1934.[14]

Table 5-1

The Five PCUS Hospitals in Korea in 1934

	Chonju	Kunsan	Kwangju	Mokpo	Soonchun
Admissions	639	1,120	1,120	176	2,800
Days treated	8,316	12,63	8,34	2,144	32,950
Major operations	230	188	209	126	825
New outpatients	2,275	1,873	3,846	1,685	7,207
Outp't treatm'ts	7,645	5,201	11,220	4,159	24,020
Yen receipts	13,760	16,449	15,900	6,073	59,909

Although fire destroyed two of the original hospitals (Kwangju in 1933 and Chonju in 1935), both were quickly replaced. The fact that local Koreans contributed substantial amounts to the rebuilding of both hospitals was tangible proof of the general acceptance of the work of the mission.

The first venture of the PCUS into formal medical education in the Cholla region was the founding of a nursing school at the Kwangju hospital in 1934 by Margaret Pritchard, R.N., a 1929 graduate of Columbia University Hospital School of Nursing in New York. By 1940, when the hospital closed, the school had graduated ten nurses, all of whom passed examinations and were licensed by the Japanese government.

The leprosy program continued to expand and to experiment with innovative ways to provide a better life for the victims of this dread disease. The Japanese recognized the value of the work and, in 1928, Dr. R. M. Wilson was called to Tokyo, where he was decorated and presented with a poem written by the empress dowager, who had taken a special interest in the problem of leprosy. Translated, the poem reads as follows:

When the lepers are worried and sad
Be kind and comfort them.
I wish to go and comfort them
But as this cannot be
You please comfort them for me.[15]

In 1934, when six malcontents burned down the building at the leprosy colony in which the empress dowager's poem was hung, a tense situation developed. As reported to the Executive Committee of Foreign Missions in Nashville, Tennessee, the "dastardly act can be explained by no other reason than bolshevism and the old demon himself."[16] Japanese officials called on Dr. Wilson and pointed out that, by Japanese custom, atonement for this outrage to the empress dowager would be the suicide (hara-kiri) of the person in charge. The mission contemplated a hasty furlough for Dr. Wilson to the United States when, luckily, word came that one of the jailed arsonists had committed suicide. This act seemed to satisfy the Japanese authorities.

In the late 1930s, morale of the mission rose with the appointment of four medical missionaries: Elizabeth Woods, R.N., for Kunsan in 1937; John F. Preston Jr., M.D., for Kwangju in 1938; and James S. (M.D.) and Edna Mae (R.N.) Wilson for Kunsan in 1939.[17] But as the tensions leading to World War II steadily increased, the ability to operate under Japanese rule became ever more difficult. In the fall of 1940 all the medical institutions except for the leprosy colony closed, the missionaries evacuated, and supplies and equipment were distributed to Korean staff. Despite continued harassment from the

Japanese, many of the Korean staff were able to carry on medical practices in small clinics.

Summary
When PCUS missionaries left Korea in 1940, the PCUS medical program had been operating there for forty-four years. Over that time, thirty-nine medical personnel had participated: twenty-two physicians (two women), sixteen nurses, and one dentist. These medical professionals made up 27 percent of the total of 142 regular service PCUS missionaries who served in Korea. Physicians arrived with the pioneers and helped to open doors to the gospel message through their ministry to the sick. Five one-doctor/one-nurse hospitals were established in each of the five mission stations, and, together with the leprosy colony, conveyed the gospel message in a tangible concrete form.

Although sadness and bitter disappointment accompanied the passing of this era of missions in Korea, the decades after the war saw the emergence of a vibrant Korean Christian church. Just as the doctors and nurses had been in the vanguard of those establishing the church in Korea, the medical program of the PCUS shared in the preparation that led to this astonishing growth.

ATKINSON MEMORIAL HOSPITAL
Kunsan
Kunsan was a small fishing village on the banks of the Kum River about 150 miles south of Chemulpo (Inchon) in 1896, when A. Damer Drew, M.D., and the other pioneers arrived to establish a PCUS mission station. Under the Japanese, Kunsan developed into a port serving the rice-growing plain that stretched east to the mountains. Rice from this plain, considered the best in the Japanese empire, supplied the imperial household in Tokyo. Kunsan was the primary port of entry to the North Cholla region until the building of the railroads in 1912; small coastal steamers made irregular calls at Kunsan.

In April 1896 two families, the Drews and the Junkins, set sail for Kunsan on a Japanese sailing junk because the SS *Sea Dragon*, the regular steamer, was in port for repairs. The voyage took four days instead of the usual fourteen hours. Accounts of the voyage vary.

According to Rev. William M. Junkin, the voyage was "four days in a chicken coop,"[18] whereas Dr. Drew wrote that it was "a very pleasant trip to all, except the two ladies who were seasick and much cramped for room. The children especially seem[ed] to enjoy . . . the delight-fully pure sea breezes."[19]

The missionaries were first housed near the river in Korean straw-roofed, mud-floor houses; one of the houses regularly flooded during the rainy season. Eventually, the mission station was established on a hill at the village of Kunmal, some three miles up the Kum River. Because of the high tides along Korea's west coast, the view from this hill alternated between a lovely seascape and wide stretches of mud flats.

The Beginning (1896–1902)

A. Damer Drew, M.D., was thirty-four years old when he arrived in Korea in 1894. Two weeks after his arrival, he and Rev. William D. Reynolds made the first extensive overland exploratory trip through the Chollas. The trip lasted six weeks and covered most of the terri-tory later to become the focus of PCUS work. Dr. Drew's blistered feet prompted his plea to place a station at the port city of Kunsan, where water travel was the usual mode of transportation.[20]

In Kunsan, Dr. Drew promptly set up a clinic in a Korean house, which a visiting executive from the United States described as a "hovel."[21] He flew a flag with a red cross during clinic hours and the Stars and Stripes on Sundays and other times when the clinic was not open. Dr. Drew, who was known as "one of the most brilliant men turned out from the University of Virginia" (M.D., 1891),[22] soon attracted large numbers of patients. He bought a boat with his own money and spent much time traveling and providing medical services to people living along the Kum River and the seacoast.

By 1899 Dr. Drew, according to Dr. Samuel H. Chester, executive secretary of foreign missions of the PCUS, was "known all over the country" and "by reason of his work has, I believe, more influence than any other man, native or foreign, in southern Korea."[23] The early positive response to the Christian message by the people in the Kunsan area was thought to be due in large measure to the drawing power of Dr. Drew's medical work.

By 1901 Dr. Drew's health was seriously impaired by repeated illnesses and overwork. He went back to the United States and, although

A. Damer Drew, M.D. (1893–1904) was the first PCUS medical missionary to Korea. Above, Dr. Drew's sailboat. Both photographs courtesy of Virginia Somerville.

never able to return to Korea, remained interested in the mission and in the Korean people. He is reported to have taken Koreans into his home in San Francisco during the time of the great earthquake.[24]

A. J. A. Alexander, M.D., arrived in Kunsan in November 1902 as Dr. Drew's replacement. Although he was met on arrival in Korea with news of his father's death and had to return to the United States after just two months, he contributed significantly to the PCUS medical work in Korea by taking back with him a promising young Korean student, Oh Kyung-Son, whom he put through the Hospital College of Medicine, Louisville, Kentucky (since 1922, the University of Louisville School of Medicine). Upon graduation, Dr. Oh returned to Korea and worked in two of the mission's hospitals (Kunsan and Mokpo) before joining the faculty of Severance Union Medical College in 1913 where, as has been noted, he became its first Korean president in 1931; he retired in 1936. Dr. Alexander also contributed substantial funds for the construction of hospitals and schools in Korea and in China.

A New Beginning (1904–1909)

Thomas Henry Daniel, a graduate of the University of Virginia (M.D., 1902), arrived in Kunsan in 1904. He showed unusual linguistic ability and was described as being "much in earnest" about his work and "having a great heart."[25] Under his leadership and with the help of Ethel Esther Kestler, R.N., who arrived in 1905—the first nurse to be appointed to Korea by the PCUS—the medical program in Kunsan grew rapidly and was established on a firm foundation.

Dr. Daniel began his work with minimal equipment or facilities. In a letter written in 1905 he spoke of needing a microscope ("there is not one in our mission") and trial lenses for fitting glasses ("there is so much eye trouble that it constitutes a considerable part of our work.")[26] Patients came in great numbers. Clinic was held in a room of a vacant residence, and postoperative patients were sent to a nearby inn. By 1906 Dr. Daniel, with funds sent in part by Dr. Alexander, began construction on the first unit of the Frances Bridges Atkinson Memorial Hospital, named for the wife of Ethel Kestler's former pastor. This first PCUS hospital in Korea consisted of an operating room and two wards with a total capacity for eighteen patients.

In 1907 Dr. Oh Kyung-Son returned to Kunsan from the United States and joined Dr. Daniel. In 1909, when the Daniels went to the United States on an emergency health furlough, Dr. Oh was put in charge of the Kunsan medical program. On their return the Daniels moved to Chonju, Dr. Oh to Mokpo, and Jacob Bruce Patterson, M.D., was assigned to Kunsan.

Dr. Patterson's Potato Vine (1910–1924)

Dr. Patterson, an honors graduate of Washington University in St. Louis (M.D., 1907), arrived in Korea in 1910. Four nurses served with him: Ethel Kestler (until she transferred to Chonju in 1912), Elizabeth Johanna Shepping (1914–18), Lillie Ora Lathrop (1919–27), and Annie Isabell Grey (1921–25).

During the fourteen years that Dr. Patterson served in Kunsan, the hospital grew into what was described as the largest one-doctor hospital in all Korea. Besides being a highly regarded physician and thorough diagnostician, Dr. Patterson is remembered for three things:

1. the complex of buildings that became known as "Patterson's Potato (or Cucumber) Vine" because, as more space was needed, he constructed Korean-style buildings of various shapes and sizes until gradually, like a vine, the hospital covered the side of the hill;

2. his special talent in training Korean medical personnel;

3. and the policy that the medical work should be primarily self-supporting.[27]

Dr. Patterson believed that the hospital should be constructed in the Korean style, with the patients sleeping on the warm floors (*ondol*) to which they were accustomed. He also encouraged relatives to become involved in the patient's care and feeding.

He was a gifted teacher. He trained a number of doctors, who became licensed after passing examinations. He also trained indigent and handicapped patients; a man with one leg and another with no arms were trained to be skillful helpers in the hospital.

Because his practice was very large and receipts were "remarkable," the hospital was largely self-supporting and was able to care for many charity cases. Among his patients were many well-to-do Japanese, who were willing to pay almost anything for his care.

Dr. Patterson was among the missionaries who contracted sprue, a digestive disorder associated with enteric infection and nutritional deficiency. Between 1917 and 1921 this disease had reached epidemic proportions among the missionaries in Korea. In 1924 Dr. Patterson resigned as the result of overwork and poor health.

Elizabeth Johanna Shepping, R.N., was a truly notable missionary. Born in Germany of Catholic parents, she converted to Protestantism while in nursing school in New York City and became a PCUS missionary in 1912. She pursued her nursing profession full time while in Kunsan (1912–18) and then spent a year at the Severance Nursing School in Seoul. Subsequently, she transferred to Kwangju where, at her request, she was given an educational/evangelistic, rather than a medical, assignment. At her death in 1934 after a long illness, she was mourned "by hundreds from low and high estate."[28] In 1969 the Korean government posthumously honored her "in recognition of outstanding contribution to the Koreans in the 1920s."[29]

Lillie O. Lathrop, R.N., was first assigned to Mokpo (1911–19), where she was often the only medical missionary on location; the same was true during her eight years in Kunsan. Lillie Lathrop's special concern was for the orphans left at the hospital. Many of these she succeeded in placing for adoption in Christian homes.

Final Years (1925–1940)

After Dr. Patterson's departure, the Kunsan hospital steadily declined, largely because of frequent changes in personnel. Physicians assigned to Kunsan served relatively briefly. Nurses, with the help of Korean staff and visits of doctors from the other stations, carried the major responsibility. Nonmedical missionaries (Rev. John E. Talmage and Miss Willie B. Greene) assisted in the administration.

The three physicians assigned to Kunsan during these years were Louis C. Brand (1924–29), who transferred to Kwangju when Dr. Wilson moved to Soonchun with the leprosy colony; William Hollister (1931–36), who required a health furlough (1933–35) and finally resigned after his wife developed a brain tumor; and James S. Wilson (1939–40). The nurses were Lillie O. Lathrop, Anna Lou Greer (Walker), and Elizabeth B. Woods. Anna Lou Greer began her service in Korea in 1913, helping to found the hospital in the newly opened station at Soonchun. In 1929, because of her administrative competence, she was asked to help with the hospital in Kunsan. While on furlough in 1932 she married George M. Walker, but, by special request because of Hollister's health problems, she returned without her husband to Kunsan for two years (1933–35). (George Walker visited her twice in Korea during that time.)

Elizabeth B. Woods, R.N., fresh from a modern medical center in New York, described "Dr. Patterson's Potato Vine Hospital" in 1937:

> The hospital in Kunsan was without a missionary physician and the buildings were a series of Korean mud and straw structures up the side of the hill. Patients slept, Korean style, on the floor. The problem of nursing a patient on the floor was no small challenge. Two Drs. Hong, father and son, staffed the hospital. The son was a recent Severance graduate; the father had started [under Dr. Patterson] as an errand boy, had no medical school experience, and stood examination for his medical license. There were no graduate nurses on the staff. Nursing was done by nursing helpers. Perhaps my chief accomplishment was to provide uniforms for the "nurses."[30]

Relations with Japanese authorities became tense. The missionaries were treated as though they were spies; officials would come into their homes at any time of the day, and permits were required for travel of any kind. However, the work in the hospital was varied and interesting. The two Korean doctors were good internists. Dr. Wilson, who concentrated on surgery, remembers removing in one month three ovarian cysts weighing over twenty-five pounds each. "I saw a lot," he commented.[31]

Elizabeth Woods's marriage to Rev. Otto DeCamp of the Northern Presbyterian mission, which took place in Kwangju in December 1940, was the last social event for the missionaries still in Korea. The closing of the mission hospitals and the evacuation of the missionaries to the United States brought an end to the PCUS medical program in Kunsan.

McKowen Memorial Hospital
Chonju

Chonju, the capital of North Cholla Province, lies at the foot of mountains on the eastern edge of the largest rice-growing plain in Korea. A walled city when the PCUS missionaries first arrived, Chonju was the family seat of the Yi Dynasty's royal family and had an ancient and proud history. The people of Chonju were conservative and suspicious of the missionaries, who first arrived in 1893.

The PCUS missionaries bought property south of the city in 1893 but, because of civil disturbances, were unable to begin the work in Chonju until 1898. In the fall of 1897 Mattie Barbara Ingold, M.D., arrived to join Rev. William D. and Mrs. Patsy Reynolds, Rev. Lewis B. Tate and his sister, Miss Mattie S. Tate, and Rev. William B. Harrison. Mattie Ingold, on graduating from the Women's Medical College, Baltimore (M.D., 1896), was awarded the gold medal for highest academic achievement and received the prize in "Principles and Practice of Medicine." As part of his preparation for missionary work, William Harrison had briefly attended Louisville (Kentucky) Hospital Medical College but soon chose to confine his activities to the evangelistic aspect of the work.

The Lady Doctor

Dr. Mattie Ingold's primary assignment for the first year was to study the language. She was then given a two-room Korean home, eleven by twelve feet, which served as a clinic until, in 1902, a substantial dispensary was built. Lewis Tate, whom she later married, supervised the construction which, she wrote, has "doubtless been a heavy burden to him, though I have heard no complaints."[32] Because there were no regular inpatient facilities, patients requiring close supervision slept in the waiting room for days, weeks, and even months.

Dr. Ingold's diary, annual reports, and articles in *The Missionary* portray a keen perception of Korean culture and customs; they also

Mattie B. Ingold (Tate), M.D.,
treating a patient. Photograph
courtesy of Paul Crane.

reveal the conflict between her professional training and her responsibility to the evangelizing concerns of the mission:

> I am anxious yet fearful to begin the medical work. Successful treat-
> ment is a great power for good, but, if unsuccessful I fear it may be
> as great for evil . . . I have tried to follow the suggestion made at our
> last meeting, that whatever was done in this line should be only
> recreation . . . The medical work I regard merely as an evangelizing
> agency which is only an aid, and always subordinate, to the evan-
> gelical work.[33]

One of Dr. Ingold's first patients was a woman who was deaf as
the result of accumulated ear wax. The dramatic restoration of
hearing when the wax was removed created a sensation in the town.
In another case, Dr. Ingold reduced a woman's dislocated jaw under
chloroform—the first use of an anesthetic in Chonju.

Dr. Ingold restricted her medical practice to the care of women and
children and steadfastly resisted pressure to provide medical care to
men. However, she made at least one exception in the case of a
distraught young woman who begged for medicine for her husband.
After learning that the husband was only twelve years old (the
marriage of a boy to an older woman was a common practice in Korea
at that time), Dr. Ingold instructed the young woman to take his hair
down from the topknot that denoted his adulthood, plait it into a braid
such as a boy would wear, and carry him into the clinic on her back. It
was then proper for her to examine him and prescribe medication.

Dr. Mattie Ingold's clinic, c. 1898. Photography courtesy of Virginia Somerville.

Although Dr. Ingold is credited with reducing suspicion and winning friends for the mission in the Chonju area, the work in the dispensary appears to have been sporadic at best. The care of sick missionaries and their children, among whom there were several deaths, was a major responsibility; because of stress on her own health, she was forced to take a number of breaks of several weeks or months at a time. She went with other missionaries on a number of preaching trips to country villages, some lasting for a week or more. She taught a children's Sunday school and prepared a children's cate-chism that was widely used for many years. Before she left for the United States on furlough in 1904, she reported that the dispensary had been open for six and one-half months in 1902 (1,586 patients), for five months in 1903 (1,523 clinic patients and 35 inpatients among whom two deaths occurred), and for six months in 1904 (2,107 dispen-sary patients, 67 inpatients, and 106 visits to 58 homes).

Upon her return to Korea, Dr. Ingold married Rev. Lewis Tate. Her assignment in 1906 was "medical, itinerating, school, and evan-gelistic.[!]"[34] She eventually withdrew from medical work except in emergencies.

Wiley Hamilton Forsythe, M.D. (1904–1905)

Dr. Forsythe, an unusually winsome and handsome young grad-uate of the Hospital College of Medicine, Louisville, Kentucky (M.D., 1898), arrived in Korea in 1904 at the age of thirty-one and was assigned to Chonju to take up the medical work begun by Dr. Mattie Ingold Tate. Not long after arriving in Chonju, Dr. Forsythe was called to the home, some fifteen miles away, of a wealthy man who had been attacked by robbers. As reported to the mission's headquarters in Nashville, Tennessee:

> Sunday [Forsythe] attended church at Sunji dong . . . and went back Sunday night to sleep in the wounded man's house. At about 4 A.M. Monday robbers rushed in and dragged Forsythe out of bed saying he was a Korean soldier and that they had come to kill him. He protested he was not and his Korean hosts tried to shield him, but they beat him with guns into unconsciousness and then a dastardly coward cut him across the right ear, an awful gash severing ear and bone and going in over an inch. He bled profusely and has been semiconscious ever since.[35]

Dr. Forsythe was moved to the Daniel's home in Kunsan, where he was tenderly nursed over a period of weeks. This incident had a profound influence on the Chonju community. Educated and well-to-do Koreans who had previously been indifferent or antagonistic to Christianity became open to hearing the Christian message. After some months, Dr. Forsythe left for the United States to regain his health. On his return to Korea in 1909, he was assigned to Mokpo.

Between 1904 and 1910 the medical program developed unevenly. Drs. Joseph Nolan and Ferdinand Birdman served for brief periods, and Dr. Mattie Ingold Tate continued to work with women and children. The arrival of Emily Cordell, R.N., in 1907 brought some relief until she moved to Mokpo following her marriage to Rev. (Henry) Douglas McCallie in 1910.

Medical Work in Chonju Stabilized (1910–1940)

From 1910 until 1940 the medical program in Chonju enjoyed continuity of personnel. Physicians who served in Chonju during that period were Thomas Henry Daniel (1910–16), Moorman Owen Robertson (1916–21), Henry Loyola Timmons (1922–25), and Lloyd Kennedy Boggs (1925–40). Following the tragic death in 1911 of Laura May Pitts, R.N., after only six months in Korea, Ethel Kestler transferred from Kunsan and provided a continuing nursing presence (sometimes in the absence of a missionary physician) until the hospital closed in 1940.

Laura May Pitts, who arrived in Chonju in 1910, had enthusiastically begun to learn the language and practice her nursing skills. In February 1911 she and Anabel Lee Nisbet, the wife of Rev. John S.

Nisbet, decided to travel by horseback to Kwangju, some sixty miles to the south, spending the night in a village en route. During the first day's travel in rain and snow, a bridge collapsed under Laura May Pitts, landing her and her horse in a shallow river. She did not seem in any way affected by the fall. During the night, however, Mrs. Nisbet awoke and realized that Laura May Pitts was dead; it was later determined that the cause was an aneurysm that broke loose in the fall.[36]

The control of the omnipresent Japanese reached even to this remote village. Mrs. Nisbet was grilled for hours by Japanese police, who assumed that the younger woman had been murdered because of jealousy in an imagined love triangle. It took eighteen terrible hours before missionary help arrived from Chonju, but local Christians rallied to support Mrs. Nisbet throughout her ordeal.[37]

In 1912 Dr. Daniel acquired the land for and oversaw the construction of a substantial thirty-bed hospital and outpatient facility with four wards, four private rooms, operating rooms, an office, and an apartment for the missionary nurse. Stone from the Chonju city wall, torn down in 1909 by the Japanese, went into the building. Funds were provided in memory of W. R. McKowen of Jackson, Louisiana. The two-story hospital (with basement) occupied a commanding location on top of a hill.

Dr. Daniel, a well-trained, capable physician, carried a heavy load during his time in Chonju. In addition to supervising construction of the hospital plant, he had a very large practice that included an increasing number of Japanese patients. Dr. Daniel also taught physiology in the boys' high school, helped prepare three medical helpers for entrance into Severance Union Medical School, and served as

McKowen Memorial Hospital, Chonju, was built in 1912 and destroyed by fire in 1935. Photograph courtesy of Paul Crane.

"captain" of Chonju's "Heathen Sunday School."[38] The doctors were expected to engage in evangelistic efforts and were commonly assigned responsibility for the "Heathen Sunday Schools," a highly successful missionwide movement to provide schools for children of non-Christian families. Overwork, and the responsibility for a family of seven children, became overwhelming. The arrival of Moorman Owen Robertson, M.D., made it possible for Dr. Daniel to spend a satisfying final year in Korea (1916–17) as professor of internal medicine at Severance Union Medical School in Seoul.

When Dr. Robertson resigned in 1921 because of ill health, Henry Loyola Timmons, M.D., who was then in practice in Columbia, South Carolina, agreed to serve a short term (1922–25) until a permanent replacement could be recruited. He had previously spent an orientation year in Chonju (1912–13) before going to the newly opened station at Soonchun (1913–16).

Lloyd K. Boggs, a graduate of the University of Georgia School of Medicine, Augusta (M.D., 1924), became known in Chonju as "Dr. John 3:16" because he repeated this biblical verse to all with whom he came in contact. During Dr. Boggs's stay in Chonju, the hospital acquired the name *Yasu* or *Jesus* Hospital by which it is known in Korea to this day.

In 1935 the hospital burned as the result of loose electrical wiring or a bad flue. No life was lost, but the building and most of its

McKowen Memorial Hospital after the fire (1935). Photograph courtesy of Virginia Somerville.

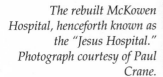

The rebuilt McKowen Hospital, henceforth known as the "Jesus Hospital." Photograph courtesy of Paul Crane.

contents were destroyed. With insurance and donations, many from the Korean community, a neat, modern forty-bed facility was built.

By 1940 the pressure from the Japanese had become increasingly severe. Dr. Boggs had the unhappy experience, when arriving to visit a rural church, of having the local church leaders dismiss the congregation, who then filed out without a word of greeting. When orders came to install miniature Shinto shrines in each hospital, the mission hospitals closed rather than comply, and the missionaries left for the United States.[39]

CHARLES W. FRENCH HOSPITAL
Mokpo

In 1897 the Japanese made Mokpo, a small fishing town like Kunsan, a treaty port. It then became a large city and was, until the railroad was built in 1912, the port of entry for the PCUS missionaries into the South Cholla region. A backdrop of jagged mountain peaks gave Mokpo a dramatic setting. Some three thousand islands of the Korean archipelago were served from Mokpo.

Early Days (1898–1904)

Rev. Dr. Clement C. Owen and Rev. Eugene and Mrs. Lottie Witherspoon Bell moved to Mokpo in 1898 to open the PCUS mission work in South Cholla Province. A small dispensary was among the first structures built and, as was true elsewhere in Korea, it was deluged with patients. Lottie Bell died in 1901, and in 1904 Mokpo station was closed in order to concentrate missionary personnel on the development of the more centrally located city of Kwangju.

Dr. Owen and his wife, Georgiana Whiting, M.D., a Northern Presbyterian missionary whom he married in Seoul in 1900, are good examples of the conflict these early missionaries to Korea experienced in reconciling their medical profession with their evangelistic calling. After moving to Kwangju in 1904, Dr. Owen devoted himself to full-time evangelistic, rather than medical, work.

Clement Owen, a scion of a wealthy Virginia family, received his theological training at Hampden-Sydney College and in Scotland. After volunteering to be a missionary, he decided to undergo medical training in order to better equip himself for service overseas. Thus he attended the University of Virginia (M.D., 1896) and took a year of postgraduate study in New York, before sailing for Korea in 1898. In the meantime, realizing the urgent need for workers, he offered to support a substitute, and A. Damer Drew, M.D., went to Korea in 1894 in his stead. (The Drews named their son for Dr. Owen).

Before her marriage, Georgiana Whiting, a graduate of the Woman's Medical College in Philadelphia (M.D., 1894), had an active medical practice in Seoul. She was appointed physician to the Korean queen and did heroic work during the severe 1895 cholera epidemic. However, after her marriage, she chose to concentrate on educational work. The Owenses accepted no pay for their missionary service.[40]

A New Beginning (1907–1940)

The arrival of a bumper crop of new missionaries made it possible to reopen Mokpo in 1907, but the medical program in Mokpo suffered from a lack of continuity in personnel. Educational institutions and work among the islands flourished; the medical work did not.

A succession of doctors served for short periods of time; often, one of the nurses would be left to assume full responsibility for the work. Ferdinand H. Birdman, M.D., came to Mokpo in 1908, transferred to Chonju after a few months, and soon returned to his home in Germany.

Wylie H. Forsythe, M.D., returned to Korea in 1909 and was assigned to Mokpo. He combined compassion for the sick with an intense evangelistic zeal and is described as going "up and down the streets and roads of Mokpo dispensing gospel tracts with one hand

and medicines with the other." After he had served only two years, ill health forced him to return to the United States in 1911. His name, however, will always be associated with the dramatic "Christ-like episode" described in the next section (Kwangju) that stimulated the establishment of a leprosy program in Korea by the PCUS.[41]

In 1910 Dr. Oh Kyung-Son transferred to Mokpo to help Dr. Forsythe oversee the construction of a new dispensary and handle the heavy load of patients (some 3,785 in a three-month period). Dr. Oh was also put in charge of the "Heathen Sunday School" program of Mokpo.

Maynard C. Harding, M.D., who arrived in 1911, spent his brief stay in studying the language and developing plans for the construction of the hospital.

Roy S. Leadingham, M.D., came to Mokpo in 1912. His eight years, the longest served by any missionary physician in Mokpo, encompassed the construction in 1916 of the hospital in memory of Charles W. French of St. Joseph, Missouri, whose legacy provided the funds for its construction. Dr. Leadingham taught at Severance Union Medical School for one year before resigning in 1921 because of ill health.

William P. Gilmer, M.D., a highly decorated veteran of World War I, arrived in Korea in 1921 and, in 1925, married Kathryn (Kate) Newman, a teacher of missionary children in Kwangju. He resigned after her death in 1926, just twelve days after their child was born.

In 1927, after being evacuated from the PCUS mission in China, James B. Woods Jr., M.D., and Philip B. Price, M.D., served briefly in Mokpo. They found things quite primitive. Octavia Price, R.N., wrote:

> It was not so easy for Phil in the hospital . . . There was an American nurse but upon examining her, Phil sent her right up to Seoul for an abdominal operation. Phil's only interpreter was a young Korean technician who knew a few words of English. The Korean nurses spoke Japanese but no English. . . . Patients in the Mokpo hospital scorned the American hospital beds and spent their days on mats on the floor. This made treatment difficult. They also brought attendants with them, sometimes the whole family. The equipment was scanty. Doing a hernia operation, Phil found he had only three clamps whose points met firmly. He would clamp off three blood vessels, sew them with catgut, and proceed with the three clamps again.[42]

William Hollister, M.D., arrived in 1927 but spent part of his time in language school in Seoul and, in 1931, transferred to Kunsan. After 1931 no missionary physicians were appointed to Mokpo, and Korean doctors provided the medical services there. The nurses who really held things together in Mokpo were Lillie Lathrop, Mary Bain, Esther Matthews, and Georgiana Hewson. Other nurses, all of whom were the wives of evangelists, were Emily Cordell McCallie, Margaret Edmunds Harrison, and Virginia Kerr Cumming.

Visits to the many islands were an important aspect of the mission's activity in Mokpo. Rev. Douglas McCallie acquired a sailboat and spent most of his time in such travel. Emily Cordell McCallie accompanied her husband on his trips and held clinics for the island people wherever they went. Much of the success of that work is attributed to her.[43]

Margaret Edmunds arrived in Korea in 1903 under the auspices of the Women's Foreign Missionary Society of the Methodist Episcopal Church; she joined the PCUS after marrying Rev. William B. Harrison. Although she apparently did not actively practice nursing after her marriage, Margaret Edmonds made a significant contribution to the nursing profession in Korea by establishing Korea's first nurses' training school in Seoul in 1903 in connection with the Methodist Women's Hospital.[44] She also, with the help of her language teacher, coined the Korean word *kanowan* for *nurse*.[45] The current term for nurse *Kanosa* is a derivative, which reflects the improved status of women.

Virginia Kerr Cumming thought Korea very beautiful. She remembered the mountains, the fields ripe for harvest, the red peppers drying on straw roofs, and the beautiful mud walls. She was not shocked by the rather primitive medical facilities because, she said, she had few preconceptions. The hospital was small but fairly well equipped, and it had running water and electricity. She noted that some patients were indeed on the floor, and treating them there took getting used to. However, she observed that under the Japanese colonial rule the Koreans had a medical system that included provincial hospitals and public health clinics, and she thought that the level of medicine was not bad for the time.[46]

The PCUS medical work in Mokpo never reached its full potential because of lack of personnel and the shortage of funds during the depression. The hospital continued to operate until 1940 with a Korean staff and a small mission subsidy.

ELLEN LAVINE GRAHAM MEMORIAL HOSPITAL
Kwangju

Kwangju, the capital of South Cholla Province, was a creation of the Japanese. It developed into the largest and most influential city in the two Chollas and became a center for commercial, educational, and government activities. But Kwangju lacked the stability of a Confucian cultural heritage and from its inception has been a center for feisty political activity.

The PCUS purchased some thirty-five acres of land south of the city on a crescent-shaped hill with a stunning view of beautiful Mudung-san (a 4,500-foot mountain). Because hilltop land was considered undesirable (and unlucky), the purchase price was low. Once it was planted with some 2,000 shade trees of various kinds, Kwangju station was considered unsurpassed for its beauty. Early construction included a church, a boys' and a girls' school, a Bible school, a dispensary and hospital, nine residences, and more than a mile of graded roads. Ample space for expansion was available.

Seven adults[47] (and seven children) made up the pioneer group that moved in 1904 and 1905 from Mokpo to establish the new mission station in Kwangju. By June 1907 they reported that "the longed-for release from building and moving operations [afford] an opportunity for fuller service."[48]

Dr. Nolan's Clinic (1905–1907)

Joseph Wynne Nolan, a recent graduate (M.D., 1904) of the Hospital College of Medicine (Louisville, Kentucky), began seeing patients during his first week in Kwangju; nine patients came the day the clinic opened. Within the first six weeks, 293 treatments were recorded, including two major operations and a number of minor ones. This heavy pace in a primitive setting proved overwhelming, and Dr. Nolan resigned in 1907 to accept a job with an American mining company in northern Korea.

The principal developers of the medical program in Kwangju before World War II were physicians Robert M. Wilson and Louis C. Brand and nurses Esther Matthews, Georgiana Hewson, and Margaret Pritchard. James K. Levie, D.D.S., arrived in 1923 and broadened the program by the establishment of the dental department.

Medical Dispensary, Kwangju.
Photograph courtesy of Virginia
Somerville.

Dr. Wilson's Years in Kwangju (1908–1928)

Robert Manton Wilson, M.D., a 1904 graduate of Washington University School of Medicine in St. Louis, was twenty-eight years old when he arrived in Kwangju in 1908. He proved to be an able administrator and imaginative innovator. Although Dr. Wilson is perhaps best remembered for his work with leprosy patients, he also built the Ellen Lavine Graham Hospital, where he gained a wide reputation as a surgeon; trained Korean nationals (twelve "home-made" doctors were taught and sent out to practice); wrote many articles and letters to publicize the medical work and its needs; and headed the Heathen Sunday School program (as did Dr. Daniel in Chonju and Dr. Oh in Mokpo).[49]

While returning from furlough in 1923, Dr. Wilson and his family were on a ship that arrived in the harbor at Yokohama just after the devastating earthquake struck, killing an estimated 74,000 persons. Dr. Wilson helped care for earthquake victims.

Dr. Wilson served on the board of Severance Medical School and supported the concept of training Korean nationals for medical careers. In later years he expressed frustration at the promptness with which interns he trained left to set up their own practices. "Getting a new doctor every year or so, as is often the case, is hard on the work, and one's own trained assistants [without medical school education] will often do better work."[50]

Dr. Wilson's involvement in leprosy (a disease that existed in every province of Korea but was concentrated in the south) grew out of an incident that became legendary. In 1909, as Dr. Forsythe was en route by horseback from Mokpo to Kwangju, he saw a woman in the last stage of leprosy lying by the wayside. She called out to him for help, and Dr. Forsythe stopped, lifted her onto his horse, and led the horse some thirteen miles into Kwangju. Because of the outcry from the patients in the hospital, shelter was arranged for the woman in an abandoned brick kiln, and Dr. Forsythe helped her, loathsome from disease, filth, and long neglect, over the rough path to the kiln.[51]

The woman died soon after, but the Kwangju missionaries were so moved by Dr. Forsythe's compassionate care that they determined to find a way to provide help for victims of this dread disease. With funds collected mainly from the missionaries, Dr. Wilson built a small "home" for six to eight leprosy patients. Thus began the leprosy program, which many Koreans consider to be the most significant medical contribution made by the PCUS in Korea before World War II.

Wylie Hamilton Forsythe, M.D., whose encounter with a woman suffering from leprosy resulted in the beginning of PCUS leprosy work. Photograph courtesy of Virginia Somerville.

The PCUS furnished personnel and managerial expertise to the leprosy program but not capital funds or operating budgets. Dr. Wilson marshaled the resources needed to do the leprosy work. Both the British and American Leprosy Societies made annual contributions, and, in 1912, the Society for Lepers (with headquarters in Scotland) underwrote expenses for building the Leprosy Home on the outskirts of Kwangju. This colony grew to have some 800 patients.

The Japanese authorities, stimulated by the concern of the empress dowager for leprosy victims, also supported the leprosy colony with

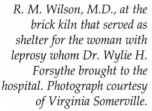

R. M. Wilson, M.D., at the brick kiln that served as shelter for the woman with leprosy whom Dr. Wylie H. Forsythe brought to the hospital. Photograph courtesy of Virginia Somerville.

annual subsidies of 3 yen ($1.50) per month for each patient. Once, the
story goes, when Dr. Wilson experienced difficulty in securing the
promised subsidy, he drove a truckload of patients to the entrance of
the provincial headquarters, where he threatened to deposit them.
This action produced speedy results from the officials, who were
deathly afraid of the disease.

As the colony expanded, the people of Kwangju pressured the
Japanese government to move the colony away from the environs of
the provincial capital. Dr. Wilson negotiated for some land on a beautiful peninsula fifteen miles south of Soonchun. The move, paid for in
part by the Japanese, took place in 1926 and the *Ai Yang Won* (Home
of Love) grew to have 1,200 patients and gained an international
reputation. The Wilsons moved to Soonchun in 1928.

The English name of the colony evolved from the "Biederwolf
Leper Colony" (named for a famed evangelist who visited and later
raised funds for the colony) and the "R. M. Wilson Leprosy Colony"
to the "Wilson Leprosy Center and Rehabilitation Hospital." The
Koreans still call it *Ai Yang Won*.

Dental Department (1923–1940)

James Kellum Levie (Atlanta Southern Dental College, D.D.S.,
1918) was appointed to Korea in the belief that the lack of proper
dental care during the seven years between furloughs contributed to
the poor health of the missionaries in Korea. Dr. Levie's extraction of
fifty-eight infected teeth from missionaries during his first year in
Korea gave credence to this belief.

Dr. Levie once packed his portable chair, dental equipment, and a
number of missionary children into a Model T Ford and headed to
Soonchun, where a missionary suffered a dental emergency. As the
Model T was climbing the great Tombok Pass on a narrow one-lane dirt
road, it stopped and refused to go farther Not long before on the same
lonely road, a tiger had attacked a postman, and his bones, bicycle, and
mailbag were all that were found of him. When darkness descended on
the Levie's vehicle, the children spent a terrifying night anticipating the
tiger's reappearance. Early the next morning repairs were completed,
and the travelers safely made their way into Soonchun.[52]

Although Dr. Levie's primary assignment was the care of missionaries' dental problems, he did not limit his practice to the
missionaries. He set up a dental department with three chairs and (in

the early days) drills powered by foot pedals. At times he accompanied the evangelists on rural trips, and he is reported to have pulled 1,000 teeth in one day! He also trained assistants, who were placed in other PCUS mission hospitals. Dr. Levie wrote, "I am delighted with the dental clinic in Dr. Roger's Hospital in Soonchun. This young man is a graduate of the Kwangju Boys' School, grammar [school] department, but in spite of lack of education, he is doing good dental work with the few months' training that I was able to give him."[53]

Dr. Brand and Miss Pritchard (1929–1940)

Louis C. Brand, M.D., a 1922 graduate of the University of Virginia, was reassigned from Kunsan to Kwangju in 1929 to fill the vacancy left by Dr. Wilson's transfer to leprosy work in Soonchun. Margaret Pritchard, R.N., also arrived in 1929 and described the hospital:

The hospital was in a very discouraging condition, not having had a missionary doctor or a nurse in [several] years. There were no graduate nurses in the hospital; the nursing was being done by widows whose nursing knowledge and skill had been gained only from experience in the hospital. The reputation of the hospital was not good. The building was a two-story grey brick with four large rooms on each floor, one of which was the operating room. A clinic building had been added on to one side. There were no closets or storage space. The equipment was very limited, and the budget was less than $100 per month.

At that period in the mission work the emphasis was on [elementary and high] schools. This hospital was one of five small hospitals being operated by the mission. The hope was to have a missionary doctor and nurse in each hospital, but that proved to be impossible.[54]

Fire destroyed the hospital in October 1933; fortunately, there were no casualties. A new building was constructed with funds from a small insurance policy ($4,000), a $2,000 grant from the mission, plus private donations from Koreans and from the United States. Miss Pritchard wrote, "The first gift of money came from the [mission's] girls' high school students. Gifts came from Christians and non-Christians alike, all saying, 'We must have a Christian hospital.' . . . When the new building was finished it was all paid for."[55]

Ellen Lavine Graham Hospital, Kwangju, was built in 1909 and destroyed by fire in 1933. Photograph courtesy of Virginia Somerville.

Financial support for the Kwangju hospital, never adequate, worsened during the depression and prompted Dr. Brand to spend his furlough year (1931) at the Johns Hopkins Hospital, where he studied plastic surgery. Plastic surgery, a moneymaker for the hospital, helped to ease the constant pressure for more funds.

Dr. Brand also became interested in the problem of tuberculosis, which was endemic throughout Korea. Two wards, connected to the main (new) hospital, were constructed specifically for tuberculosis patients. After World War II the medical program in Kwangju continued to emphasize the treatment of tuberculosis.

Margaret Pritchard began her distinguished missionary career in Kwangju. She considered the founding of the nursing school in 1934 her most valuable contribution to the Kwangju hospital. Conventional wisdom maintained that Korean society would only accept older women (widows or cast-off wives) as nurses, but Miss Pritchard was able to recruit young high school graduates. "When we had demonstrated what could be done there was no more difficulty securing students who were well qualified."[56]

A tragic loss for Kwangju and for the mission's medical program was Dr. Brand's death in 1938 at age forty-four from a combination of amoebic dysentery, malaria, and sprue.[57] John F. Preston Jr., M.D., was recruited for Kwangju, but he arrived only months before the mission closed in 1940.

The political crisis that forced the closing of mission work in Korea was especially hard on the medical missionaries at Kwangju. The future for significant medical service had seemed bright with a new hospital building, a newly appointed well-trained young physician, a new and well-accepted nurses' training school, a busy dental program, and evidence of support from the local community.

ALEXANDER HOSPITAL
Soonchun

Soonchun station is unique in that it was based on a comprehensive plan and was adequately staffed and funded from its inception. Located near the southern coast, Soonchun was separated from other mission centers by three high mountain passes; rail service did not begin until 1932. The population was warmly receptive to the missionaries. Rev. Dr. Clement C. Owen spent much time and energy in the Soonchun area, and contracted his fatal illness (age forty-two) while on a trip there in 1909.

Rev. John F. Preston used his furlough in 1911 to present the plan for a station at Soonchun to the "home church" (PCUS churches and mission headquarters in the United States). Personnel were recruited, funds were raised for the buildings, and one donor—George W. Watts of Durham, North Carolina—provided an endowment to pay the salaries of not one missionary but the entire station complement of thirteen persons. Thus in 1913 Soonchun station, as one of its members stated, "sprang full bloom into being."[58]

The new station was located at the base of a mountain outside the walls of the ancient city of Soonchun. The mountain provided granite suitable for quarrying, and a mountain spring furnished "good" water. In 1912 and 1913, construction began on a boys' school, a girls' school, a Bible school, the Alexander Hospital (named for Dr. A. J. A. Alexander, who had served briefly in Kunsan), and four residences. Enthusiasm for their work and a sense of uniqueness were characteristic of the Soonchun personnel, despite the death from dysentery of two children in the Robert T. Coit family on the same day in 1913. The missionaries called this day their "baptism of fire."[59]

The medical program in Soonchun was fortunate in having missionary personnel who served long enough to give it continuity and strength. Henry Loyola Timmons, M.D., began the work in 1913 and oversaw the construction of the hospital. James McLean Rogers, M.D., arrived in 1917 and served until the hospital closed in 1940. He built the Alexander Hospital into the largest and most active of the mission's hospitals. Robert Manton Wilson, M.D., worked at the Alexander Hospital as well as supervising the leprosy colony. John Fairman Preston Jr., a graduate of Duke University (M.D., 1935) interned there from 1937 to 1939. The nurses, Anna Lou Greer (Walker) and Georgiana Hewson, were efficient well-trained professionals. Thelma Thumm, a graduate of the Johns Hopkins School of Nursing, died after two years from measles encephalitis contracted from a patient.

Dr. Timmons Builds a Hospital (1913–1916)

Henry Loyola Timmons, M.D., whose father was a contractor and builder, studied architecture before entering medical school (North Carolina Medical College [M.D., 1911] and Rush Medical College, Chicago). His experience in construction was useful when he and Anna Lou Greer, R.N., were assigned to begin the medical work in Soonchun.

Dr. Timmons described the celebration for the opening of the thirty-bed hospital: "For three days, streams of people came in awe and admiration . . . The greatest wonder of it all is that it was built for them—not for the Americans nor Japanese, but just the poor, ignorant, neglected Koreans."[60]

In 1916 Dr. Timmons contracted sprue and returned to the United States, where he eventually went into practice in Columbia, South Carolina. (As noted, he returned to Korea in 1922 for three years in answer to an emergency situation at the Chonju hospital.) The missionaries in Korea continued to have serious health problems. The annual

Alexander Hospital, Soonchun. Photograph courtesy of Paul Crane.

Five doctors serving in Korea in 1927 were all graduates of Davidson College. Left to right: Louis C. Brand, William Hollister, James M. Rogers, Lloyd K. Boggs, and James B. Woods Jr. Photograph courtesy of Virginia Somerville.

report for 1923 noted that twenty-six missionaries were sick with sprue, and that only two doctors were available to man the five hospitals.

Dr. Rogers, the Happy Surgeon (1917–1940)

James McLean Rogers, M.D., F.A.C.S. (Medical College of Virginia, M.D., 1917) was a workaholic, but carried on his practice, especially surgery, with such zest that people, foreigners and Japanese included, were drawn to him. As a youth he had suffered a hunting accident that destroyed a section of the humerus in his left arm but left the nerves and blood vessels intact, so that he had full use of his forearm and hand. He entertained Koreans (and missionary children) by winding his flaccid arm around his neck and performing other unimaginable acrobatics. At the operating table a nurse was always positioned to support the elbow, so that he could use his hands for surgery. For recreation Dr. Rogers acquired a twenty-four-foot, two-masted fishing junk, with which he explored the bay near the leprosy colony.

Under Dr. Rogers, the Alexander Hospital in Soonchun gained a reputation similar to that of Dr. Patterson's hospital in Kunsan in the preceding decade. Surgical patients came from all over Korea, and space became a pressing problem. In 1934 a new wing brought the bed capacity to 85 (an inpatient count of 100 or more was not uncommon). First- and second-class wards produced income and made it possible for the hospital to operate on the subsidy from the mission of around $1,800 per year. The hospital was described as one of the most attractive and up-to-date plants in Korea. A visitor to the hospital in 1927 had this to say about it:

> The spotlessly clean floors and walls strike your attention at once. You ask how can the place be kept in such spick-and-span order, and we

are told that Miss A. L. Greer, the nurse in charge, has spent weary days and sleepless nights drilling it into the nurses, until the Korean nurses and hospital boys are taking a pride in keeping it clean.

The cases in the hospital on one particular day included a middle toe amputation, empyema, removal of a piece of bamboo from a heel, bladder stones in a five year old, kidney trouble, T.B. of the knee joint, T.B. of the spine, gall stones, lung abscess from which a quart and a half of pus was removed, leg amputation made necessary from applications of Korean medicine, stomach ulcer, abscess of the hip, cancer of the face, an amputation caused by a native doctor who had needled the knee so that it was full of pus, amputation of a gangrenous leg, diphtheria, an obstetrical complication, and a Buddhist priest with tuberculosis.

We inquire about the charity work and find that 62 percent of all patients are absolutely charity patients. The establishment is run very efficiently, the plant being almost self-supporting. . . . We ask the doctor if he does not get tired working for those people. And he tells us that he enjoys it. [We] realized the secret of his success. He loved his work. His face as well as his actions showed it.[61]

WILSON LEPROSY COLONY
Yosu

Dr. Wilson, the Leprologist (1928–1941)

Equally impressive was the activity of Robert Manton Wilson, M.D., at the leprosy colony for which, as noted, he was known internationally and was decorated on several occasions by the Japanese government.[62]

The location for the new colony, on a hilly peninsula surrounded by sea and mountains, could hardly be equaled in beauty. In due time the peninsula was covered with fields and trees, dotted with villages made up of stone cottages, and crowned with a central complex containing church, hospital, school, and facilities for the severely handicapped. Students at Davidson and Flora Macdonald colleges raised the money to help build the cottages for a men's and a women's village. A school, constructed outside the gate for the "clean" children

Wilson Leprosy Colony, Yosu, after relocation in 1926 to a beautiful peninsula near Soonchun. Note the distant mountains, bay, beach, and patient village. Photograph courtesy of Paul Crane.

of patients with leprosy, became an integral part of the program.

Dr. Wilson had overall responsibility for the administration and the medical affairs of the colony. He was assisted by Rev. J. Kelly Unger, who, in addition to being the principal of the Soonchun Boys' School, had responsibility for education and religious instruction at the colony. He upgraded the vocational training programs in order to help patients whose disease had been arrested to return to regular society. An executive committee, made up of twenty-two patients, oversaw the day-to-day operation of the colony.

"Dr. Wilson was always short of funds," wrote another missionary, "for his big heart could not resist taking in more lepers."[63] The 1940 budget illustrates the level of funding for the colony:

Receipts:

American Mission to Lepers	Yen	40,077
Japanese government		39,036
Imperial Household		18,140
Gifts (mostly missionaries)		8,350
Lepers (entrance fee)		14,028
	Yen	121,631 ($24,326.20)
Expenses:	Yen	111,010.[64]

The hospital at the Wilson Leprosy Colony, Yosu. Photograph courtesy of Virginia Somerville.

In order that expenses might be reduced to a minimum, able-bodied patients worked to make the colony as self-supporting as possible. They built the buildings and produced most of the food. A sixty-foot sailing junk, acquired primarily for hauling supplies, was also used for fishing. Dr. Wilson wrote in 1934:

> There are 25 blind and 50 with poor vision . . . 300 are able to work and 461 unable, 12 wear peg legs of their own making. . . . There are 20 pigs, 1,000 rabbits, 4 plow cows, 6 carpenters, 4 masons, 4 stone cutters, 30 wells, two and half miles of highway within our grounds . . . There are 126 leper children in school taught by leper teachers. They study half a day and work the other half.

> Last month at the colony we planted over 25,000 trees, mostly pine and oak, as well as many flowers. We have to grow our own fuel and thus must plant many trees. The place is taking on a beautiful form now with green barley and crops about.[65]

An innovative policy was the establishment of villages for married couples. Couples were allowed to marry after the male was given a vasectomy. Each couple was given twenty-five dollars to build their own house, assigned garden space, and allowed to adopt one or more

A mass wedding at the leprosy colony. Photograph courtesy of Stuart Wilson Manson.

children with leprosy. Some eighty-three couples participated in the program and Dr. Wilson writes of a ceremony in which thirteen couples took their marriage vows.

The administration of chaulmoogra oil by injection or by mouth was the accepted treatment of the day for leprosy. Some 750 subcutaneous injections were administered each week at the colony. A staff of twenty-nine patients were trained to run the hospital, administer the injections, and perform simple surgical procedures.

Dr. Wilson was deeply concerned with early detection of the disease. His special joy was to find cases in the early stages so that, when the disease became quiescent, patients could be discharged free of the stigmata of the disease.

In Korea, as elsewhere, patients with leprosy suffered not only physical pain and mutilation but also serious emotional and mental stress. They were looked upon with fear and contempt, ostracized from normal social activity, and discriminated against. Most leprosy patients outside the colony lived as homeless beggars; they slept under bridges and in culverts and obtained money by terrorizing ordinary people, who had an exaggerated fear of the disease (which those with leprosy quickly learned to exploit). It was rumored that they stole children in order to eat the livers, hoping thereby to cure their disease. Leprosy was found among all classes of society. The wealthiest man in Soonchun had leprosy and was reported to eat gold shavings in the hope of a cure. He isolated himself in his home compound behind a high wall. Dr. Wilson found the daughters of a pastor and of a deacon to have leprosy.

The church at the colony exerted an important influence on the communal and social life of the colony. A full religious program began with predawn prayer services and included Bible classes and evangelistic rallies. Blind patients held contests in which they memorized large portions of scripture; one blind woman was able to recite the entire book of Romans perfectly. Leprosy patients, elected by their peers, served as elders and deacons.

While he was in the United States in 1937, Dr. Wilson visited the U.S. Public Health Service Leprosy Hospital at Carville, Louisiana. He was struck with how kind, gentle, and attentive the doctors and nurses were; patients were treated like millionaires. Yet, he noted, patients in Korea were more cheerful and the results from treatment were consistently better. Dr. Wilson attributed the better results to the religious faith of the people (which was the very heart of the colony), and to the work program, which required the patients to work in their gardens to grow their food and vegetables. The patients improved physically, developed better appetites, and slept better.

In addition to his responsibilities at the leprosy colony and at Alexander Hospital, Dr. Wilson, who was ordained by the Ouchita Presbytery (Arkansas) during his furlough year in 1929, participated in evangelistic and public health outreach. In 1934 he reported visiting twenty-seven different churches, often accompanied by his

Carpenters at the leprosy colony were patients. Photograph courtesy of Stuart Wilson Manson.

wife, Bessie Knox Wilson. It was his custom to treat the sick, search for early cases of leprosy, and extract a lot of teeth, as well as to hold a religious service. He wrote a tract, titled "Health for the Soul and Body," which received wide distribution; a special edition was produced for use with children. Physical examinations were held in the local schools, where tuberculosis, as well as leprosy, was common.

Dr. Wilson attributed his long term of service (forty years) to his frequent breaks for hunting and fishing, for which he was sometimes criticized by his more driven coworkers. He wrote:

> When I get a bit tired looking at the sick I take my dogs to the hills for a chase . . .

> It's quite a remarkable thing that this little country, the size of Kansas with 22 million people, has such an abundance of game—pheasants, deer, wild pig, bear, leopards, and tigers. . . . The animals do great damage to the crops, and the villagers have to sit up at night in the fall to prevent destruction of their rice crops. They will often beg and plead that we come and shoot the game destroying their crops.

> During Christmas week we bagged 23 deer. . . . Ed [Wilson's son] fell into one of their tiger wells one day and he said his first thought as he went down was whether there was already a tiger in that trap.[66]

One year the residents of what became known as "Bear Village" sought Dr. Wilson's help with a bear that had mauled five persons (killing one) and wreaked havoc in their fields. Expecting to find a small bear, Dr. Wilson confronted instead a mammoth beast but managed to kill it with birdshot to the head. "Bear Village" became "100 percent Christian" for a while, though backsliding was reported with the passing of time.

It seems no accident that eight of thirteen missionary boys growing up in Soonchun during this period became physicians (four of them missionary doctors). With Dr. Rogers allowing them to hold retractors in the operating room and Dr. Wilson taking them hunting for deer and wild boar, they perceived a medical career as one of great usefulness and satisfaction.[67]

Dr. Wilson, when he departed Korea in the spring of 1941, left the colony in a surprisingly prosperous financial state. He accomplished this by going to Beijing, China, then occupied by Japan, where American banks exchanged U.S. dollars for Japanese yen at a rate many times more favorable than was possible in Korea. This imaginative, but not illegal, exchange process prompted a number of missionaries to go sight-seeing in China and made it possible for Dr. Wilson to provide the colony with funds for the fiscal year 1941–42. The leprosy colony continued in operation under Japanese management and was the only PCUS medical institution in Korea to stay open throughout World War II.[68]

Notes

1. Place names in Korea have undergone a number of changes in spelling, including the names imposed by the Japanese (Fusan for Pusan; Keijo for Seoul; Chosen for Korea). However, the spelling used in recent PCUS writing (as adopted here) is not difficult to identify: Soonchun has been Sunchon or Sunchun; Chonju has been Chunju and even Jeonju.

2. Donald Stone Macdonald, *The Koreans: Contemporary Politics and Society* (Boulder & London: Westview Press, 1988), 36–37.

3. Charles Allen Clark, *The Nevius Plan for Mission Work: Illustrated in Korea* (Seoul, Korea: Christian Literature Society, 1937), 77.

4. Ibid., 81.

5. Ibid., 17, 84–85, 211–12.

6. G. Thompson Brown, *Mission to Korea* (Seoul, Korea: Presbyterian Church of Korea, Dept. of Education, 1984), 26.

7. The Methodist and Catholic missions accepted the Japanese rationalization that obeisance at the shrines was a political and not a religious act; their mission schools remained open.

8. Brown, *Mission to Korea*, 148–61.

9. The four missionaries who remained in Korea were Rev. J. V. N. and Mrs. Eliza Emerson Talmage, Miss Florence Root, and Miss Mary Dodson.

10. Martha Huntley, *To Start a Work* (Seoul, Korea: Presbyterian Church of Korea, 1987), 341–46.

11. "Personalia," *Missionary Survey*, April 1915, 316.

12. Brown, *Mission to Korea*, 125.

13. Ibid., 107–08.

14. Ibid., 145.

15. Robert M. Wilson, M.D., letters to "Friends," Oct. 19, 1933, collection lent by son, John Knox Wilson, M.D.

16. James Kelly Unger and Robert M. Wilson, M.D., "Report of the Leper Hospital Committee," April 29, 1934.

17. Three were second-generation missionaries: Elizabeth Woods was the daughter of Dr. James B. Sr and Mrs. Bessie Woods of China; John Preston Jr. and James Wilson were sons of pioneers to Korea (Rev. John F. Sr. and Mrs. Annie Preston and Dr. Robert M. and Mrs. Bessie Wilson).

18. William M. Junkin, "Moving to Kunsan," *Missionary*, 1896, 457.

19. A. Damer Drew, M.D., "Korea," *Missionary*, 1886, 316.

20. George Thompson Brown, *Mission to Korea*, 29.

21. Samuel H. Chester, "What Do Medical Missions Accomplish?" *Missionary*, Oct. 1913.

22. History of Kunsan Medical Work, typescript, Nov. 1930.

23. Samuel H. Chester, *Lights and Shadows of Mission Work in the Far East* (Richmond, Va.: Presbyterian Committee of Publication, 1899), 117.

24. Virginia Bell Somerville, R.N., has done in-depth research on the PCUS missionary personnel serving in Korea. Her records are on file at Honam University, Taejon, Korea, and can also be accessed through the Dept. of History, P.C. (U.S.A.), Montreat, N.C.

25. *History of Kunsan Medical Work*, typescript.

26. Thomas H. Daniel, M.D., letter quoted in Missionary, 1905, 377.

27. *History of Kunsan Medical Work*, typescript.

28. Brown, *Mission to Korea*, 121.

29. Elizabeth Johanna Shepping, R.N., personnel files of the Board of World Missions, Dept. of History, P.C.(U.S.A.), Montreat, N.C.

30. Elizabeth Woods DeCamp, R.N., interview, Feb. 1990.

31. James S. Wilson, M.D., phone conversation, 1993.

32. *Minutes of the Korea Mission*, 1902, 4.

33. Mattie Ingold Tate, M.D., a bound book containing a diary, articles, and reports, Dept. of History, P.C.(U.S.A.), Montreat, N.C.

34. *Minutes of the Korea Mission*, 1906, 56.

35. William M. Junkin, letter to Dr. S. H. Chester, Mar. 14, 1905.

36. Marian Sterling, "And They Twain: A Family Chronicle for My Grandchildren," typescript, Dept. of History, PC(USA), Montreat, N.C.

37. Brown, *Mission to Korea*, 104–05.

38. Ibid., 91–92.

39. Ibid., 157–61.

40. W. H. Manning Jr. and Edna A. Manning, *Our Kin* (Augusta, Ga.: Walton Printing Co., 1958), 576–78.

41. Brown, *Mission to Korea*, 103, 105.

42. "Octavia: Her Life As She Remembers It," typescript by family of Octavia Howard Price, 78–79.

43. Brown, *Mission to Korea*, 63.

44. L. George Paik, *History of Protestant Missions in Korea, 1832–1910* (Seoul, Korea: YMCA Press, 1929), 165–66.

45. Margaret E. Harrison, *The Mustard Seed* (Nashville, Tenn.: PCUS Executive Committee of Foreign Missions, 1941), 6.

46. Virginia K. Cumming, interview, 1990.

47. The Rev. Eugene and Margaret B. Bell (the second Mrs. Bell), the Rev. Clement C. (M.D.) and Georgiana W. (M.D.) Owen, the Rev. John F. and Annie W. Preston, and Joseph W. Nolan, M.D.

48. *Minutes of the Korea Mission*, 1907.

49. Robert M. Wilson, M.D., letter, Dec. 9, 1933.

50. Robert M. Wilson, M.D., "Annual Report, June 1919,"*Missionary Survey*, 1919, 734.

51. Brown, Mission to Korea, 105–106.

52. Paul S. Crane was one of the children on this hair-raising trip.

53. James K. Levie, D.D.S., "American Dentistry in Korea," *Presbyterian Survey*, Aug. 1928, 482–83.

54. Margaret Pritchard, R.N., "The Life Story of Margaret Frances Pritchard," typescript, 1980, 4.

55. Ibid., 12–14.

56. Ibid., 11.

57. Virginia Brand Francis (Dr. Brand's sister), interview, May 21, 1990.

58. Brown, *Mission to Korea*, 92–95.

59. Ibid., 94.

60. Henry L. Timmons, "The Opening of Alexander Hospital, Soonchun, Korea," *Missionary Survey*, Aug. 1916.

61. G. Raymond Womeldorf, "The 'Jesus Hospital' at Soonchun," *Presbyterian Survey*, 1927, 613.

62. Robert Manton Wilson, M.D., information and quotations in this section are gleaned from a collection of letters lent by John K. Wilson, M.D., his son.

63. J. V. N. Talmage, "A Prisoner of Christ Jesus," typescript in the Dept. of History, P.C. (U.S.A.), Montreat, 1942.

64. Robert M. Wilson.

65. Ibid.

66. Ibid.

67. The eight who became physicians were James S. Wilson, John K. Wilson, Paul S. Crane, and J. Fairman Preston Jr., all of whom served as missionaries in Korea; and Robert M. Wilson Jr., Joseph F. Wilson, David R. Rogers, and Rhea S. Preston.

68. Talmage, "A Prisoner of Christ Jesus."

Chapter Six

Korea
(1947–1983)

K orea in 1945, following World War II, differed vastly from the
Korea that the PCUS evacuated in 1940. The oppressive
Japanese presence was gone, but the euphoria of liberation was soon
tempered by the tragic division of Korea and the Korean War.
Without attempting a comprehensive survey, some of the major
developments, particularly those affecting the PCUS medical work,
can be summarized.[1]

The tragic division of Korea resulted from the decision at the end
of World War II to divide the country at the 38th parallel into two
zones in order to allow the Japanese forces in northern Korea to
surrender to the Soviets and those in the south to surrender to U.S.
forces. The "temporary" military occupations solidified into separate
political entities that reflected the ideology and great-power rivalry of
the Soviet Union and the United States. The Korean problem needs to
be viewed in the context of the cold war tensions of the period.

In North Korea, the Soviet occupiers moved quickly to establish
the Communist Party as the central organ of control. Kim Il-Sung, an
anti-Japanese guerrilla who had joined the Soviet army, emerged
(with Soviet backing) as head of the Democratic People's Republic of
Korea. He eliminated opposition, collectivized the land, nationalized
industry, and organized the Korean People's Army under Soviet tute-
lage. Religions, including Christianity, were suppressed. Well over a
million people—professionals, technical people, property owners,
and Christians—fled to the South.

In South Korea, a reluctant U.S. military occupation began in some
confusion. The Americans, initially combat forces brought in from

133

Okinawa, were ill-prepared to provide the needed resources and expertise to help rebuild Korea. Despite mistakes, the U.S. military government (1945–48) "generally acted with diligence and fairness, pragmatically working within very limited resources to meet basic human needs, revive the economy and infrastructure, and expand education."[2] A lightly armed constabulary with no offensive capability was put in place. General elections, held in 1948 under United Nations supervision established the Republic of Korea with Syngman Rhee as its president. "On the whole, the display of U.S. goodwill outweighed the mistakes of the administration and the individual sins of the foreign occupiers"; South Koreans continued to admire and respect the United States.[3]

Although Korea was not the target of Allied bombing and thus was not physically destroyed during World War II, the country by the end of that war was in a deplorable state. The Japanese departure left the country bereft of most of the professional and managerial skills that had kept the wheels of society running smoothly. Although the sudden exodus of more than a million Japanese from their former colony was achieved without violence or vengeance on the part of the long-oppressed Koreans, the Japanese departure created a vacuum that further contributed to the general chaos.

The Korean War began on June 25, 1950, when, without warning, North Korea attacked South Korea all along the 38th parallel. A hastily organized United Nations command came to the aid of South Korea.[4] Gen. Douglas MacArthur's successful amphibious landing at Inchon in September led to the defeat of the North Korean army but precipitated the intervention of China with its army of a million "volunteers." The war devastated both North and South Korea: up to 4 million lives are estimated to have been lost on both sides (including 33,729 Americans); millions more were disabled or became refugees.[5] An armistice agreement, which South Korea has never signed, was set in place in July 1953 by the UN Command, North Korea, and China. An almost impenetrable demilitarized zone separated the two Koreas and an uneasy peace, marked by mutual animosity and distrust, endures to this day (1997).

The political and economic history of South Korea since 1953 has been a mixed bag. The problems were basically manageable, and the country, aided by its small size, homogeneous culture, and work ethic, plus massive injections of aid from abroad, surprised the world by the rapidity with which it progressed from being one of the world's poorest countries to a major economic power in Asia.

Three governments through 1983 (the period covered in this work), under Presidents Syngman Rhee (1948–60), Park Chung-Hee (1961–80), and Chun Doo-Hwan (1980–88), held power by autocratic suppression of political opposition. Traditionally the Koreans are accustomed to strong leadership and seem to lack the concept of "Her Majesty's loyal opposition"; the government generally views any political opposition as subversive. Tensions resulting from the suppression of basic freedoms sometimes erupted in student and worker demonstrations that, on occasion, turned violent. South Koreans enjoy many freedoms; the freedom to oppose or criticize the government is not among them.

North Korea, even more devastated than South because of strategic bombing by Allied forces, faced enormous postwar political and economic challenges. Kim Il-Sung was able to consolidate and maintain political control. He, like Stalin, encouraged a personality cult in which he was glorified as "Our Great Leader." He initiated a philosophical dogma of self-reliance called *juche*, which, he claimed, represented a higher form of communism, transcending Marxism-Leninism. This strong ideology combined with centralized control brought economic recovery that, at first, outdistanced the south's. Since the 1970s, however, the south has forged far ahead.

Until the 1970s the United States was generally held in high regard in South Korea—as the liberator from Japan and the savior from North Korean aggression. In recent years the historic Korean xenophobia has reasserted itself, and some Koreans now blame the United States for perpetuating the division of Korea. This feeling is most violently expressed by a radical minority of students born since the Korean War.

Christianity in South Korea

South Korea is a country with a visible Christian presence: church bells ring, steeples and crosses dot the skyline, remote villages have one or more church buildings. Described as "the most fruitful field in Asia for Protestant missions," the story of the Protestant church in Korea is unique in church circles.[6]

In Korea, unlike in some countries where Christianity was associated with a colonial regime, the word *missionary* is not a pejorative term. Missionaries were generally held in high regard.

Like the country as a whole, the church emerged from World War II and the Korean War in a sad state, with property destroyed, organization disintegrated, and leadership depleted. Under the Japanese, many Christians were imprisoned and tortured; stories of heroism under pressure abound.[7] The Japanese imprisoned most of the Christian clergy, apparently out of a belief that they would be a potential fifth column when the anticipated Allied invasion took place. Many Korean Christians believe that the dropping of the atomic bombs (August 6 on Hiroshima and August 9 on Nagasaki), which precipitated the Japanese surrender on August 15, 1945, miraculously saved the lives of the many ministers who were scheduled for execution on August 17.[8] During the Communist occupation of North and South Korea, more than 500 Christian leaders (one-half of all the Protestant ministers) vanished.[9]

If the 1950s were a time of recovery from devastation for the Presbyterian Church in Korea, the 1960s were a period of development of national leadership. By the mid-1980s the Christian community comprised 30.5 percent (11.5 million) of the population.[10] Christians made up such a large proportion of the Korean population that mission institutions could afford to employ only baptized Christians, irrespective of denomination. The Presbyterian Church, although the largest denominational grouping, was divided into four major and a host of smaller bodies. Schisms, factionalism, and the fracturing into many diverse groups characterized the Protestant movement in the postwar years.[11]

Education and medicine continued to be major emphases of the Protestant movement in Korea. By 1982, the Ministry of Education legally recognized eleven Protestant colleges and universities, eighty-five high schools, seventy-nine middle schools, and innumerable primary schools. Twenty-one Protestant hospitals and a great number of smaller clinics had legal status under the Ministry of Health and Social Affairs. Severance Medical College of Yonsei University was recognized as one of the largest and most influential medical institutions.[12]

In recent years Korean Christians have assumed the leadership in various institutions, their overseas mission work (a tradition in the Korean church since 1913) has expanded to some twenty-three countries including the United States, and Koreans have become leaders in international church bodies.

The PCUS in South Korea

In the 1950s and 1960s, the PCUS maintained a strong presence in South Korea. Although emergency relief activities absorbed the mission's energies during the war, education and development of leadership remained priority concerns.

In the 1960s, the PCUS and the Korean church developed a church-to-church partnership. The role of the "mission" consisted primarily of providing the logistical support for the missionaries. Qualified Koreans began to assume positions of responsibility in the institutions.

Between 1970 and 1983, the PCUS had a reduced presence in Korea, but continued to send funds and personnel to conduct special programs in hospitals, colleges, and seminaries. The PCUS also helped support Korean missionaries to other countries (Bangladesh, Taiwan, and Indonesia).

The PCUS Medical Program

The history of the PCUS medical program in Korea after World War II, like the history of the country itself, is one of development and accomplishment. The demand for Western medical services remained overwhelming and pushed the medical missionaries to the limits of their abilities and strength.

The PCUS medical mission seized the opportunity to participate in Korea's development process by training medical leadership and by addressing major health problems, such as tuberculosis, leprosy, parasites, and cancer. The special pleasure of teaching eager, receptive, talented, Christian young people added zest to the mission's medical activities, and the medical missionaries regarded their teaching as the most important, as well as the most satisfying, aspect of their work.

The PCUS teaching hospitals became major referral centers for difficult and complicated cases. After a few years, "simple" surgeries such as appendectomies and hernias were usually taken care of in the local hospitals. The missionary surgeons daily performed cases that demanded the most advanced surgical skills with remarkable results.[13] Although the Cholla area in which the PCUS operated was considered a backwater, the PCUS institutions were recognized for their quality, and they attracted patients from the major urban centers. Staff members regularly published papers in Korean and U.S. medical journals.

As the level of medicine improved generally in Korea, the mission hospitals found their unique contribution to be their concern for the whole person. The practice of medicine in a Christian environment demanded not only high-quality care but compassion for individual patients.

Between 1947 and 1983 the PCUS sent to South Korea a total of forty-five regular service medical missionaries (twelve doctors, two dentists, eighteen nurses, four medical technologists, one occupational therapist, one physiotherapist, one pharmacist, and six hospital administrators).[14] Short-term workers numbered twenty-two (nine doctors, one dentist, two full-time and three part-time nurses, two occupational therapists, three physiotherapists, and two administrators). Medical volunteers, because air travel made it feasible for them to serve for short periods of time, made a valuable contribution to the quality of care offered at the mission's institutions.

The government expressed its official appreciation of the role of the PCUS medical work by conferring National Merit and Presidential awards on medical personnel who served for an extended time. Among the recipients were Drs. Codington, Crane, Dietrick, Seel, and Topple; Miss Margaret Pritchard, R.N.; and Rev. E. T. Boyer (administrator of the leprosy colony).

By 1983 the ultimate goal of "working oneself out of a job" seemed to be coming to reality. Boards made up chiefly of Koreans operated the hospitals. Korean physicians headed both the Kwangju Christian Hospital (Dr. Huh Chin-Duk, director) and the Wilson Leprosy Center and Rehabilitation Hospital (Dr. Yoo Kyung-Un, director). Two PCUS physicians wrote books that wrestled with the question of the future role of mission medical work overseas: David J. Seel, M.D., author of *Challenge and Crisis in Missionary Medicine*,[15] and Ronald B. Dietrick, M.D., *Modern Medicine and the Mission Mandate: Thoughts on Christian Medical Missions*.[16]

PCUS Medical Work between the Wars, 1947–1950

The health care situation in Korea following World War II was bleak, mainly because of the lack of trained medical professionals and the low level of medical practice. The Japanese had permitted little advanced training for Koreans so that there were few qualified medical professionals, and these tended to congregate in Seoul. The precipitous departure of the Japanese in 1945 stripped hospitals and public health facilities of their staffs. Moreover, clinical medicine under the Japanese system had deteriorated under wartime pressures.

Aseptic surgical techniques and blood transfusions were rare, and the concept of fluid balance not fully appreciated. There were epidemics of smallpox, cholera, polio, and measles; tuberculosis affected more than 10 percent of the population; over 90 percent were infected with parasites; and leprosy patients, who lacked support in their colonies, had left them to beg from and terrorize the general populace. The backlog of neglected and advanced surgical conditions, such as large goiters, cysts, cleft palates, burn contractures, and tuber-cular orthopedics, along with acute conditions of gastric malignancies, gall bladders, tuberculous lungs, and hernias, was a smorgasbord of opportunity for a surgeon.

Robert Manton Wilson, M.D., was the first of the former PCUS missionaries to return to Korea. He arrived in January 1946 as a Department of the Army Civilian (DAC) assigned to the military government and was asked to take over the direction of all leprosy work in Korea. His son, Captain John Knox Wilson, M.D., was assigned by the military to help him in this work.

Dr. Wilson stepped into an acute crisis. Conditions in the leprosy colonies were deplorable: the large government facility at Sorokdo (Deer Island) and the three colonies established by missionaries at Soonchun (PCUS), Pusan (Australian Presbyterian), and Taegu (Northern Presbyterian). Disease was rife; a smallpox epidemic had claimed fifty lives. Other people had succumbed to malnutrition resulting from poor food (bean fertilizer mixed with a little barley was fed patients at the Soonchun colony during the latter days of the war). As the Japanese left Sorokdo, patients rioted and made a rush for the warehouse where food was kept. Eighty people died when the guards opened fire, and many patients escaped into the hills where they survived by begging.[17]

Dr. Wilson made Soonchun his headquarters for the leprosy program. He moved into his former mission residence and was soon joined by his wife, Bessie. The Korean Christians and the Soonchun community were overjoyed at the Wilsons' return. Dr. Wilson succeeded in getting the leprosy colonies operating, provided food and drugs for all, and expanded the facilities to care for some 9,000 patients. He began a program for the early detection and treatment of the disease and encouraged the settlement of leprosy villages where discharged patients could be self-supporting.

By 1946 research for new and effective drugs offered hope, for the first time, of a cure for leprosy. Sulphones emerged as the drugs of choice. John Wilson remembers that his father was sent enough dapsone, also called DDS (diaminodiphenyl sulphone), to treat thirty patients. Dr. John Wilson, the pediatrician, chose fifteen children for the experiment, while Dr. R. M. Wilson chose fifteen adults.

In 1947 the Wilsons returned to the United States, and the Biederwolf Leprosy Colony in Yosu was renamed the R. M. Wilson Leprosy Colony.

Return of Missionaries

For a variety of reasons, Margaret Pritchard, R.N., was the only former PCUS medical missionary available to return to Korea after World War II. In late 1946 the Board of World Missions approached First Lieut. Paul S. Crane, M.D., U.S. Army Medical Corps, and asked whether he would consider going to Korea if the board could get him released from the army. Dr. Crane, the son of missionaries to Korea, had formerly applied for mission service and readily agreed to go. The U.S. Army, which was in the process of demobilizing, gave him an honorable discharge for this purpose.

In the fall of 1947 Dr. Crane and his wife, Sophie, who had taken a crash course in basic laboratory techniques, set out with Margaret Pritchard, R.N., to "reopen" the PCUS medical work in Korea. They took with them what amounted to two boxcars of equipment and supplies, which they had assembled from three main sources: (1) an $8,000 start-up grant from the PCUS that, because of U.S. Army surplus sales, translated into approximately $150,000 worth of medical supplies, including complete sets of surgical instruments, two steam pressure autoclaves, 100 metal cots, 500 blankets, and laboratory centrifuges, reagents, and glassware; (2) a generous supply of White Cross linens from the PCUS Women of the Church; and (3) donations of new and secondhand supplies from interested persons.

A friendly rivalry developed between Thomas M. Barnhardt of the Barnhardt Absorbent Cotton Company, Charlotte, North Carolina, and H. N. Smith of H. N. Smith & Nephew Ltd. of London, England, manufacturer of orthopedic plaster, as to which would donate the most and which could get its product to the destination in the shortest time. Barnhardt's generous contributions later included donations to Zaire and other mission fields as well.

The medical team's first assignment was to survey the situation in Korea and make a proposal to the mission about the future of the medical work. In carrying out this assignment Dr. Crane and Margaret Pritchard found themselves in perfect agreement that the major goal of the medical work should be training.

In support of this basic premise, they recommended to the mission the formation of a comprehensive medical plan rather than a return to the five small (one-doctor/one-nurse) hospitals. The plan contained four main features: (1) a centralized training center to be located in Chonju for the training of doctors (interns and residents), nurses, and laboratory technicians; (2) a tuberculosis hospital and control program to be located in Kwangju; (3) continuation of the leprosy colony in Yosu near Soonchun; and (4) a public health program in Mokpo with outreach to the islands. The mission adopted this basic plan and more or less carried it out in the ensuing years. The public health program in Mokpo failed to develop to its full potential because the annual request for public health personnel remained unfilled, but the three other institutions developed strong public health components.

This shift in medical policy—accepting medical missions, in and of themselves, as a significant component of the good news of the gospel and moving away from using local medical units primarily as tools for evangelistic activity—represented a radical change in the philosophy of medical missions as practiced in Korea by the PCUS. A major tenet of the shift was that medicine practiced in the name of Christ, along with a compassionate concern for the individual patient, should be of the highest quality possible; the training of indigenous Christian medical leadership became a priority concern. The establishment of diverse pilot projects was intended to involve the PCUS in a comprehensive program that reduced duplication and competition between the institutions for the PCUS personnel and resources.

Severance Medical College in Seoul continued to be the basic Christian training institution for medical students. During World War II the college remained in operation, with Japanese physicians in control. Eventually, Severance united with Yonhi University, an institution of the Northern Presbyterian Church, and became the medical college of Yonsei University. (The name *Yonsei* was formed by combining the *Yon* of *Yonhi* with the *Sei* of *Severance*). The PCUS continued to support Yonsei University Medical School and was represented on its board of directors.

Medical Work Begins
    The Presbyterian Medical Center/Jesus Hospital (PMC), initially an overly optimistic title (it continued to be known in Korea as "the Jesus Hospital"), opened its clinic on April 1, 1948, and its inpatient department (forty-five beds) on May 1, in the buildings of the former mission hospital in Chonju. These buildings, which had been used for storing straw, lacked windows and doors, plaster and plumbing. Strenuous effort went into making the buildings functional; the Cranes lived in the apartment in the hospital that had formerly been occupied by Ethel Kestler, R.N.
    The Korean staff consisted of a graduate of Severance Medical School (Dr. Song Chung-Suk), several licensed nurses (graduates of the Kwangju nursing school begun by Miss Pritchard), four interns[18] (recent graduates of Severance), and a number of former employees. Among the last group was Chung Qui-Bing, X-ray technician, who had somehow managed to preserve the 1920s-vintage X-ray machine, which he now restored to the hospital. Morale was high; long hours and hard work were the norm. During the first eleven months, 7,000 new patients were treated, 338 major operations were performed, and inpatient days totaled over 8,000. Beds lined the halls, keeping the daily inpatient census well over 60.
    By June of 1950 the place began to resemble a medical center. New missionary appointments included Ovid B. Bush Jr., an internist; Mariella Talmage, R.N., director of nurses in the hospital (freeing Margaret Pritchard for the nursing school); Gene Lindler, medical technologist; and Howard B. Smith, business administrator, who, with his wife Agnes, arrived in mid-May 1950.
    There were ten interns and residents in what was Korea's first five-year intern/residency program. A blood bank was established. Clinical research was undertaken to find a treatment for the dread infestation of the liver by *clonorchis sinensis*, the liver fluke that posed a major health problem in Korea, China, and Southeast Asia. The results of this study were published in 1955 in the *Transactions of the Royal Society of Tropical Medicine and Hygiene*.[19]

The opening ceremony for the newly constructed School of Nursing was held on June 1, 1950. On June 15 the cornerstone was laid for an addition to the hospital that would raise the number of beds to 160. Both buildings were funded by the Program of Progress, a PCUS postwar rehabilitation program.[20]

Other parts of the mission's medical plan began to fall into place. Rev. Elmer T. Boyer, an evangelistic missionary who began service in Korea in 1921, took over administration of the leprosy colony; Dr. Crane, accompanied by a Korean resident, provided medical supervision through monthly visits from Chonju.

Herbert A. Codington, M.D., and his wife, Page Lancaster Codington, R.N., began their missionary service in 1949 at the Mokpo Hospital, with language study as their primary assignment. This hospital, while primitive, was in a reasonable state of repair and was being operated by Dr. Chai Sup, a Korean physician previously associated with the mission.

The Kwangju hospital began to be rehabilitated as a tuberculosis unit. Dr. Codington and Virginia K. Cumming, R.N., (Mrs. Bruce), a former PCUS missionary in Kwangju, were scheduled to develop the program to combat tuberculosis there.

War

On June 20, 1950, the mission (some fifty persons) held its annual meeting in the newly completed nursing school in Chonju. Despite rumors of conflict between North and South Korea, the mood was optimistic. In South Korea, the political situation had stabilized with the election of President Syngman Rhee, the economy had improved, the church was growing, and twenty-two new missionaries had joined the prewar veterans; much had been accomplished, and great days lay ahead. Expansion of all phases of the work was being considered.

At the close of the church service on Sunday, June 25, however, came word of North Korea's massive attack on South Korea and of the U.S. embassy's instructions for the mission to prepare to leave for Pusan, the designated port of evacuation. In a state of shock, the missionaries prepared to leave and the evacuation took place on Tuesday and Wednesday, June 27–28.

A skeleton force of ten volunteered to stay behind: Rev. and Mrs. William A. Linton (Chonju), Mr. and Mrs. H. Petrie Mitchell and Miss Florence Root (Kwangju), and five medical personnel: Paul Crane,

M.D., Ovid Bush, M.D., Gene Lindler, M.T., and Mariella Talmage, R.N., in Chonju; and Herbert Codington, M.D., in Kwangju/Mokpo. Margaret Pritchard, R.N., was asked to accompany the evacuees who included four pregnant women, nine small children, and a number of frail adults. Drs. Crane and Bush went with the caravan to Pusan and saw them off on the SS *Letitia Lykes*, bound for Japan.

The Korean War, 1950–1954

The war reached the PCUS area in southwest Korea some three weeks after the evacuation of the mission, and the North Korean army remained in control until after General MacArthur's famous landing at Inchon in September. On July 17, upon receiving word that the Kum River line (thirty miles from Chonju) had broken, nine of the ten missionaries who had remained behind left for the safety of the Pusan perimeter. Miss Florence Root (Kwangju) refused to leave and spent the summer hiding in the hills under the protection of a group of Christians.

Dr. Codington remained in Pusan, where he volunteered his services to the Korean 5th Army Hospital. He assisted in the blood bank that had been initiated by Dr. Y. U. Kim, a resident from PMC, and was able, at critical times, to solicit blood from U.S. sources for severely wounded Korean casualties. Page Codington and their three-month-old son stayed in Japan.

The four medical persons from Chonju (Ovid Bush, Paul Crane, Gene Lindler, and Mariella Talmage) proceeded to Japan. They took with them the hospital truck, which they had filled with basic medical supplies, including all their surgical instruments except for one pack inadvertently left behind in the autoclave. These supplies contributed to the speedy start-up of the hospital following their return to Chonju in the fall.

Drs. Bush and Crane joined the staff of the U.S. Army General Hospital in Osaka. This hospital, which expanded from a small 120-bed station hospital to a general hospital with over 5,000 beds, became one of the major receiving-hospitals for casualties from Korea, many of whom were flown directly to the hospital from the battlefield. At this early stage of the war, antitank bazookas held a higher priority for transportation from the United States than did medical personnel; because the shortage of doctors was acute, the two hardworking missionary physicians from Korea were able to make a significant contribution in Japan.

The Osaka Army Hospital processed some 18,000 admissions during the time Drs. Bush and Crane were there. Among these were a group of Korean marines, casualties of the Inchon landing, who, because of the "buddy system" that paired them with U.S. marines, were evacuated to Osaka along with the American casualties. Dr. Crane was given charge of this group who, at first, were deeply resented, especially by the U.S. Army nurses. Dr. Crane's Korean language abilities and cross-cultural understanding brought about a gratifying change in attitude. Some years later Dr. Crane was accosted on a street in Seoul by a veteran of this experience, who proudly bared the scars of his wounds for inspection.

Two of the mission's evacuees benefited from the services of the Osaka Army Hospital: Florence Bush, who contracted bulbar poliomyelitis, and Sophie Crane, who delivered the Crane's first child.

Chonju

In mid-October, following the Inchon landing, Drs. Crane and Bush received permission to return to Chonju. Except for this three-month period when occupied by the North Koreans, the Presbyterian Medical Center/Jesus Hospital remained fully operational during the Korean War.

The two men (and their truck) returned to a Korea profoundly changed from the one they had left. The countryside was ravaged, bridges were out, roads were in poor repair, villages were burned and sacked, and tanks and other armor littered the fields. But it was the human devastation that most seared the heart. The South Koreans, in addition to the hardships caused by fluctuating battle lines, had experienced the systematic elimination of whole classes of people that takes place wherever Communist rule has been imposed. Tens of thousands are estimated to have died in South Korea as a result of this policy. The Communists executed over 3,000 civilians during their occupation of Chonju; twenty-four bodies were found on the hospital property. Drs. Crane and Bush spent the first days after their return listening to streams of people tell their harrowing stories of peril, terror, hunger, and death.

The mission buildings in Chonju had been the headquarters of the North Koreans and the nursing school, of the secret police. Maj. Gen.

William Dean, who had been captured in July, was temporarily
housed in one of the residences. The cement, which had been stock-
piled for use in building the four-story extension to the hospital, had
been used to form a three-foot bomb-proof roof on the partially
completed first floor. Windows were bricked up and space divided
into small prison cells. Large caves were dug into the hillside for
bomb shelters; these caves later proved useful for storing gasoline,
diesel, and other volatile products.

The hospital was soon in operation but the character of its service
changed radically as the result of guerrilla activity and the influx of
masses of refugees.

After the Inchon landing (September 1950), which cut off their
retreat, the bulk of the North Korean army took to the mountains of
the two Cholla provinces and engaged in savage guerrilla operations
that terrorized the countryside and were not brought under control
until after the armistice in 1953. Curfews were enforced, travel took
place only in daylight and in armed convoy, ambushes were
common, and villages were pillaged. An estimated 200,000 died of
what was called the "red plague."[21]

The Chonju hospital became an official support-hospital for the
antiguerrilla campaign and received equipment and supplies from the
UN Command for this purpose. The intern training program was rein-
stituted with a total of ten interns. The nursing school reopened in
January 1952 with ten of the original twenty students who had enrolled
just weeks before the outbreak of war. The wards were filled with casualties from the fighting, and guards were posted to protect the hospital
property and personnel. On one occasion, a group of youths, gathered
to inspect an unexploded grenade, were tragically wounded.

Despite the guerrilla problem, southwest Korea became the
refugee center for the nation because it was out of the path of the
two opposing armies. Thousands subsisted in deplorable conditions; to find a family allotted space measuring four by seven feet
was not uncommon. In Chonju, 600 children in two orphanages
showed signs of malnutrition. An official of an international refugee
organization is reported to have written, "In all my experience, I
have never seen destruction and human suffering on so large a scale
as in Korea."[22]

The nursing school building became the hospital for sick refugees
and, in the winter of 1951, admitted some 260 patients desperately ill

with smallpox. Teams went daily to orphanages and refugee camps to immunize and to distribute milk and other food. The hospital opened a ward for abandoned babies, which, by 1961, had admitted 520 infants; 204 were adopted into Christian homes.[23]

A massive infusion of relief supplies poured into the country through the army, the UN Civil Assistance Command Korea (UNCACK), Church World Service, and other relief (including church) agencies. All the PCUS missionaries (not just the medical) were involved in relief activities. Personnel from other missions came to Chonju to help. In 1952 the hospital and its staff received the highest commendation from UNCACK for its "unselfish and invaluable aid."[24]

In May 1951 Gene Lindler, M.T., and Mariella Talmage, R.N., received permission to return to Chonju from Japan; Margaret Pritchard, R.N., returned in the fall. During the summer, Dr. Crane left for the United States on furlough, which he spent in advanced surgical training at the Union Memorial Hospital in Baltimore. His return, scheduled for June, was delayed until December 1952 because his eleven months' service in 1946–47 did not meet the twenty-four-month requirement of the doctors' draft law of 1950. The PCUS Board of World Missions was able to arrange his release because of the urgent need in Chonju, but he later (1956–58) was called back into the army and served the two years in Korea.[25]

Kwangju

In October 1951 Dr. Codington, with the assistance of Virginia K. Cumming, R.N., opened the Graham Memorial Tuberculosis Hospital in Kwangju. The sharp rise in the incidence of tuberculosis under war conditions created a critical need and, within two years, the hospital doubled in size.

Virginia Cumming and her husband, Rev. Bruce Cumming, veterans of eleven years' service (1927–38), had returned to Korea in June 1950 just before the outbreak of the Korean War. Bruce Cumming became a civilian chaplain attached to the army and worked primarily with North Korean prisoners of war. Virginia Cumming stayed in Japan, where she worked for ten months as a head nurse in the U.S. Eighth Army Station Hospital in Kobe. This experience updated her nursing skills and prepared her for her leadership role in the founding and operation of the tuberculosis hospital in Kwangju.

Soonchun

Rev. Elmer T. Boyer returned to Soonchun after the Inchon landing in 1950. As he was the only missionary in Soonchun, his presence contributed to the general morale of the city. The Soonchun area was a center of guerrilla activity; raids at night were common. He is remembered for having undertaken to repair an American tank that had been abandoned in Soonchun after crashing through the pavement into a water main. He solicited spare parts from the U.S. Army and was able to put the tank into operation. Every night the tank roared up and down the streets of Soonchun giving the citizens a welcome sense of security. Each morning a check was made to see if the "Reverend Po" was still in town.[26]

Rev. Elmer Boyer continued to supervise matters at the leprosy colony and saw that the patients received adequate relief and food supplies. One of the most poignant stories of the Korean War came from the leprosy colony.

Rev. Sohn Yang-Won, pastor of the church at the leprosy colony, had two teenaged sons, Tong-In and Tong-Shin. In 1948, when Communists took over the area in what became known as the "Yosu Insurrection," both boys were condemned as anti-Communists and executed by a fellow student, Ahn Chae-Sun. After the rebellion was put down, Ahn was arrested and sentenced to death. Pastor Sohn pleaded for the life of his sons' murderer, offering to act as the boy's guarantor. The military judge granted this unusual request and Pastor Sohn took the boy into his home and instructed him in the Christian faith. This act of forgiveness became known throughout Korea and around the world. However, two years later, when the North Korean Communists invaded the area, Pastor Sohn was arrested and shot. A monument to the "Graves of the

Graves of martyrs, Pastor Sohn and his two sons. Photograph courtesy of Paul Crane.

Three Martyrs" in the cemetery at the Wilson Leprosy Center marks the final resting place of Pastor Sohn and his sons.

In 1954 the military and political situation in Korea stabilized. Missionary families were allowed to return and normal mission activity resumed. A number of new missionaries who were studying the Korean language in Tokyo received permission to enter Korea. PCUS prepared to do its part in rebuilding the devastated nation.

PRESBYTERIAN MEDICAL CENTER/JESUS HOSPITAL (PMC) *Chonju*

The story of the Presbyterian Medical Center/Jesus Hospital (PMC) after 1954 divides neatly into two periods, that of the "old" and that of the "new" hospitals. The "old hospital" period (1948–71) was one of building staff (Korean and Western) and laying the foundation for a multispecialty teaching center. The "new hospital" period (1971–83) saw the fruition of an extensive building plan, new initiatives, and transfer of leadership from the missionaries to Koreans. Dr. Paul Crane was the primary director during the "old hospital" period and Dr. David Seel, during the "new hospital" period.

The Old Hospital (1948–1971)

The "old hospital" occupied the top of Taga San, a steep hill also known as Dragon Head Ridge. A four-story extension to the sturdy facility built by Dr. Boggs in 1934, begun just before the outbreak of the Korean War, was completed in 1954. This addition provided outpatient facilities and increased the bed capacity from 45 to 160; the operating rooms were expanded from one to three. Funds for this addition came from a PCUS Program of Progress development grant plus $50,000 from the United Nations Korea Reconstruction Agency (UNKRA). UNKRA also donated equipment and supplies, including a forty-bed surgical unit. Built with the inferior materials available at the time and without benefit of an architect, this enlarged facility soon proved inadequate to handle the crowds that pressed in upon it. As additions were made here and there, the building began, as one visitor observed, to bulge at many peculiar angles. The hilltop site constricted further expansion.

The practice of modern medicine had outgrown the "one-man show" of the past and required the specialized skills of a team of

Presbyterian Medical Center/ Jesus Hospital, Chonju, the "Old Hospital." Photograph courtesy of Paul Crane.

trained medical professionals. This team spirit was undergirded by a Korean staff made up of baptized Christians who were hired with the endorsement of their local churches. The Korean staff often initiated ways to witness for Christ to the patients and their families. Teams composed of physicians, nurses, and evangelists went each weekend to outlying villages to check on discharged patients, hold clinics, and conduct worship services. Many staff members became elders and deacons in their local churches and contributed generously to the support of church programs.

Immediately after the Korean War, PMC maintained a number of war-related services in addition to its regular program: an amputee rehabilitation center, a special six-month internship for military doctors under the "Kim Plan" (a Korean Army plan similar to the U.S. Army "Barry Plan," which was designed to upgrade the proficiency of military medical personnel), and, as noted, a nursery for abandoned babies. Relief money and supplies poured in; barrels of sample drugs, collected from physicians in the United States, augmented the pharmacy's stock. U.S. military personnel from nearby bases volunteered their time and helped with painting, carpentry, and the sorting of sample drugs. After it was discovered that the neck of a whiskey bottle fit the coupling for intravenous tubing, jeep loads of empty Jack Daniel, Wild Turkey, and George Dickel bottles ended up suspended over the patients' beds dispensing blood and intravenous fluids.

The Korean government relied heavily on voluntary agencies and foreign aid to meet the medical needs of the people during this period. One Korean official stated frankly that, initially, health care was given a low priority in government planning; economic recovery was considered more important, and resources were inadequate for both.

By the 1960s, however, the Korean government and the Korean medical profession had become actively involved in dealing with the health problems of the nation. Public health clinics, in which Peace

Corps volunteers participated, were established throughout the country, and a national health insurance plan went into effect in 1977.

The antiparasite campaign of 1958–64 raised the average hemoglobin of patients with hookworm (*Necator americanus*) from eight to fourteen grams and reduced the infestation of roundworm (*Ascaris lumbricoides*) from 90 percent (1956) to 3 percent (1988). The resulting increase in the energy of the Korean people undoubtedly contributed to the country's remarkable advance as a modernized society.

Dr. Crane became involved in the antiparasite effort after a nine-year-old girl was admitted to the hospital with intestinal obstruction. At surgery she was found to have 1,063 (by count) roundworms blocking her intestines. The child died, but the article that Dr. Crane felt impelled to publish (in a monthly column he wrote for the *Korean Times*) sparked nationwide interest in the problem and brought together many national leaders and agencies in the successful eradication of this debilitating public health menace.

In 1960 Korean specialty boards were established to raise and control the quality of medical practice. At first, missionaries who had U.S. board certification had no problem acquiring Korean board certification; in later years, because of language requirements, certification became increasingly difficult.

The staff at PMC

Fundamental to the success of PMC were the high quality and the dedication of its missionary staff. Five missionaries provided continuity of leadership. These were Paul Crane, surgeon (1947–69); Margaret Pritchard, nurse (1947–70); David Seel, surgeon (1954–90); Janet Talmage Keller, nurse (1954–76); and Merrill Grubbs, hospital administrator (1961–89). Those serving for ten years or more included Frank G. Keller,

These 1,063 ascaris from the abdomen of a nine-year-old child sparked a national parasite eradication program. Photograph courtesy of Paul S. Crane.

Missionary physicians at the "Old Hospital" (1965). Left to right: Frank G. Keller, David J. Seel, Joanne Smith T, and Paul S. Crane. Photograph courtesy of Presbyterian Medical Center.

pediatrician and the first PCUS physician to Korea to have board certification (1955 until his death in 1967); David Chu, internist (1967–88); John Shaw, board-certified orthopedic surgeon (1971–83); Rebecca Balenger, nurse (1968–78); Ruth H. Folta, nurse (1977–83); Mary Seel, medical technologist, A.S.C.P. (1954–90); Ocie Respess, medical technologist, A.S.C.P., (1954–64); George Patton, medical technologist, A.S.C.P., (1964–78); and Sharon U. Shaw, occupational therapist, (1971–83).

A number of short-term persons made special contributions. Among them were Joanne Smith T, internist (1963–66); John K. Wilson, pediatrician (1968–71); Ronald B. Dietrick, surgeon (1958–61, to Kwangju); Dorothea Sich, an East German obstetrician/gynecologist (1966–70), Burton B. Butman, anesthetist (1975–81), and (John) Chun Jung-Youl, surgeon (1976–79). Biographical sketches of some of these missionaries follow.

Paul Crane, F.A.C.S. (Johns Hopkins University, M.D., 1944) is credited with the vision and the leadership that led to the establishment of a qualified training center for Christian young professionals. He considers his most enduring contributions to have been the introduction of the training of interns and residents (including programs

initiated in thirty-six Korean army hospitals in 1956–58) and participation in the parasite eradication program. He authored *Korean
Patterns*, a book designed to enhance understanding of Korean
culture. Dr. Crane resigned in 1969 when his furlough year coincided
with the completion of the planning and the initial fund-raising for
the new hospital. Missionary and Korean staff were ready and able to
assume leadership and implement the development plans for PMC.

Margaret F. Pritchard (Columbia University Hospital School of
Nursing, New York City, R.N., 1929), the only PCUS medical person
to return to Korea after World War II, occupied a place of high honor
and respect as the doyen of PMC. Affectionately called the "Tiger"
because of her inflexible adherence to high standards and impatience
with sloppy performance, she was much beloved by her students.
After her retirement, her alumnae twice paid for her to return to Korea.

David J. Seel, F.A.C.S. (Tulane University, M.D., 1948) piloted the
construction, organization, and administration of the new hospital.
Within six months of his arrival in Chonju in 1954, he was diagnosed
with active tuberculosis. He elected to remain in Chonju for treatment
and used the period of enforced rest to study and master the Korean
language. His love of teaching, his organizational talents, and his
concern for the spiritual welfare of staff and patients contributed
significantly to the PMC program.

*Margaret F. Pritchard, R.N., director of the nursing school, with a class of student
nurses. Photograph by Raymond Provost.*

Mary B. Seel, A.S.C.P. (Charity Hospital, New Orleans, M.T., 1952) worked for a while in the laboratory, where she set up the histopathology department. When family responsibilities and poor health caused her to give up this work, she turned her considerable talents toward, among other things, setting up the cancer registry, publicity and public relations, and paramedical training (secretarial, photography, computers, inventories, etc.). She is credited with persuading the Kresge Foundation to donate funds for the construction of the new nursing school.

Frank G. Keller, F.A.A.P., and Janet Talmage, R.N., were married in the PMC chapel in April 1956. Dr. Keller (Washington University, St. Louis, M.D., 1967) came to PMC in response to the emergency created by Dr. Seel's illness. The morning after his arrival in Chonju at 11 P.M., Dr. Keller was up and at work in the hospital. This spirit of teamwork and dedication distinguished his service. He had special concern for sick children and the babies in the abandoned baby nursery. During Dr. Crane's stint in the army from 1956 to 1958, Dr. Keller served as director pro tem of PMC. He died in 1967 of a coronary occlusion while climbing the hill from the hospital to his home; the Koreans liked to say he "kept walking into heaven."

Janet Talmage Keller, the daughter of Rev. and Mrs. J. V. N. Talmage of Kwangju, returned to Korea in 1949 as a missionary assigned to educational work. When the Korean War started, all "nonessential"

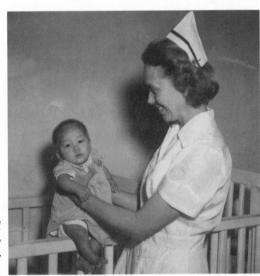

Janet Keller, R.N. with child in the abandoned baby nursery. Photograph by Raymond Provost.

missionaries were evacuated, whereas medical missionaries, including her sister, Mariella Talmage, R.N., stayed at their posts. This experience caused her to make a career change, and she spent the Korean War years at the Washington University School of Nursing (R.N., 1953). At PMC she became superintendent of nurses at the hospital, taught at the nursing school, and became director of the nursing school when Margaret Pritchard retired. She performed a major service in expediting the transfer of the nursing school to Korean leadership.

David Chu (Baylor University, M.D., 1951) responded to the call for an internist following Dr. Keller's death. He introduced the implantation of pacemakers and set up and trained staff for the intensive care unit in the new hospital. Dr. Chu was a member of a distinguished Chinese American family. He made contact with the Chinese community in Chonju and was able to serve their medical needs as well as witness for Christ in that community.

Ocie Respess, A.S.C.P. (Crawford Long Hospital, Atlanta, M.T., 1936), a thoroughly experienced technologist and a perfectionist, brought the PMC laboratory to a high standard and began the two-year training program for Korean technologists. The PMC 1963 annual report notes that the laboratory staff of seventeen "all speak with a Georgia accent" because she did her teaching in English.

Dorothea Sich (Humbolt University, Germany, M.D., 1957), a native of East Germany, was especially concerned with prenatal care, a concept poorly understood in Korea at that time.

(John) J. Y. Chun, F.A.C.S. (Seoul National University, M.D., 1952) grew up in Chonju, emigrated to the United States, became an American citizen, but wanted to contribute to his native land. A brilliant academic and surgeon, Dr. Chun contributed significantly both to the clinical and to the training program at PMC.

The training programs, as already noted, benefited from the work of professionals from the United States who, thanks to jet travel, found it practical to volunteer their expertise for weeks or months at a time. Most of the major specialties were represented among those who came. These board-certified specialists substantially enhanced the quality of training of the house staff through lectures and demonstrations.

The contributions of the Korean staff cannot be underestimated. Most carried cruel histories from recent war years. Among them were: Mr. Kim To-Su, the anesthetist, who was living in Nagasaki at the time of the atomic bombing there; Dr. (Andrew) Pak Yung-Hoon,

PMC residents, K. Y. Song, M.D. and Y. H. Pak, M.D. Photograph courtesy of Paul S. Crane.

who, after becoming separated from his bride as they were escaping North Korea, joined a guerrilla unit in an unsuccessful attempt to find her; and Dr. Im Kyung-Yul, who, like many other refugees from North Korea, lost communication with family members in the north. Mr. Yu, a triple-amputee, was given three prostheses (two legs and an arm) and trained to be a laboratory technician; he then married one of the nurses and became the chief technician at the Wonju Methodist Hospital in central Korea.

A mission scholarship program made it possible to send a number of the staff to the United States for advanced training. Among those sent during the "old hospital" period were Dr. Im Kyung-Yul (ophthalmology at the Wilmer Eye Clinic of Johns Hopkins University), Dr. (Andrew) Pak Yung-Hoon (neurosurgery at Hartford Hospital, Hartford, Connecticut, and the University of Tennessee Medical School Hospital, Memphis), Dr. Yune Hun-Yung (radiology at Vanderbilt University Medical Center, Nashville), and Miss Helen Um Chai-Chung, R.N. (Medical College of Virginia and Cook County Hospital, Chicago).

As they became qualified, Korean staff moved into positions of responsibility. Physicians with their Korean specialty board certifications headed some of the departments. In 1963 Ms. Kong Soon-Ku, a graduate of the nursing school, became superintendent of nurses in the hospital.

Unfortunately, many doctors and nurses trained to world-level standards in Korea found their expertise a passport for employment abroad, especially in Germany and the United States. In 1969 it was estimated that more than 3,000 of 13,401 physicians had left South Korea.[27] In 1967 the PMC nursing school reported 35 of its 260 graduates were working in seven countries.[28] Some graduates of the PMC residency programs found positions in the United States, and one became a professor in an American medical school. Most PMC-trained medical personnel, however, stayed in Korea. Some became professors in Korean medical schools, some joined the staffs of mission and private hospitals. Among those who went into private practice were many who shunned the big cities to work in the more remote areas.

Practice at PMC

By 1969 PMC had competent specialists in surgery, internal medicine, pediatrics, obstetrics/gynecology, otolaryngology, ophthalmology, pathology, and radiology. It had a modern laboratory, a radiology department with diagnostic and therapeutic capabilities, a blood bank, and a medical records department organized in accordance with the standards of the American Hospital Association.

As in most mission hospitals, the surgical department at PMC was the largest department, and it provided the major financial support for the hospital. Stomach cancer, a rare condition in the United States, was one of the surgical challenges most frequently encountered. The esophageal bypass for lye stricture of the esophagus, usually incurred in suicide attempts, was a procedure rarely performed in the United States; sixty operations were done in one year at PMC. Other common conditions were amoebic liver abscesses, surgical complications of tuberculosis and of parasites, and plastic repair of cleft palates, burns, and leprosy lesions (including the cosmetic replacement of eyebrows).

Dr. Seel was challenged by the plight of patients with advanced cancer, particularly those involving the head and neck. During an extended two-year furlough required by his wife's health problems, he studied at Memorial-Sloan Kettering Cancer Center in New York City. After returning to Korea in 1960, Dr. Seel set up the first cancer registry and tumor clinic in Korea. The registry provided follow-up for patients with cancer and generated data that led to the eventual designation of PMC as a Cancer Research Center. Dr. Seel also introduced the use of cobalt-60 teletherapy and radioisotope therapy.[29]

In 1954 the nursing school was awarded the Florence Nightingale Cup for excellence, and its graduates regularly placed high in national examinations. In 1962 the nursing school became an accredited junior college; in 1970 its name was changed to the Margaret Pritchard Junior College of Nursing.

The laboratory, described by a visiting physician as "one which any hospital in America could be proud of,"[30] trained technicians on an apprenticeship basis, after which they were certified by examination. Graduates were in demand all over Korea.

Preventive Medicine

The program at PMC expanded into preventive medicine and community health after the arrival of John Wilson, a board-certified pediatrician (as previously noted, Dr. John Wilson, while in the army, had worked with his father, Dr. R. M. Wilson, at the leprosy colony). Dr. John (Jefferson Medical College, Philadelphia, M.D., 1943) began an outreach project to serve some 10,000 persons in a mountainous area near Chonju. Molly Holt, R.N., a public health nurse, took a leave from her mission (the Team Mission) to help start the program. An initial grant of $10,000 from the Medical Benevolence Foundation (MBF) provided a Land Rover, a portable X-ray machine, and a small subsidy for four village health workers. The site was chosen in response to the request of a deaf Korean minister who said to Dr. Wilson, "We can see the light of the Jesus Hospital, but it does not reach us."[31]

Finances

Financing, a perennial problem in medicine everywhere, became desperate due to the costs of operating a teaching institution and of keeping pace with the enormous technological advances in the practice of medicine. In Korea the high rate of inflation and, ironically, the increasing number of highly qualified Korean staff added to the problem. Salaries for Korean physicians were comparatively high, so that replacing a missionary with a qualified Korean placed a financial burden on the institution.

Before World War II it had been possible for the mission hospitals to be more or less self-supporting. Some hospitals were even able to generate funds to support significant charity work and carry out some capital improvements. Not only was self-support now an unrealistic goal, but sources of funds were restricted by the PCUS policy of an "equalized budget" (incoming monies were to be divided equally among all programs). Eventually, church policy was changed to allow designated giving to approved projects.

As has been noted, the establishment in 1962 of the Medical Benevolence Foundation (MBF), largely through the initiative of Dr. Crane, opened the way for PCUS church members in the United States, primarily those in the medical profession, to send contributions (over and above their regular church pledge) to the medical institution of their choice. The MBF was also eligible to receive grants from foundations prohibited by their charters to give directly to a church body. In addition, MBF collected new and used equipment and sponsored the volunteer participation of medical professionals for short-term service.

Merrill Grubbs (Medical College of Virginia, M.H.A., 1968), the hospital administrator who arrived in 1961, established a sound business administration organized on American Hospital Association systems, with necessary modifications. He was initially shocked to find that patients were charged any fees in a mission hospital; they all seemed so poor. However, the hospital was expected to meet operating expenses and, although the "ability to pay" system was applied, no patient was refused admittance because of a lack of funds. Grubbs took a keen interest in the financial problems of the staff, as well as those of the patients, and set up a Mutual Benefit Association with a revolving loan fund for the employees. He also experimented with insurance plans and credit unions. Between 1967 and 1977, when a national health insurance plan was instituted, he operated a reasonably successful missionwide insurance plan. The insurance concept was new and took a while to catch on; after three months one presbytery wanted to cancel coverage because no one had gotten sick.[32]

Plans for a New Hospital Become a Reality
In the 1960s, as Korea began its amazing economic progress, the deteriorating condition of the PMC physical facilities became critical. Wards were overcrowded and beds again lined the corridors; housing for house staff and graduate nurses was substandard; electrical, plumbing, and heating systems needed overhauling. Visitors from a U.S. military post pronounced the place a firetrap and the plumbing "unethical." The paying patients, on whom the hospital depended for its operating budget, began to go to the newly constructed modern hospitals in Seoul; top graduates of medical schools, who had previously chosen to work at PMC, began to look elsewhere for training opportunities.

The construction of the modern Presbyterian Medical Center/Jesus Hospital, which has been dubbed "the Miracle of Dragon Head Ridge," came about as the result of three events.

First, in 1961 PMC applied for the 1965 Birthday Offering of the (PCUS) Women of the Church. The women responded enthusiastically by raising $411,000, by far the largest sum raised to that date.

Second, in 1963 Charles Davis, an architect from Birmingham, Alabama, volunteered his professional expertise. He recommended that, rather than try to renovate the existing facility, the PCUS should erect a new plant on a spacious piece of mission property formerly occupied by the mission's school for girls. He prepared preliminary plans for a new hospital (250 beds) and a home for nurses with an estimated cost (construction and equipment) of two million dollars.

Third, in 1964, at the request of the mission, the PCUS Board of World Missions sent a survey team to make recommendations for the future of the medical program. This team, consisting of L. Nelson Bell, M.D. (former missionary to China and member of the PCUS Board of World Missions), Theodore J. Stephenson, M.D. (the Northern Presbyterian medical secretary), and Warfield M. Firor, M.D. (retired professor of surgery at the Johns Hopkins University Medical School), recommended that, if the money could be raised, Mr. Davis's plan should be adopted.[33]

Raising the money was no small matter. Four sources provided the needed funds.

1. The generous Birthday Offering posed a problem: $411,000 was not enough to build a new medical facility but was too much to invest in the old plant, where it would disappear with relatively little visible result. Through some fortuitous circumstances and imaginative financing, however, the $411,000 became the seed-money for building the "new hospital." The Women of the Church deserve credit for and can take pride in the results of their enthusiastic support of PMC.

2. In a very real sense the Korean government contributed substantially to the building of the new medical center. PMC secured permission from an initially reluctant Mission Board in the United States to invest the Birthday Offering in Korean government banks while seeking other sources of funds. Korea, desperate at that time for hard currency, had authorized its

Selecting the site for the new medical center. Paul S. Crane with a representative of the German Evangelical Central Agency for Development Aid. Dr. Dorothea Sich (left) and Dr. K. Y. Lee (right). Photograph courtesy of Presbyterian Medical Center.

banks to pay an annual interest rate of 37 percent on eighteen-month deposits of U.S. dollars. The $411,000 investment (with additional donations) eventually generated more than $1.5 million. PMC was also able to arrange for duty-free importation of building supplies and hospital equipment.

3. Additional funds were donated. Among these were $22,000 by the Mary Lynn Richardson Foundation in Greensboro, North Carolina; $70,000 by the Covenant Presbyterian Church in Charlotte, North Carolina; $50,000 by the Benjamin Clayton Foundation in Houston, Texas (the supporter of L. Nelson Bell, M.D., in China); and some $360,000 through MBF by many individuals and church groups (seventy-two people made contributions of at least $1,000).[34]

4. And finally, the Evangelical Central Agency for Development Aid (EZE) of West Germany made the crucial matching grant. The four years it took to process the grant was, for the PMC staff, a learning experience in Korean/German/American cross-cultural relations and in patience. Dr. Crane made three trips to Germany, and German architects twice submitted plans to the EZE before approval came in the fall of 1969 for a grant of $1,350,000. When word finally came, on October 10, 1969, Dr. Seel ordered the chapel bell to peal the good news.

A German contractor, Gerhard Nomrowski, worked with a PMC building committee to supervise the construction. The resulting plant, meeting German standards, was a larger and grander facility in many ways than anyone at PMC had dreamed of proposing.

Presbyterian Medical
Center/Jesus Hospital, the
"New Hospital." Photograph
from Presbyterian Medical
Center brochure.

The New Hospital (1971–1983)

The November 10, 1971, dedication of the new Presbyterian Medical Center (PMC) was a gala event attended by dignitaries and visitors from Germany, the United States, and Korea. The spacious, modern, 253-bed facility had become in fact the multispecialty teaching institution envisioned for so many years; its continued Christian witness was affirmed by its Korean name, the Jesus Hospital, and by the beautiful sculptured relief portraying the healing Christ, which graced the entrance hall.

The two decades following the dedication of the new hospital coincided with the most expansive period of modernization and progress in South Korea. The medical center continued to develop in the face of new opportunities and new challenges: Korean leadership and responsibility increased, construction and expansion continued, new programs were inaugurated (rehabilitation, research, community health), and the evangelistic program expanded to include an overseas outreach.

Although Dr. Seel served as director of PMC after Dr. Crane's resignation in 1969, more and more responsibility was delegated to the Korean staff. With the exception of John Shaw, M.D., and his wife,

Sculptured relief at the PMC "New Hospital." Photograph courtesy of David Seel.

Dr. David J. and Mary B. Seel.

Sharon U. Shaw, O.T., the PCUS Mission Board appointed no new regular service missionaries to the hospital after 1971. Short-term workers and an increasing number of volunteer specialists continued to contribute their expertise in specific areas.

In 1971, in compliance with PCUS policy changes, PMC came under an independent board of directors made up of missionaries and Korean nationals. Initially six of twelve directors were missionaries; in 1983 the number of missionaries on the board was down to four. The Korean directors represented the community, sister Christian hospitals, and PMC alumni, as well as church leaders.

The orderly transfer of responsibility to the Koreans proceeded at an increasingly rapid pace. In 1973, Um Chai-Chung, R.N., became the first Korean director of the nursing school. She was followed by Hong Shin-Young, R.N., Ph.D, the retired director of Severance Nursing School, who held Korea's first doctorate in nursing educa-tion. Kim Chung-Jai became supervisor of the laboratory department, while the laboratory training program came under the direction of D. K. Chung, M.D., an anatomical pathologist with training at Southwest Medical School in Dallas, Texas.[35]

The administration of the medical center with its sophisticated technical equipment and ongoing building program offered a special challenge. In 1979 (Daniel) Oh Yong, following a period of study in the United States, became hospital administrator. Merrill Grubbs took the title of director of planning and development, with responsibility for internal audit, reports, recordkeeping, and grant applications for donor agencies. Lawrence J. Burns, an electrical engineer (1971–73), set up the engineering department and was followed by Shin Jin-Woo, who went for six months' special training in hospital maintenance at Dallas Presbyterian Hospital in Dallas, Texas.

Every institution in Korea is closely monitored by, and must work within the guidelines set by, various government agencies in Seoul. The hospital comes under the rules and regulations of the Ministry of Health and Social Affairs. However, the nursing school, deemed a school rather than part of the hospital, is under the Ministry of Education and operates under a board of directors separate from the hospital's. Both government ministries require frequent reports, and ministry approval is needed for major changes such as curriculum revisions and appointment of the director and board members. Meeting these government regulations takes considerable time and money.

The nursing school, as was the case in nursing education in the United States, became more academic in orientation. When it was founded, the student nurses paid no tuition and performed a major portion of the nursing for the hospital. The hospital not only paid the nursing school a subsidy for this work but paid each student a small sum as well. As graduate nurses became available to fill nursing positions, the situation changed. Nursing students paid tuition, and hospital duty was designed primarily to enhance the students' learning experience rather than to meet the hospital's nursing needs. Courses became more academic, and the school became a junior college under Ministry of Education guidelines.[36] By 1980 the Margaret Pritchard Junior College of Nursing had graduated a total of 601 nurses; the student body doubled that year, with the admission of 80 students into its first-year class.[37]

In 1977 Ruth Folta (Columbia University School of Nursing, R.N., 1954) joined the nursing school staff at their invitation to "help us fulfill our potential as Christian nurses." She taught a course for which she wrote a textbook titled *Bringing Hope Through Spiritual Care: How to Give Christian Health Care*. She also wrote a *Deaf Primer*, a *Manual for Medical Workers*, and newspaper articles on breast-feeding.[38]

Construction

Construction and expansion of the PMC facilities continued as grants and donations became available. The Medical Benevolence Foundation, in addition to substantial annual grants to the hospital, became the agent through which money was channeled to PMC. Support for major expansion came from three main sources:[39]

1. The Kresge Foundation of Troy, Michigan, provided $250,000, which, with the $197,000 from the sale of the "old hospital," made possible the construction of the nursing school on property adjoining the "new" hospital. Stan Kresge's arrival via helicopter for the dedication brought high drama and excitement to the event.
2. The U.S. Agency for International Development (AID) through its American Hospitals and Schools Abroad (ASHA) program gave $3 million. AID grants began in 1973.
3. The EZE in West Germany granted $1.2 million in addition to the original $1.35 million. EZE's experience with PMC had been good. For example, one year PMC sought to start a credit union in one of the rural villages where the community health program was being developed and applied to EZE for matching funds. When the villagers failed to produce the local funds by a particular dateline, which had been extended several times, PMC canceled the application. EZE was impressed by this unusual cancellation of a request for funds. Another time, when PMC had not applied for a grant, EZE asked, "Where is your application for this year?"[40]

See Table 6-1 for major construction at PMC after the initial dedication of the new hospital in 1971.

Medical Practice

Medical practice at PMC continued to emphasize compassion, high-quality service, and training. Hospital equipment, including computers, ultrasound, and a CT scanner, kept pace with worldwide

---

Table 6-1

Major PMC Construction (1971–83)

1975 Nursing School built; funded by the Kresge Foundation
1976 Memorial Chapel dedicated in memory of Dr. Y. H. (Andrew) Pak and Mrs. Jean Williams (sister of Mary Seel); hospital expanded to 269 beds
1978 Medical Library; funded by AID grant
1980 Rehabilitation wing; funded by AID grant; hospital expanded to 293 beds
1981 Critical Care Annex; funded by AID grant, hospital expanded to 338 beds
1982 Hospital expanded to 350 beds
      Kosan Branch Hospital; funded by EZE grant
1983 Seventh-floor addition begun; funded by EZE grant; hospital to expand to 401 beds

development of medical technologies. Seven operating rooms reflected the continued strength of the surgical department. The new intensive care unit, maternal/infant care wing, emergency room, medical library, and rehabilitation wing improved service. The statistics in Table 6-2 reflect the development of PMC.

The twenty-four-hour emergency service and disaster plan were put to the test in 1977 when a boxcar of explosives blew up in the railyard at Iri, nineteen miles away. Within an hour 165 seriously wounded patients flooded the facilities. The government subsequently recognized PMC for its response to this emergency, and Dr. Seel received the Presidential Second Order of Merit.

Three new programs deserve special mention: rehabilitation, research, and community health.

Rehabilitation

Dr. John Shaw (Washington University, M.D., 1965) was appointed to PMC in 1971 to help cope with the "epidemic" of major trauma cases resulting, to a large extent, from the increased number

Table 6-2
Statistical Comparison of the "Old" and the "New" Hospitals

	1970 (old)		1983 (new)	
Beds	160		353	
Staff doctors	8	(1963)	43	
House staff (interns and residents)	34		73	
Nurses	70		177	
Nurse's Aides	0		102	
Laboratory	22	(1963)	42	
Employees	224		774	
Chaplains	2		5	
Missionaries	8		7	(1 in 1990)
Outpatients	35,853		168,895	
Admissions	4,462		12,142	
Surgical operations	2,879	(1968)	8,301	
Deliveries	606	(1968)	2,063	
Percent charity	17%		12%	

*Compiled from PMC annual reports

and speed of vehicles on the newly constructed highway system. Sharon Shaw (Washington University, B.S., O.T., 1963) contributed occupational therapy expertise.

In his orthopedic practice, Dr. Shaw became aware of the prevailing prejudice against disabled persons; in "old Korea" persons with handicaps were kept hidden from public view. Dr. Shaw pioneered the establishment of the Rehabilitation Medicine Department, or Rehabilitation Institute, as it was sometimes called, which provided physiotherapy and occupational therapy for persons crippled by poliomyelitis, skeletal tuberculosis, burns, and accidents. Facilities for blind people were instituted as well. In 1980 a twenty-four-bed rehabilitation wing was added to the hospital.

The special problems of disabled children were a major concern, and what became known as "peripheral clinics" were established on Cheju island, in Masan, in Kunsan, and in Taejon. Resident staff from PMC visited regularly. The Good Samaritan Children's Rehabilitation Center in Masan developed into a fifty-bed hospital/school.

Research

The study of diseases commonly found in Korea remained a major preoccupation of the PMC staff; in 1983 some thirty-five papers were published in Korean and American medical journals. The tumor registry, set up in 1961, and the tumor clinic, established in 1983, began to provide significant statistical data.[41]

Community Health

An important new development during the "new" hospital era was the establishment of the Department of Community Health. Building on the work started in 1970 by Dr. John Wilson, this department sought to intervene in an organized manner in the health practices of communities in order to prevent disease and to raise the health standards of the poor. After Dr. Wilson left in 1971, a dynamic Australian public health nurse, Dorothy Knight, R.N., carried on the program until a strong national leader, Dr. K. S. Kim (M.D., M.P.H., Ph.D.), was found.

The PMC program offered a comprehensive approach in which the medical center not only acted as the tertiary referral center but also led in primary care. Credit unions and medical insurance cooperatives were established to encourage community ownership of the health program.

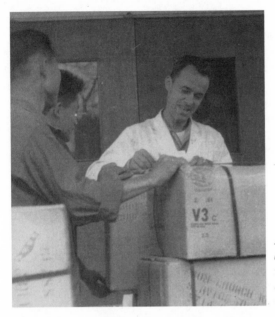

Merrill Grubbs, PMC hospital administrator, checks out a shipment of sample drugs. Photograph courtesy of Presbyterian Medical Center.

EZE became very much interested in the program and provided a major portion of the funding—$50,000 per year for five years.[42]

PMC's community health projects were located in one urban and three rural areas. In Kosan, a township of 43,000 in a remote mountainous area, the role of a highly successful regional health center was expanded in 1982 by the construction of the Kosan Branch Hospital. Affectionately known as the "Baby Jesus Hospital," this ten-bed facility, with its operating room and a simple laboratory, became a model of a rural primary care facility.

Evangelistic Outreach

The evangelistic emphasis continued to be an essential part of PMC. While five chaplains and evangelists were employed to work with the patients, the real strength of the Christian witness lay in the dedication of the staff. The Evangelistic Society, supported by the employees with 0.5 percent of their salaries, encouraged the staff to both speak and act out their faith in every patient encounter. The Evangelistic Society also engaged in a variety of church-related activities in the community, and a PMC choir won nationwide acclaim and recognition.

In 1979 the Evangelistic Society entered overseas mission work by sending Dr. (John) Lee Yong-Ung, a PMC-trained surgeon, and his wife as missionaries to Bangladesh. Miss Pak Hae-In, R.N., a graduate of the Margaret Pritchard Junior College of Nursing, joined the Lees in 1981. All three worked at the Tongi Clinic, a primary health clinic established and operated by the PCUS near Dacca in Bangladesh.

Conclusion

In 1983 the Presbyterian Medical Center in Chonju was well on the road to becoming an inde-pendent, Korean, multispecialty

Pharmacy full of sample drugs. Photograph courtesy of Presbyterian Medical Center.

teaching hospital with a strong community health program. The facili-ties were modern, largely as a result of grants from foundations and governments (U.S. and German). Although the dream of founding a Christian medical school had not been realized, the training of nurses, technicians, and Korean physicians had become well established. Although Dr. David Seel remained director of PMC until 1987, Korean leadership was in place; the missionaries played a supportive role. The primary challenges ahead for the Korean leaders would be to maintain standards, secure adequate financial support, and deal with the increasing pressure for secularization.

KWANGJU CHRISTIAN HOSPITAL (KCH)
Kwangju

The post–World War II medical program in Kwangju began with a tuberculosis facility, the Graham Memorial Tuberculosis Hospital, and developed into a multispecialty general hospital, the Kwangju Christian Hospital (KCH). The general hospital, however, maintained a strong emphasis on tuberculosis treatment and prevention.

Graham Memorial Tuberculosis Hospital (1951–1964)

The Graham Memorial Tuberculosis Hospital opened in October 1951 at the height of the Korean War under the leadership of Herbert A. Codington, M.D., and Virginia Cumming, R.N. War conditions had aggravated the already serious problem of tuberculosis, and the forty-bed hospital, closed since 1940, was rehabilitated with $25,000 from the Program of Progress development funds. In two years the bed capacity nearly doubled.[43]

Dr. Codington brought to his service in Kwangju a dedication to the healing of both body and soul that was reminiscent of Dr. Wylie Forsythe's in an earlier era. His sensitivity to the needs of people in trouble became legendary and, at times, strained the already limited resources. At the same time his selfless spirit and sincerity attracted support, and he was able to generate financial backing from many sources for the tuberculosis work.

During the early years, Virginia Cumming had the primary responsibility for the day-to-day running of the institution—a situation, she has noted, the Koreans sometimes found hard to accept. A

Virginia Cumming, R.N., and Herbert A. Codington, M.D. Photograph courtesy of Paul Crane.

Aerial view of Kwangju, Korea, showing the Graham Memorial Tuberculosis Hospital as it appeared in 1954. This building was constructed in 1934 following the fire. Photograph courtesy of Kwangju Christian Hospital.

fine Korean woman doctor, Dr. Yuh Soong-Sook, supervised the tuberculosis medication, and, when Dr. Codington was on furlough or with his family in Japan, Dr. Crane from PMC provided regular medical coverage. On several occasions Virginia Cumming was able to successfully intercede with Korean army officials for the return of members of the staff who had been drafted for military duty. "They must have venerated my greying hair and my ancient years [early fifties]," was her comment.[44]

Virginia Cumming described the hospital as "in terrible shape" in 1951. It had been completely stripped; it had no water or electricity, no heat, no glass in the windows, and no mattresses. She stuffed mattresses with bamboo shavings and cheap cotton and had carpenters make wooden bedsteads. The cold of that first winter was not to be forgotten. The hospital was unheated except for small oil stoves in the nurses' stations, and patients were given hot bricks wrapped in cloth to put in their beds.

Beds increased to 150 in 1954 when an 80-bed charity ward was built with the help of funds from the UN Korea Relief Agency (UNKRA) and materials donated by the U.S. Army; the inpatient count often exceeded 180. During the summer while construction took place, patients were housed in three large tents donated by the U.S. armed forces. As one of the physicians who later served at Kwangju remarked, "We always called it the AFAK building after the Armed Forces Aid to Korea. . . . The year it was built AFAK was building only school buildings. Thus the structure was built like a typical grammar school under the AFAK plan for such."[45]

Thanks to White Cross supplies, relief grain, and drugs from the government and from Church World Service, the hospital was able to serve the largely indigent patient population, many of whom were refugees from all over Korea. Because the work was heavily subsidized, as much as 68 percent (in 1956) of the care was given free of charge.[46]

Before antibiotics speeded the healing process for tuberculous patients, occupational therapy occupied an important place in the program. Sewing, knitting, weaving, barbering, and the raising of chickens, bees, and rabbits were some of the activities in which the patients were engaged.

As the situation in Korea stabilized, so did the hospital. In 1954 the UN Command allowed the return of dependents. Page Codington, R.N., joined her husband and assisted in emergency situations. Astrid Kraakenes, R.N., the Norwegian nurse who served in Chonju, followed Virginia Cumming as director of nurses.[47] James K. Levie, D.D.S., returned in 1956 and revived the dental program.

The 1957 Birthday Offering of the PCUS Women of the Church of $107,615 for "Tuberculosis Work in Korea" was a welcome assist to getting tuberculosis under control in the PCUS areas. In Kwangju, it purchased a portable X-ray unit for making mass surveys, provided basic improvements to the physical plant (including a dormitory for graduate nurses), and created an endowment fund for the support of poor patients. Birthday Offering funds also went to strengthen the chest surgery unit at PMC and to build a tuberculosis ward at the Wilson Leprosy Center.[48]

In 1958 Laurence Simpson, a young surgeon from Australia, was recruited to develop a surgical program at Kwangju. Before he arrived, surgical treatment of the tuberculous patients was done some sixty miles away at the Presbyterian Medical Center (PMC) in Chonju. Dr. Simpson commented:

> The practice of medicine was so totally different to that in which I had done my training, it was almost a new experience. The diseases faced were different, the patients' responses to those diseases were different, as were the facilities that were available. In addition to

this, I had little or no help . . . as I was the only surgeon in the province undertaking chest surgery.[49]

The arrival in 1959 of John M. McBryde, hospital administrator (Duke University, MHA, 1953), and his wife Sally, a physiotherapist (Duke University, P.T., 1949), greatly strengthened the staff. The hospital when McBryde arrived was essentially a tuberculosis sanatorium in a rather primitive condition. His goals were to place the hospital on a financially sound basis and to train Koreans in hospital administration. The business office (in 1959) was run by a man greatly respected in the community whose methods were those common in Korean offices: bookkeeping was by the Korean ledger system and most office personnel were relatives. McBryde wisely did not rush change, and only after this employee resigned did he attempt to restructure the administration. Making ends meet was always a problem, and work on an extensive construction program occupied much time and energy.[50]

The Graham Memorial Tuberculosis Hospital contributed significantly to the eventual successful control of tuberculosis in South Korea. Thanks to the introduction of new antibiotics, it was possible to offer, for the first time, effective cures for the dread disease in all its many manifestations: lung, bone, meninges, peritoneum, kidney, and lymph nodes. In addition to inpatient and outpatient treatment of the disease, the Kwangju hospital conducted classes in preventive education in the schools, identified cases of tuberculosis through mass X rays, and conducted research on the effectiveness of certain drugs. Dr. Simpson, at the request of the Korean government, tested the effectiveness of thiacetazone in drug-resistant cases; this drug proved to be quite toxic.[51]

In 1957 the first of what became annual meetings of the Korean National Tuberculosis Association was held at the Graham Memorial Tuberculosis Hospital, and in 1958 Dr. Codington participated in the International Conference of Chest Diseases in New Delhi, India, and in the National Tuberculosis Conference in Pusan. In 1960 Codington received a citation from the Ministry of Health for an "outstanding contribution in the field of Public Health."[52]

In its tenth year (1961) Graham Memorial Tuberculosis Hospital reported treating 1,200 inpatients and 12,000 outpatients.[53] The 1973 report states, "More cases of tuberculosis are treated through this facility and its satellite clinics than any other private hospital in Korea."[54]

Kwangju Christian Hospital (KCH) (1964–1983)

By 1961 the government's energetic application of new drug therapies for tuberculosis had begun to bring the tuberculosis problem under control and, as in the United States, diminish the need for inpatient care of persons with this disease. Pressure for a multispecialty service increased as patients suffering from a variety of surgical conditions sought the services of the qualified Western surgeon. Moreover, the income-producing potential of an active surgical department stood in sharp contrast to a tuberculosis service whose patients were unable to pay for the required extended hospitalization. In the meantime the city of Kwangju had developed into the major urban center in southwest Korea. Industrial plants and educational institutions proliferated. Kwangju was no longer a small provincial capital, but a city of political and economic strength. It was a challenge for the hospital to keep pace with the city's development.

In 1961 after the completion of Dr. Simpson's term in 1960, Ronald B. Dietrick, M.D., transferred from Chonju to Kwangju as chief of surgery. With the encouragement of Dr. Codington, the director, Dr. Dietrick began to develop an intern and residency program. Although the hospital continued its special emphasis on

Kwangju Christian Hospital's new building (1983). The 1968 (brick), 1974, and 1977 buildings can be seen in this photograph. Photograph from Kwangju Christian Hospital brochure.

tuberculosis, it gradually evolved into a multispecialty hospital with an intern/residency training program and a nursing school.

In 1964 the Medical Survey Committee (sent at the mission's request to survey the medical program in Korea) recommended that the Kwangju hospital become a modern multispecialty hospital.[55] This new focus, as previously noted, was reflected in the change of name in 1964 from Graham Memorial Tuberculosis Hospital to the Kwangju Christian Hospital (KCH). The new name identified the location of the hospital (in Kwangju) and the nature of the hospital (i.e., Christian).[56]

The outstanding achievements of the Kwangju Christian Hospital (KCH) included the development of a modern general teaching hospital under Korean leadership; a public health program in rural areas and in Soonchun; a strong dental department with an emphasis on teaching; and a hospital chaplaincy program that offered training to students of the Honam Theological Seminary.

The Staff at KCH

Drs. Herbert A. Codington (1949–74) and Ronald B. Dietrick (1961–87) provided continuity of leadership at KCH, the former in tuberculosis and public health and the latter in general surgery. Dr. Codington was director from 1950 to 1967; Dr. Dietrick, from 1967 to 1976. In 1976 Dr. Huh Chin-Duk[57] was appointed the director, and KCH became the first PCUS medical institution in Korea to be headed by a Korean national. Dr. Huh provided fine leadership for a smooth transition from a mission-operated institution to one under Korean direction. Dr. Dietrick continued as the director of medical affairs, and the secretarial help provided by Mrs. Bess Dietrick was invaluable during the transition. Information regarding specific key staff serving at KCH follows.

Herbert A. Codington (Cornell University, M.D., 1944) has already been described as a caring person sensitive to the needs of the poorest of the poor. He has also been described as an "idea man" looking for ways to improve care for suffering people. In 1974 his concern for the plight of people in Bangladesh led him to persuade a reluctant Mission Board in the United States to begin a medical relief program in that sad country and led to his assignment in 1974 from Korea to Bangladesh to implement that work (see Bangladesh).

Ronald B. Dietrick, F.A.C.S., (University of Pennsylvania, M.D., 1953) was a highly trained and capable surgeon whose dedication to

Christian medical missions combined the practice and teaching of high-quality medicine with an unequivocal Christian witness. He became deeply interested in supporting the healing ministry in the church and skillfully articulated his interest in the subject.

W. Laurence Simpson, M.D. (University of Melbourne, Australia, M.D., 1954) was first supported at KCH by Inter Church Aid (1964–67) and returned in 1964 for a four-year term under PCUS support. He set up the first surgical unit at the Graham Memorial Tuberculosis Hospital and said that his most satisfying memory of his stay in Korea concerned the transformation of a poor-quality tuberculosis center into a modern hospital facility. Dr. Simpson's genial personality endeared him to Koreans and his fellow missionaries alike. The devastation he felt when his two-year-old daughter suffered a serious burn from ingesting lye was shared by all who came to know him and his family.

Albert H. Bridgman, F.A.C.S., (Louisiana State University, M.D. 1956) was the son of missionaries to China (see Eleanor Bridgman, R.N., Yencheng and Taizhou). He served at KCH for four years (1967–71) and did what was described as "seminal work in getting TB surgery on a firm footing."[58] He commented that the medical profession in Korea was then in a period of transition: Medical students were well taught but lacked "hands on" experience; the residents had "good attitudes and were a pleasure to teach." The workload was heavy, but patients seemed to respond well to treatment; in fact, he said, the percentage of good results compared favorably with those in the United States. Colleagues at the Veterans Administration Tuberculosis Hospital in Oteen, North Carolina, supplied him with discards such as gloves and grafts. They also sent a discarded Russian surgical stapling machine, which proved useful in vascular surgery; one of the Korean dentists made staples for the machine.[59]

Adrian J. Wolbrink, F.A.C.S. (University of Minnesota, M.D., 1965) completed his orthopedic residency at Mayo Clinic in July 1972 and left in August with his wife and two sons for a three-year tour at KCH. Under his leadership, the Department of Orthopedic Surgery was established and received accreditation.

There were relatively few missionary nurses and none, except Juanita Coyer (Aultman Hospital, Canton, Ohio, R.N., 1950), served for more than one term. KCH was able to recruit a number of missionaries other than those assigned by PCUS. Among these were

Staff at the Kwangju Christian Hospital c. 1968. Missionaries on front row, left to right: Herbert A. Codington, M.D., Ronald B. Dietrick, M.D., Albert H. Bridgman, M.D., and Dick Nieusma, D.D.S. In 1976, Dr. Huh Chin-Duk (left of Dietrick) became director, the first national to direct a PCUS hospital in Korea. Photograph courtesy of Kwangju Christian Hospital.

two nurses of the United Church of Canada Mission: Margaret Storey, public health nurse (1972–74), and Marian Pope, nursing education (1973–76), whose contributions were outstanding. Others were Esther Cooksey, R.N., public health; Lloyd and Melsa Shout, physiotherapy; and Susan Fleming, radiology technician. The hospital also benefited from a large number of short-term volunteers, many of whom were sent through MBF.

Four Korean physicians were of key importance, especially in setting up the intern/residency program. The director, Dr. Huh Chin-Duk, an endocrinologist, served for a number of years as the chief of internal medicine. Dr. Kim Ki-Bok, who interned at PMC and studied in Germany and the United States,[60] headed the pediatric department; Dr. Pak Hong-Bae, internist; and Dr. Im Hun-Jung, chief of the OB/GYN department. Many of the Korean nurses and some technicians received their training at PMC in Chonju.

The Practice

The presence of highly qualified surgeons at KCH drew many patients, and the diversity of surgery undertaken was reflected in the papers published by Dr. Dietrick. In addition to covering tuberculosis-related problems (thoracoplasty and lobectomy), these papers dealt with such subjects as surgical treatment of intussusception, stricture of the esophagus, stomach cancer, duodenal and gastric ulcers, liver abscess, paragonimaniasis, and ascariasis.[61]

In 1969 the number of beds approached 200; half were for tuberculosis patients and half for general medical and surgical patients.[62] In 1983 KCH had 450 beds.

Training Program

As at PMC, the importance of training Korean physicians to care for their own people was perceived as an extremely important aspect of missionary medicine at KCH. An intern/residency training program became an integral part of the program. However, by the early 1960s, the government and medical societies had established many rules and regulations that made it very difficult to set up the program. Although KCH received government approval as an intern/resident training hospital in 1965, the training program, in Dr. Dietrick's words, "took [us] the better part of 15 years to fully accomplish." In the early days, PMC helped by sending surgical residents to KCH on rotation, and Dr. Keller provided coverage for the pediatric department until Dr. Kim Ki-Bok got her Korean pediatric board-certification.

KCH developed a good relationship with the Chunam University Medical School, and an exchange of lectures and seminars was mutually beneficial. Many graduates of Chunam University entered the postgraduate program at KCH, and nursing students received public health training at KCH.

Nurses' training at KCH began in 1973 in cooperation with the Speer Nursing School, a department of Speer Girls' High School. Marian Pope, the Canadian nurse, is credited with the idea. She helped implement the plan for Speer to provide the academics, while KCH provided clinical and ward training. In 1982 the nursing school became Kwangju Christian Hospital School of Nursing.[63]

Paramedical training was carried out in cooperation with the Kwangju Health Junior College (Seowon Junior College) which operated under the Honam Christian Educational Foundation. KCH provided practical experience in X-ray and medical technology, dental hygiene, and dental laboratory technology.[64]

Hospital Development

The hospital occupied a large piece of property fronting on what became one of the major highways leading southwest out of Kwangju. When first established, the hospital was on the outskirts of the city, but as the city grew, the hospital became more centrally located. The transformation of the 200-bed tuberculosis facility into a 350-bed general hospital took place step by step. Major construction was as follows:

1966–68: A modern four-story hospital building, funded by the Presbyterian Development Fund ($87,000) and the Evangelical Central Agency (EZE) of Germany ($260,000), increased the beds to 200. This building had water, electricity, and heat. In 1969 KCH received a grant for $1.25 million from EZE to equip and furnish this new building.[65]

1972: A dormitory for the doctors and the nurses was built with funds ($60,000) raised by the Medical Benevolence Foundation (MBF).[66]

1974–75: A three-story wing provided beds for the obstetrical service and outpatient clinics (OB-GYN, general surgery, ENT, orthopedic, and dental clinics). MBF raised $100,000 for this project.[67]

1977: The L. Nelson Bell Surgical Wing contained a central laboratory, operating rooms, delivery rooms, a recovery room, and a surgical ward; beds increased to 250. Funds were raised by MBF.[68]

1983: A four-story unit, built primarily with funds from EZE, provided space for clinics, wards, and an intensive care unit. The beds increased to 350.[69] Two short-term workers, Donald B. Kinder (1971–73) and Wesley Wentworth (1977–79), supervised construction and maintenance.

Community Outreach

The outreach into the surrounding communities had its historic beginnings in the volunteer weekend evangelistic teams that went to nearby villages to hold services and clinics. In time this community outreach became a well-organized part of the KCH program and was funded, in part, by the Oxford Committee of Famine Relief (OXFAM).[70] Services, directed primarily at tuberculosis (identification by mass X-ray examination, prevention, and follow-up), were expanded to include immunizations, family planning, maternal and child health care, rehabilitation of crippled children, and examination of school children. The Canadian nurses, Margaret Storey and Marian Pope, were instrumental in getting these public health programs under way.[71]

One aspect of the outreach program—repair of harelips—got started this way. One day while Dr. Dietrick was out hunting, he saw a child with a harelip standing by the side of the road. He gave the child a scrap of paper saying that if he came in to KCH, the harelip could be fixed free. Several months later the family brought the child and the well-worn note to the hospital; the child was admitted and the lip was operated on. The word spread and other children with this defect appeared and were treated free-of-charge. Later the Korean army started its own harelip-repair program, and the source of harelip patients soon dried up.[72]

Sixty miles away in the city of Soonchun where Dr. Rogers had once headed the largest PCUS hospital in Korea, Betty Linton (Mrs. Hugh) became concerned about the plight of the many poorly supervised tuberculosis victims and decided to take action. Although not a medical professional, she began the Soonchun Christian Clinic in 1962 in order to better supervise some 300 tuberculous patients under treatment in their homes. In time she added a simple eighty-bed rest home for the tuberculous and a thirty-bed hospice for the terminally ill. Physicians from KCH visited regularly to provide the medical supervision needed. Dr. Dietrick reported that working three days a month in this clinic was one of the more pleasurable duties of his work in Korea.[73]

KCH also provided support to a clinic on the island of Cheju. Sylvia Boyer, R.N., while assigned to Mokpo (1962–68) and Kwangju (1968–77), accompanied her husband, Rev. Kenneth Boyer, on visits to Cheju island; in 1972 they organized a low-cost medical clinic there. Physicians from both KCH and PMC assisted local Korean doctors in the program. The Cheju Clinic became involved, among other things, with tuberculosis surveys and treatment, parasite control, cancer detection, immunizations, rehabilitation for disabled children, dental work, and classes in public health.[74]

Dental Department
James K. Levie, D.D.S., returned in 1956 for a three-year term and revived the dental department he had founded in Kwangju before World War II. As before, he spent a major portion of his time working

on missionaries and their children. Dr. Levie was followed by Dick H. Nieusma Jr. (University of Michigan, D.D.S., 1956), who built up an outstanding training center for Korean dentists and paradental personnel.

Dr. Nieusma began his missionary service in Korea with two years of intensive language study in Seoul, during which he developed a relationship with the dental school at Seoul National University, the only dental school in Korea at that time. This relationship proved helpful in the development of the dental residency program.

While Dr. Nieusma attended language school, the dental clinic in Kwangju was renovated and enlarged to a three-chair unit furnished, in part, with used equipment sent from the United States. Dr. Nieusma, with the help of local machinists, also designed, built, and repaired equipment. Construction in 1974 of the three-story wing to the hospital included a new dental clinic with space for fourteen chairs.

In September 1963 the three-year dental training program began operation with the assistance of Dr. Sam Pak (Pak Choong-Sam), a graduate of Seoul National University Dental School and an ordained minister. Two students were accepted each year for a one-year internship and two-year residency. The program had government accreditation in prosthodontics and was approved under the R.O.K. Army's "Kim Plan," for military deferment. By 1983 some forty students had been through the program; one of the first two students was a woman.

Dr. Nieusma characterized the dental program at Kwangju as "on a high level." He added:

> Many different types of treatment were available including maxillofacial prosthesis, a sophisticated procedure accompanying surgery for cancer of the mouth. Koreans desire good dentistry and are willing to pay for it. They seem more willing than Americans to undergo treatment that would preserve the teeth. This attitude contributed to the success of the dental program and may be linked to the Korean dislike of prosthesis of any kind that reflects a handicap.[75]

Dr. Nieusma credits more than forty visiting dentists and members of the U.S. military stationed in the area with enhancing the quality of the training program. Among those who served briefly in

Kwangju were Drs. Fred Willard and Biff Oliver, dentists; Nancy Kane, dental hygienist; Sandra Koostianti, dentist, who went to Kwangju from Indonesia under the PCUS "Partners-in-Mission" program; and Dr. Sandy Marks, a former PCUS dental missionary serving in Zaire, who spent three months in Kwangju in 1980 while en route back to Zaire to revive the dental training program there.

As noted previously, the dental laboratory technician training program (begun in 1965) and the dental hygienist training program (begun in 1976) were carried out in cooperation with the Kwangju Health Junior College. Technicians became certified after completing three years of study and passing a licensing examination. Some twenty to twenty-five students had completed this program by 1983 and were able to obtain good-paying jobs. Nancy Kane, a dental hygienist who later became a member of the dental faculty of Loyola University of Chicago, helped set up the program for the dental hygienists. Graduates of the two-year program (following high school) received junior college accreditation. Classes that began with forty in a class expanded to eighty.

A mobile dental clinic, housed in a twenty-six-passenger bus, participated in the KCH village health care program. Some 6,000 persons a year received dental attention in this manner

Graduates of the dental program were active in the Korean Dental Missionary Society, which studied missions, operated a charity clinic among the poor in Seoul, and sponsored overseas dental missionaries.[76]

Hospital Chaplaincy

The evangelistic outreach at KCH had a high priority from the beginning. A minimum of one male and two female Korean evangelists maintained contact with inpatients and outpatients. Staff participation was impressive. They formed a Christian Hospital Association to which they donated 1 percent of their salaries for support of mission work in Korea and overseas. During the time that Rev. Dwight Linton served as hospital chaplain (1968–69) a free-standing chapel, which cost about $5,000, was built with funds largely donated by members of the staff.[77]

Rev. C. Betts Huntley, who arrived in 1965, served as chaplain at KCH and taught counseling at the Honam Theological Seminary. He combined a course in counseling with practical experience in the hospital. The first year, some fifteen students signed up for the course. This number increased each year until there were eighty in the class.

Huntley enjoyed his work because it offered a successful alternative to traditional Korean pastoral counseling attitudes. Korean pastors were accustomed to occupying an authoritative position vis-a-vis the patient; their approach would be judgmental and directive. A counseling approach that emphasized listening skills and understanding without "coercive preaching or pushy evangelism" was a new concept and proved to be both exciting and productive. It became apparent, however, that, in order to meet the needs of the patients, an element of direction or "assertiveness" was necessary. How to meld the two approaches within the Korean cultural framework formed the basis for Huntley's dissertation for the Doctor of Ministry degree from Columbia Theological Seminary in September 1985.[78]

In May 1980 the so-called Kwangju Incident was a watershed event for KCH. Following the assassination of President Park Chung-Hee in October 1979, Korea experienced a period of political unrest marked by student and worker demonstrations and the imposition of martial law by the government. Bloody fighting erupted in Kwangju when the Korean military brutally suppressed a demonstration begun by students and joined in by the townspeople. The hospital was deluged with over 130 injured persons including civilians, soldiers, and police.[79] KCH gained the reputation for being a "caring hospital." One missionary reported that "the experience of anger and of fear brought him closer to the people. . . . One relates differently to people with whom you [shared] this experience."[80]

The summer of 1980 also brought a severe cholera epidemic to the Kwangju area. In the words of Dr. Huh Chin-Duk, KCH was the "right hospital in the right place at the right time."[81]

Conclusion

By 1983 when the PCUS story came to an end, Kwangju Christian Hospital was prepared to continue as an independent Korean Christian institution. The Korean director and members of its board were dedicated Christian leaders of considerable stature and, within a few years, no missionary personnel served on the staff of KCH.

Korea, as a nation, had developed economically to the point that it could support a modern medical institution. The medical professionals were trained in modern medical practice and were capable of providing the required leadership. Moreover, a national health insurance plan was in place.

The effects of the Koreanization of KCH will be interesting to observe in the future. It is to be expected that KCH will differ from a mission institution, but will continue to be concerned with the compassionate care of the sick and the poor.

WILSON LEPROSY CENTER AND REHABILITATION HOSPITAL (WLC)
Yosu

The story of leprosy work in Korea is one of the happiest chapters in the history of the PCUS overseas medical missions. Begun in 1909 in response to the plight of the victims of leprosy, the R. M. Wilson Leprosy Colony became, in 1967, the Wilson Leprosy Center and Rehabilitation Hospital. The change of name reflected the dramatic change that occurred after the successful application of sulfone drugs brought the first hope for cure of this dread disease.

The fundamental difference between the colony and the center was one of orientation. The colony provided segregated sanatorium facilities for leprosy patients and received international recognition for the innovative programs that enriched the lives of the patients. The center was dedicated to the early identification and treatment of leprosy, the prevention and repair of nerve damage deformities, and the rehabilitation of arrested cases into society. It also cared for old and severely crippled people who required special attention. Furthermore, rehabilitation services were extended to people crippled from causes other than leprosy. The acceptance of leprosy

Wilson Leprosy Center Rehabilitation Hospital. Photograph from Wilson Leprosy Center 1981 annual report.

patients into public hospital wards and clinics had become quite common, but by admitting nonleprous patients into its hospital, WLC was doing something that had never been done before.[82]

For the purposes of this account, the term Wilson Leprosy Colony will be used loosely to describe the institution from 1947 to 1965, a period in which Rev. E. T. Boyer was the principal administrator; Wilson Leprosy Center and Rehabilitation Hospital will apply after 1966, when Dr. Stanley C. Topple became the director. The *colony* was administered by missionaries of the PCUS. The *center* operated under a board of directors, the majority of whom, by 1983, were Koreans; in 1983 only one PCUS missionary couple remained on the staff.

Leprosy and *tuberculosis* are similar in many ways. Both are caused by rod-shaped acid-fast bacteria of the genus *Mycobacterium* (*M.leprae* and *M.tuberculosis*); both were devastating diseases not responsive to treatment until the discovery of effective drugs after World War II. Leprosy was not the killer that tuberculosis often became but was dreaded more because of the disfigurement and social rejection associated with it. The PCUS played a significant role in the eventual control of both tuberculosis and leprosy in South Korea.

The miracle drug for leprosy was diaminodiphenyl sulphone, commonly known as dapsone or DDS. First successfully administered in 1941 to leprosy patients at the United States Public Health Leprosy Hospital in Carville, Louisiana, dapsone proved to be "cheap, safe, effective, and eminently suitable for outpatient care."[83] Dr. Robert G. Cochrane of the British Leprosy Mission introduced dapsone to Korea in 1953; nationwide use in Korea dates from 1955.[84] Problems with dapsone resistance began to emerge in the 1960s but were successfully managed with multiple drug therapy (MDT) regimens worked out by the World Health Organization (WHO). The number of leprosy cases in Korea declined from an estimated 100,000 in the 1950s to 25,000 in 1989.[85] The census at the Wilson Leprosy Colony/Center dropped from a high of around 1,400 at the time of the Korean War (1950) to approximately 200 old and severely crippled people in 1983.

Loss of sensation in the extremities is the most serious complication of leprosy and by far the most common cause of disability.[86] The nerves that transmit pain sensations are damaged because the *leprae* bacilli grow in the sheaths surrounding the peripheral nerves, causing an inflammatory reaction that constricts the nerve. This tourniquet effect blocks the transmission of nerve impulses. People who have no feeling of pain are vulnerable to great damage. Dr. Paul Brand, world famous leprologist and orthopedic surgeon, has said that "if he had but one gift to give his patients it would be the ability to perceive pain."[87] Dr. Stan Topple relates horror stories. Some patients' anesthetic limbs were gnawed by rats while they slept; one man arrived at the center with black gangrene in both legs as the result of frostbite; another, while sleeping by an open fire, was awakened by the smell of burning flesh to find his hand and fingers severely burned.[88]

One of the outstanding leaders in the field of leprosy in Korea after World War II was Dr. Lew Joon (M.D., D.M.Sc., Ph.D.), professor of microbiology at Yonsei University Medical School and founder of the Lew Institute of Biomedical Research in Seoul. Dr. Lew, a graduate of Yonsei University and the University of California, Los Angeles, helped organize the Korean Leprosy Association and was a leading spirit in the highly successful Resettlement Village Movement.

The Wilson Leprosy Colony

The colony had a beautiful setting of a hundred acres on a peninsula off the south coast of Korea, halfway between Soonchun and the port city of Yosu. In 1949 100 or so buildings contained dispensaries, baths, industrial shops, store, barbershop, theater, church, and living quarters for patients and staff. An elected council, made up of patients, managed the daily operation of the colony. Festivals and celebrations were a common part of community life.

The colony depended on three main sources of income. The PCUS contributed the services and salaries of the missionary staff but did not contribute to the operating budget of the colony; the Korean government, continuing the practice of the Japanese colonial administration, supplied regular subsidies for basic living expenses; and the American Leprosy Mission made an annual contribution toward operating expenses. The patients also contributed by farming, fishing, and the raising of poultry and livestock.

Rev. Elmer T. Boyer (1949–1965)

Rev. Elmer T. Boyer, in addition to other responsibilities, served as administrator of the Wilson Leprosy Colony from 1949 until his retirement in 1965. Although the patients viewed him as a father figure in the Confucian tradition, Boyer described his role as being like a "mayor" of the almost self-contained agricultural/industrial community of roughly 1,000 patients.[89] He took special pride in three projects initiated during his tenure: the Bright Star Orphanage, the Seminary, and the resettlement of noninfectious ex-patients into independent villages.

The Bright Star Orphanage, built outside the main gate of the colony, provided a home for the disease-free children of leprosy patients. These children, while not inheriting leprosy, lacked immunity and were especially vulnerable to infection; they were checked regularly to see that they remained disease free. A dormitory, playground, and school served some sixty boys and girls, ages four to fourteen. A major breakthrough in public attitudes made it possible to send the children to junior and senior high school in Soonchun where Boyer was the principal; four attended college.

The Seminary at the Wilson Leprosy Colony was the "only seminary in the world exclusively for the training of persons afflicted with leprosy."[90] Its student body averaged thirty-five to forty students from all over Korea. As the treatment for leprosy became successful, students with leprosy were accepted in the regular seminaries, and this institution became obsolete.

Resettlement villages were initiated after 1963 when the compulsory segregation law, instituted by the Japanese in 1916, was repealed, and leprosy colonies all over Korea were gradually emptied of all but patients suffering from extreme disabilities. The ex-patients were encouraged to settle into villages run by the villagers themselves, not by the government, missionary societies, or charitable organizations. The responsibility for their own socioeconomic decisions fostered independence and brought prosperity to many who had been beggars and outcasts in society; according to Dr. Lew it restored dignity and "Manship." Seed money, advice, and training in modern techniques were available on request. Many ex-patients found it profitable to raise pigs and chickens and to sell eggs; eventually, one-third of the pig and poultry business in Korea was in the hands of former leprosy patients.[91]

Admissions to the Wilson Leprosy Colony, except for the very old and crippled, stopped in 1963.[92] Some ex-patients were able to return to their homes, but many found it difficult to assimilate back into their former villages. A $35,000 grant helped build three resettlement villages in the PCUS area, one in North Cholla Province and two near the colony. One, named "Boyer Village" or "Po Sung Ni" for Mr. Po

A cottage in the women's village at the Leprosy Center. Photograph by Raymond Provost.

(Boyer), was built on land adjoining the colony. This mountainous land, formerly owned by the Japanese, was purchased from the government. Here, in one summer, the former patients helped build forty-eight Korean-style duplex homes, and a new church was dedicated with a membership of 100.[93] In time, these villages, because of their up-to-date medical and farming technology, had a living standard that was often higher than that of the average Korean village.[94]

Medical Supervision

Medical supervision of the colony, before the arrival in 1959 of Stanley C. Topple, M.D., was provided by physicians (Drs. Crane, Keller, Seel, Im Kyung-Yul) and resident staff of the Presbyterian Medical Center, Chonju. In 1958 Ocie Respess, M.T., from PMC, held a training session on laboratory techniques for the paramedics, and Dr. Im performed some twenty-six eye operations. Most of the medical work was done by ex-patients, who distributed drugs, cared for leprous lesions, and performed relatively simple operations such as appendectomies and amputations. Patients needing other surgery were transported to PMC where, somewhat to everyone's surprise, they were admitted to the wards without protest from other patients.

Dr. Robert Cochrane, the dynamic British leprologist who, as noted, helped pioneer the application of the new drugs for the cure of leprosy, spent a week at PMC in 1953 and gave Dr. Crane what he called a "crash course in leprosy." Dr. Cochrane encouraged Dr. Crane to begin surgery that would provide eyebrows, the loss of which was one of the dreaded signs of leprosy. This procedure involved the surgical implantation of hair from the scalp to the eyebrow area of the face. Several days before the operation, the patient was given black paper, scissors, rice paste, and a mirror, and told to cut out and paste in place the desired shape and size of the eyebrows. After much consultation with family, friends, and sundry interested observers, the patient would arrive in the operating room with a likeness of the new eyebrows in place. The procedure, which was rather simple, was eventually performed by the paramedics at the colony.

In 1953 Dr. Crane began an experimental parasite control program at the colony. Simply by using an inexpensive compost method for "curing" night soil, the percentage of patients infested with roundworms (*Ascaris*) dropped from 99 percent to 37 percent within three years. This pilot project became the model for the nationwide parasite eradication program launched with such success in 1958 by Drs. Crane and Suh Chin-Taek of Yonsei University.

Stanley C. Topple, M.D. (1959–1981)

In 1959 Dr. Stanley C. Topple, age twenty-seven and fresh out of medical school (Emory University, M.D., 1957), internship and one year of surgical residency, arrived in Korea and found the leprosy colony at a crossroads. Revolutionary and fundamental changes in the treatment of leprosy were taking place, and a new role for the colony was being defined.

Dr. Topple was the second PCUS physician assigned full-time to the Wilson Leprosy Colony, after Dr. R. M. Wilson, who had left twelve years before. Dr. Topple's first years were spent in studying the Korean language, learning about leprosy, and upgrading the medical facilities at the colony. In 1962 he married Maria (Mia) Amundsen (Oslo University Medical School, Norway, M.D., 1955), a pediatrician with the Norwegian Missionary Alliance in Seoul.

The Topples were able to enhance their knowledge and understanding of leprosy by visits in 1962 to the Hay Ling Chau Leprosarium in Hong Kong and in 1963 to the Christian Medical Center in Vellore, South India. Six months' study in India with Dr. Paul Brand influenced

Dr. Stan Topple's decision to complete his medical training in orthopedic and reconstructive surgery, whereas Dr. Mia Topple decided to
concentrate on problems of the eye and the skin.

The medical facilities at the colony were primitive: no electricity,
no running water, no heat, no nurses. Dr. Stan Topple spoke from
experience when, in later years, he expressed the belief that good
medicine could be practiced in simple conditions.[95]

The level of medical care also was primitive: poorly kept or nonexistent medical records, inadequate administration of dapsone (DDS),
poor aseptic technique, and widespread use of ineffective drugs (such
as intravenous injections of camphor and small amounts of glucose,
calcium gluconate, and sodium salicylate). There was no lack of
patients needing surgical attention, and Dr. Stan Topple was soon
removing tumors, repairing hernias, performing hemorrhoidec-
tomies, and dealing with acute gall bladders.

Because there were no inpatient facilities, patients would walk
into the operating room and climb onto the table; after surgery they
were carried to their homes where postoperative care was given by
family or friends. The lighting in the operating room was so poor that
the operating table was pushed from one window to the other in
order to get the best light; flashlights were used at critical moments.
In winter the operating room was heated with a small coal-block
stove, which was removed when ether was administered; doctors and
patients wore many layers of woolen clothes under their surgical
gowns. Dr. Oliver W. Hasselblad, head of the American Leprosy
Mission, reported in 1966, "Never have I seen such good work,
including reconstructive surgery, accomplished under more dreadful
conditions."[96]

*Dr. Stan Topple teaches a class
at the Wilson Leprosy Center.
Photograph courtesy of Clarence
G. Durham.*

Wilson Leprosy Center and Rehabilitation Hospital

Dr. Stan Topple served as the director of the Wilson Leprosy Center and Rehabilitation Hospital from 1965 until 1978, when Dr. Yoo Kyung-Un, an orthopedic surgeon, was appointed director. Dr. Topple continued as chief of orthopedic services until 1981, when he resigned and returned to the United States. Drs. Stan and Mia Topple returned to Korea for a number of short working visits before going as missionaries to Kenya to begin another orthopedic/rehabilitation program in a medically deprived area.

Dr. Yoo came from a family that had been Christian for three generations. They lived in a rural area of Ko Hung county not far from Soonchun. He attended Chun Nam University Medical School (M.D., 1960) and had residency training at the Kwangju Christian Hospital (1961). After three years' service in the army, he went to work with Dr. Van Drogenbrooke, a Belgian leprologist, at the National Leprosy Center on Sorok Island. Dr. Yoo trained for six months in reconstructive surgery at the Leprosy Research and Training Center at Karigari, India (1969) and in 1977 visited orthopedic services at several universities in the United States. He joined the staff of the Wilson Leprosy Center in 1971 and served as vice-director until he was appointed the director in 1978.

Dr. Yoo Kyung-Un became director of the Wilson Leprosy Center and Rehabilitation Hospital in 1978. Photograph courtesy of Dr. Yoo.

The program at the Wilson Leprosy Center evolved into what Dr. Stan Topple described as a pie divided into three pieces—the Leprosy Center, Mobile Leprosy Clinics (outpatients), and Rehabilitation.[97]

The Leprosy Center

The change from the colony to the center, although gradual, was not an easy process for many patients. Some dreaded losing the security of the colony and having to deal with a society in which they had experienced rejection and hostility. The establishment of resettlement villages of "cured" ex-patients helped with the transition. Drugs and medical care were provided free of charge on an outpatient basis to the people in the resettlement villages. To promote independence and self-esteem, financial aid was limited to scholarships for the education of children and was paid directly to the schools.[98]

The last exodus of patients to a resettlement village occurred in 1976 when the number of patients at the Leprosy Center dropped to about 200 persons—all old, blind, severely crippled, or terminally ill. The hospital/dispensary building, renamed Peace House, was converted into a hospice for those requiring nursing and terminal care. The census remained stable because, as old age and infirmity took their toll, former patients returned from the surrounding communities.[99] The permanent residents were encouraged to become involved with "their" hospital and came to take pride in the new developments. Residents who were able to do so regularly visited the hospital wards, singing, talking, and visiting with the patients.[100]

The logistical and administrative aspects of the work were well organized by Rev. Clarence G. Durham, who was appointed administrator of the center in 1969. Dr. Stan Topple described Durham as a "zealous, hardworking [leader] who not only oversaw the day-to-day business operations . . . such as purchasing, maintenance, and shipping, but was an excellent communicator with overseas contributors."[101] Careful attention to economic measures (good recordkeeping, wise purchasing, prompt communication, and fiscal accountability) made it possible for the leprosy center to operate at minimal expense. Clarence Durham and his wife, Ruth, made outstanding contributions to WLC.

The leprosy center program attracted many visitors, international as well as Korean. The staff spent considerable time providing tours and orientation for these visitors. Some specialists came on working trips, staying for weeks and even months. Eventually, housing was built in a beachfront area to provide pleasant accommodations for these volunteers.

A primary aim of the center was to provide training in the field of leprosy and rehabilitation. Training programs included seminars for government health workers, sessions with ex-patients from the resettlement villages (in which they were taught improved methods of agriculture and preventive health measures), instruction for families

Clarence and Ruth Durham with friends at the Wilson Leprosy Center. Photograph courtesy of Clarence G. Durham.

in the care of patients in the home setting, and rotation in reconstructive surgery for orthopedic residents (from Seoul National and Emory universities).[102] The center also held seminars for clergy and church workers on the problems of rural societies, disabled people, and persons with leprosy.[103]

Perhaps the most important type of training was that given to paramedical personnel, most of whom had once had leprosy. Because of their own experience with the disease, they were able to deal sensitively with the psychological, as well as the physical, problems of people afflicted with leprosy. The hospital relied heavily on paramedics, the "unsung heroes" (as Dr. Stan Topple called them) who managed the mobile clinic program.[104]

The Christian commitment at the heart of the program was greatly enhanced by the faith of the leprosy patients, most of whom were Christians. As Clarence Durham said, "Instead of working in a non-Christian and hostile environment, it has been a warm, healing, humbling, vibrantly Christian one."[105] Dr. Stan Topple described that environment as follows:

> Every morning before dawn, there was a large prayer meeting filling the church. At noon every day, the church bell rang and people stopped what they were doing for a time of prayer. Each day [at the hospital] was begun with a time of worship that included scripture and prayer in which the staff and leaders of the leprosy colony gathered together for 20 to 30 minutes.[106]

Mobile Clinics/Outpatient Programs

The development of mobile clinics became central to the leprosy center's commitment to the problem of leprosy in the area. These clinics spread the word that leprosy could be cured, that no one need become mutilated, and that help was available for people who carried scars. By 1983 the mobile clinic staff regularly visited some 800 patients in five counties. The incidence of the disease seemed to be under control; only ten new cases were found in 1984.[107]

Eventually the mobile clinics reached out to persons with disabilities of all kinds, identifying cases that would benefit from surgery and following up on postoperative cases. In 1976 Lloyd Auton of Greenville, South Carolina, gave the center five Honda motorbikes, which brought great joy and prestige to the paramedics as they bounced their way up remote country roads.[108]

Dr. Mia Topple, who helped run the mobile clinics/outpatient program, described the paramedics' role as follows:

> The paramedic is the main thing in our leprosy control program. He lives on the spot. It is his job to make contact, and do the examination. It's a very ticklish problem because people don't want anybody to know that they have leprosy. It is true that the stigma has lessened over the years but people still . . . want help discreetly.[109]

Outpatient clinics for skin, eye, and bone were held on specific days of the week at the Rehabilitation Hospital and in three neighboring cities—Yosu, Chinju, and Soonchun (at the clinic operated by Betty Linton). These outpatient clinics were staffed by physicians as well as paramedics.

The Chinju Clinic, a two-story outpatient facility some fifty miles away, was built in 1976 by the Korean Leprosy Association and the German Relief Association to serve as a hub for reaching the 5,299 registered leprosy patients in the neighboring province of Kyung Sang Namdo. The government asked Wilson Leprosy Center to equip, staff, and operate this facility. Peace Corps volunteers helped make this clinic become a reality.[110]

Susan Kram, a Peace Corps volunteer assigned to the Wilson Leprosy Center in the 1970s, introduced the physiotherapist skills to the mobile clinics. Using equipment readily available on the Korean market, she treated cuts, bruises, and ulcerations; demonstrated exercises for the hands and feet; and counseled patients on the importance of preventive care of eyes and extremities. She trained the paramedics and proved to them that this kind of work could be satisfactorily carried out in the absence of a registered physiotherapist. According to Dr. Stan Topple,

> We were very much struck with how the patients received this kind of instruction when mixed with a practical demonstration, particularly an American girl getting down on her knees to clean up wounded, smelly feet. This was far more effective than cold lectures.[111]

The Rehabilitation Program

The rehabilitation program at the Wilson Leprosy Center was carried on in the Rehabilitation Hospital and in the Vocational Rehabilitation School.

The centerpiece of the program was the Rehabilitation Hospital, built in 1966–67 with funds provided by Dr. Stan Topple's home church, the Decatur Presbyterian Church in Decatur, Georgia. Dr. Topple's initial plan, in keeping with his desire for an unpretentious facility, was to renovate the original primitive hospital/dispensary, but the 1964 PCUS Medical Survey Committee encouraged him to build a new, modern hospital. He commented:

> It was felt that to have a bare bones minimal building was not good planning, but tasteful lines and a well-constructed building that was easy to maintain projected a good image for the care of the crippled. ... The public perception of the handicapped and those with leprosy

was not to be related to third-class structures of medicine. After much debate and agonizing, the choice was made to stay [on the site of the 100-acre leprosy colony]. We did not want to give the impression of deserting our leprosy patients as the work turned more and more to non-leprous, crippled young people and children.[112]

The attractive well-planned, two-story, forty-bed facility with, at last, electricity, running water, and heat was primarily an orthopedic, eye, and plastic surgery hospital. The hospital was enlarged to fifty beds in 1977 with funds donated through the Medical Benevolence Foundation. Persons disabled by burns, birth defects, osteomyelitis, and polio, as well as by leprosy, were welcomed. The leprosy patients, who accounted for 7 to 10 percent, received priority and were treated at token charges. No one was turned away for lack of money.[113]

Physiotherapy

Physiotherapy at the colony/center was begun by Ruby T. Tillman, P.T, who received her training at Harvard Medical School. She served from 1963 to 1966 and was followed by Robert and Theodora Hottentot from the Netherlands, who served from 1968 to 1970. All three concentrated on building up a staff of Koreans, most of whom were ex-patients. The former Bright Star Orphanage complex was transformed into dormitories where discharged patients needing postoperative care and physiotherapy could be cared for at nominal expense by family members.

Medical Specialists

The quality of care at the hospital was enhanced by a stream of highly trained specialists from abroad who volunteered their services for weeks, and sometimes months, at a time. The fields of orthopedic, plastic, and eye surgery lent themselves to this kind of short working visits. A waiting list of more than 1,000 patients from all over the country testified to the reputation of the institution.

Among the physicians who brought their expertise to the Wilson Leprosy Center were two short-term physicians, appointed by the PCUS, who returned several times.

(Ralph) Erskine Moore (1969–71), a board-certified orthopedic surgeon from Florence, South Carolina, covered for Dr. Stan Topple while the latter completed his orthopedic training in the United States. With the help of Dr. John Wilson, who was the acting director in Dr. Topple's absence, Dr. Moore organized the orthopedic program and had it well under way when the Topples returned. Dr. Wilson, the pediatrician stationed at PMC and the son of Dr. R. M. Wilson, brought many nonleprous crippled children for Dr. Moore's attention. His family connection and Korean language skills helped get this new program going.

John C. Frist (1974–75; Washington University, M.D., 1966), the first board-certified plastic surgeon to be appointed by PCUS, summarized his work as follows:

> There is no question that a definite need exists for my particular specialty of plastic and reconstructive surgery. Although most of my work is done at the Leprosy Center, only about 35 percent of my work is involved with reconstruction of leprosy disfigurement. Burn scar contractures with their severe crippling deformities account for most of my surgical work. It seems as if these are particularly common in rural Korea and generally found in children. Congenital abnormalities such as cleft lips and severe birth marks are another area of my concern. In all of these areas the correction or improvement of severe disfigurement and the return of needed function to the patients have given me much happiness. . . . One week out of each month I travel to the other Presbyterian hospitals in Kwangju and Chonju and to the [large government leprosy colony] on the island of Sorokdo where I perform similar surgical procedures and enter into the training program for interns and residents with specialty lectures. In summary [my experience] has been much more rewarding than I ever expected.[114]

Other physicians who volunteered their services are listed below.

Paul Gieser, M.D., a board-certified ophthalmologist from Battle Creek, Michigan, made five visits of two weeks or more each at his own expense, always bringing his R.N. wife and his own scrub nurse. Dr. Gieser was the son of Dr. and Mrs. Ken Gieser, PCUS medical missionaries to China (see TKP Hospital). While in Korea he lectured at the Christian hospitals and at Yonsei University Medical School and brought their resident physicians to the leprosy center for advanced training.

Akiko Obara, M.D., leprologist, hand surgeon, and clergywoman from Japan, served for seven years (1974–81) and returned for a number of shorter working visits. She worked in the skin and eye clinics and carried on research and treatment of children, both those with leprosy and those whose parents had leprosy. Dr. Obara was supported by a group in Japan's Christian community who also, on several occasions, sent a number of dermatologists for short periods of time.

Over a period of seven years beginning in 1976 a team of British ophthalmologists, Drs. Timothy ffytche (lowercase spelling correct), Malcolm Kerr-Muir, and Peter Fison traveled to Korea to perform cataract surgery on leprosy patients.

Among others who volunteered their services were Drs. Ed Hay, an orthopedic surgeon from Charleston, South Carolina, and Robert T. Willingham, an orthopedic surgeon from Atlanta, Georgia.

Finances
A notable feature of the Rehabilitation Hospital was the determination to keep costs as low as possible. Prices were less than one-half of what they would have been at other mission hospitals and less than one-quarter of what they would have been at university hospitals.[115] Several factors contributed to accomplishing this aim:

• The leprosy center was heavily subsidized. The contribution of personnel by PCUS and the annual grants from the Korean government and the American Leprosy Mission continued as originally planned. In later years, substantial contributions were made by a number of agencies, including the British Leprosy Mission, Christoffel Blinden mission (C.B.M. of West Germany), Germany Leprosy Relief Association, American drug and supply firms, and the Medical Benevolence Foundation. The U.S. Armed Forces gave quantities of surplus equipment. Thousands of dollars' worth of supplies were contributed from abroad each year, including the bandages, gowns, and other soft goods donated by the White Cross program of the (PCUS) Women of the Church. Many of the visiting specialists left behind the equipment they had brought to work with; the eye department became especially well equipped.

• The working visits of the volunteers kept the quality of service very high at a low cost to the institution and, therefore, to the patients.

• The rural location (where living costs were less), and the early discharge of patients to the dormitory setting, kept the charges to the patients and to their families affordable; staff members, at least half of whom were ex-patients, were willing to work for lower salaries. The rural setting, however, made it difficult to recruit Korean physicians for the permanent staff because they wanted better educational opportunities for their children.

• The hospital staff were taught a variety of skills so that they might function in many different positions. This led to respect for one another's tasks and resulted in good coverage at vacation times and for sick leaves. Compared with an American hospital, much patient care was delegated to nurses and assistants, resulting in more effective use of the doctors' time. Some paramedics became very skilled in changing casts, dressing wounds, removing (simple) pins, and much of the suturing.

• The government offered the institution a tax-free status, which helped greatly with the importation of supplies.

• Careful and imaginative use of supplies stretched the medical dollar. Shrewd purchasing and buying in bulk from a number of countries resulted in tremendous savings. Cloth goods were laundered and sterilized; even bandages and gauze were reused several times so that the use of expensive disposables was limited. Bone plates and nails, needles and syringes, and many items commonly discarded after one use in the United States were thoroughly cleaned and sterilized for reuse. Disposable diapers, cut up and sterilized, were used as dressings or padding for casts; nylon fishing line served as skin sutures. Many instruments and much of the physical therapy equipment, such as braces and prostheses, were made in local machine shops.[116]

The Vocational Rehabilitation School

The Vocational Rehabilitation School, established in 1974, grew out of the realization that people with disabilities, in order to become income-producing members of society, needed not only surgical repair of physical deformities but also help in acquiring vocational and social skills. The Korean mind-set "that to be crippled in body is to be crippled in mind" caused many, especially the young, to retreat into isolation and despair, without hope of independent living.[117]

Mr. Lee Pong-Soo, from a strong sense of Christian commitment, chose to leave a successful career in a large chemical complex in southeast Korea in order to address this problem. He and his wife began a one-year school in their home for crippled young people. Up to twenty-five young people received instruction in sewing and tailoring and in the social skills they lacked. No tuition was charged, but students were expected to provide their own living expenses.

The school was highly successful, and in 1977 a building was constructed on the former mission compound in Soonchun. Students were taught vocational skills, given basic education as necessary, and instructed in personal hygiene, deportment, interpersonal relations, and the acceptance of responsibility. Fundamental to the success was the setting in a Christian home where acceptance, love, patience, and forgiveness were practiced. Most of the students became Christians before graduating.[118]

By 1983 more than 130 students had completed the course. Most were able to make a good living; some went to work in textile factories; quite a few ended up marrying a fellow student. Reunions were held annually, and the graduates formed an association that set up a revolving loan fund to help poorer students. Clearly the Vocational Rehabilitation School accomplished its purpose in preparing its young people to become productive, happy, strong members of society.[119]

Conclusion

The Wilson Leprosy Center developed a staff of Korean Christians who were dedicated to the goals and purposes of the institution and were able to carry on without the presence of missionary personnel. The Durhams' return to the United States in 1985, two years after PCUS had ceased to exist as a separate entity, brought to an end seventy-six years of PCUS missionary presence in the leprosy program in Korea.

Dr. Stan Topple and Clarence Durham continued their association with the center through the Wilson Rehabilitation Foundation, which was incorporated in Georgia in 1984 in order to provide the center with dollar bookkeeping and accounting, overseas purchases, English correspondence, and logistics for the center.

Postscript

A small number of PCUS regular service medical professionals were assigned to Korea but not to one of the three institutions just described. For the record their names are included here.

Robert Chester Patten, M.D., and Joy Blaney Patten, R.N. (1974–78), were first assigned to the Kwangju Christian Hospital but were reassigned to work at the Kojedo Community Health Project, a primary health facility of the Northern Presbyterian mission. Dr. Patten was a family practitioner and a 1954 graduate of Cornell University Medical School, New York City.

Elizabeth Ann Boyer (Betty), R.N., (1955–96) the daughter of Rev. and Mrs. Elmer T. Boyer, grew up in Chonju. After completing one term at Presbyterian Medical Center (1955–58) and one term at Kwangju Christian Hospital (1959–63), she transferred to the Korean Christian Academy (KCA) in Taejon, where she became the school nurse and dietician. She also taught classes in hygiene and public health.

Virginia Bell Somerville, R.N., the daughter of L. Nelson Bell, M.D., and a graduate of Johns Hopkins (B.S.N. 1952), grew up Huaiyin (TKP), China, and was the wife of John N. Somerville, Ph.D., professor at Han Nam University in Taejon. Her first assignment in Korea was to Mokpo (1954–58) where, as the only missionary with medical training, she had occasion to help in medical emergencies. After moving to Taejon in 1968, she used her nurse's training in the care of students at KCA and also taught health subjects. She served on numerous mission committees where her major contribution was, perhaps, her support of the medical work.

Frances D. Batemen, R.N. (Mrs. Ben H.) and *Barbara Steele,* R.N. (Mrs. P. D.) served on a short-term basis (four years) in Taejon with their husbands.

Notes

1. Much of this historical background is based on Donald S. Macdonald, *The Koreans: Contemporary Politics and Society* (Boulder & London: Westview Press, 1988), 44–50.

2. Ibid., 47.

3. Ibid., 48.

4. Forces from sixteen countries made up this command; an American general was in charge. The UN troops were forced to retreat to a small perimeter around the southern port city of Pusan, leaving most of South Korea under North Korean occupation.

5. *Encyclopedia Britannica,* vol. 13, 1969, 475.

6. David B. Barrett, ed., *World Christian Encyclopedia* (Oxford & New York: Oxford University Press, 1982), 442.

7. G. Thompson Brown, *Not By Might: A Century of Presbyterians in Korea* (Atlanta: Presbyterian Church (U.S.A.), 1984), 14.

8. G. Thompson Brown, *Mission to Korea* (Seoul, Korea: Presbyterian Church of Korea, Department of Education, 1984), 171.

9. Brown, *Not By Might,* 17.

10. Barrett, *World Christian Encyclopedia,* 441.

11. Brown, *Not By Might,* iv.

12. Barrett, *World Christian Encyclopedia,* 442–45.

13. Laurence Simpson, M.D., letter, April 1987.

14. Seven of the eighteen nurses were married; their primary responsibility was to their homes. Some worked part-time in the medical institutions and were the source of strong support in mission meetings and on mission committees.

15. David J. Seel, M.D., *Challenge and Crisis in Missionary Medicine* (Pasadena, Calif.: William Carey Library, 1979).

16. Ronald B. Dietrick, M.D., *Modern Medicine and the Mission Mandate: Thoughts on Christian Medical Missions* (Woodville, Tex.: Medical Benevolence Foundation, 1984).

17. Brown, *Mission to Korea,* 171.

18. The first PMC interns were Drs. Lee Kyung-Yul, Kim Young-U, Im Kyung-Yul, and Song Kyung-Jin.

19. Ovid B. Bush, M.D. and Paul S. Crane, M.D., "Treatment of *Clonorchis scinensis* with Chloroquine and Methiscol," *Transactions of the Royal Society of Tropical Medicine and Hygiene,* vol. 49, 1955, 68–70.

20. Nursing School, $50,000; hospital, $80,000.

21. Brown, *Mission to Korea,* 194.

22. Ibid., 195.

23. PMC Report, *Minutes of the Ad Interim Committee,* Dec. 1961, 17.

24. Brown, *Mission to Korea,* 197.

25. Maj. Paul Crane served as chief of surgery at the 121st Evacuation Hospital near Seoul and as commanding officer of the 44th M.A.S.H. unit (of television fame). American officials often called on his proficiency in the Korean language and understanding of the Korean culture. In 1961, 1965, and 1966, he served as the interpreter for Presidents John F. Kennedy and Lyndon B. Johnson on four state visits in their meetings with President Park Chung-Hee.

26. Elmer T. Boyer, *To Build Him a House* (Seoul, Korea: Posung Press, 1976).

27. Paul S. Crane, M.D., "An Unresolved Problem for Developing Countries: Korea as Exhibit A," *JAMA,* vol. 29, 1969, 2039.

28. Margaret Pritchard, R.N., "The Life Story of Margaret Frances Pritchard," typescript, 1980, 86.

29. David J. Seel, M.D., interviews, April 1988, March 1996.

30. L. Nelson Bell, M.D., report to "Members of the Korea Mission," 1956.

31. John Wilson, interview, October 1984.

32. Merrill Grubbs, interview, March 1984.

33. Survey Committee, *Report*, April 1964, 6.

34. PMC, "Investment in Healing," 1971, 14.

35. In 1987, Dr. Y. T. Chung, an ophthalmologist, was appointed hospital director. Dr. Seel served as director of the medical center (an honorary position) until his retirement in 1990.

36. PMC Annual Reports.

37. Pritchard, "The Life Story," 85.

38. Ruth Folta, R.N., correspondence, April 1986.

39. PMC Annual Reports.

40. Grubbs, interview, March 1984.

41. This interest in research led in 1986 to the building of PMC's Christian Medical Research Institute. Researchers from the United States, including David Talmage, M.D., a former dean of the University of Colorado School of Medicine and Neville Sue Rapp, Ph.D., a biochemist from Washington University, took part in this program.

42. Grubbs, interview, March 1984; Christian Medical Research Center, *Fairness and Economy in Health Care: Community Oriented Health and Education Program in a Rural Area in South Korea* (Chonju, Korea, 1987), 7–9, 65.

43. Brown, *Mission to Korea*, 197.

44. Virginia K. Cumming, R.N., interview, April 1990.

45. Ronald Dietrick, M.D., correspondence, March 1996.

46. Annual Report, Board of World Missions, 1956, 114.

47. Astrid Kraakenes, R.N. (1955–59), took discharge from the Norwegian Medical Unit in Korea in order to, in her words, "do" mission work.

48. Brown, *Mission to Korea*, 215–16.

49. Laurence Simpson, M.D., letter, April 27, 1987.

50. John M. McBryde, interview, June 1990.

51. Simpson, letter, April 1987; Dietrick, correspondence, March 1996.

52. Annual Report, 1961, 106.

53. Ibid., 1962, 106.

54. "This Gift of Love," *Report* (Nashville, Tenn.: Board of World Missions, 1973), 19.

55. Survey Committee, *Report*, April 1964.

56. Dietrick, correspondence, March 1996.

57. Huh Chin-Duk, Chunam University, Kwangju (M.D., 1956); Massachusetts General Hospital, Boston, internal medicine resident (1960–63); Massachusetts Memorial, Boston, fellowship (1963–64); University of Texas at Dallas (1974–75).

58. Dietrick, correspondence, March 1986.

59. Alfred Bridgman, M.D., interview, 1986.

60. Kim Ki-Bok, Chunam University (M.D., 1958); University Children's Hospital, Freiburg, Germany (1960–63); University of Rochester, N.Y. (genetics, 1972–73). Dr. Kim became the director of KCH when Dr. Huh retired in the 1990s.

61. Ronald B. Dietrick, M.D., curriculum vitae.

62. McBryde, interview, June 1990.

63. Dietrick, correspondence.

64. *Korea Mission Report*, 1978, 71, 75; Dick H. Nieusma, interview, Dec. 1989.

65. Brown, *Mission to Korea*, 267.

66. *Korea Mission Report*, 1973, 6–8.

67. Ibid., 1976, 1.

68. Ibid., 1977, 12.

69. Brown, *Mission to Korea*, 267.

70. *Korea Mission Report*, 1974, 2.

71. Dietrick, correspondence.

72. Ibid.

73. Ibid.

74. *Korea Mission Report*, 1975.

75. Dick H. Nieusma, D.D.S., interview, Dec. 1984.

76. Ibid.

77. Dwight Linton, phone contact, March 1996.

78. C. Betts Huntley, interview, 1990; his dissertation for the doctor of ministry degree was titled "A Balanced, Participatory Model for the Minister's Role and Function in Pastoral Counseling/Care in Korea," Columbia Theological Seminary, Sept. 1985.

79. *Korea Mission Reports*, 1981, 17.

80. Huntley, interview, March 1990.

81. Hu Chin-Duk, *Korea Mission Reports*, 1981, 17.

82. Carol Cameron Shaw, "The Wilson Leprosy Center and Rehabilitation Hospital," typescript, 1976, 113.

83. Anthony Bryceson and Roy E. Pfaltzgraff, *Leprosy* (New York: Churchill Livingstone, 1990), 77–79.

84. Joon Lew, "MDT and the Role of People: Experience in Korea," (paper presented in Beijing, China, at the Asia/Pacific Regional Conference on Rehabilitation, October 26–31, 1990), 2–3.

85. Lew, "MDT," 1.

86. Bryceson and Pfaltzgraff, *Leprosy*, 138–39.

87. Quoted in ibid., 139.

88. Shaw, "The Wilson Leprosy Center," 120–21.

89. Boyer, *To Build Him a House*, 12.

90. Ibid., 12.

91. Joon Lew, *A Korean Model for the Healing of Leprosy* (Seoul, Korea: Lew Institute for Biological Research, 1993), 46.

92. Clarence G. Durham, interview, 1986.

93. Boyer, *To Build Him a House*, 164, 173.

94. Lew, *A Korean Model*, 54.

95. Shaw, "The Wilson Leprosy Center," 113.

96. Ibid., 97.

97. Ibid., 70.

98. Ibid., 99.

99. Durham, interview, Jan. 1986.

100. Stanley C. Topple, M.D., "Lessons from a Korean Experience in Rehabilitation Mission Work," typescript, c. 1985, 5.

101. Ibid., 9.

102. Ibid., 6–7.

103. Durham, interview, Jan. 1986.

104. Shaw, "The Wilson Leprosy Center," 100.

105. Durham, interview, Jan. 1986.

106. Topple, "Lessons," 1.

107. Durham, interview, Jan. 1986.

108. Shaw, "The Wilson Leprosy Center," 100.

109. Ibid., 109.

110. *Korea Mission Report*, 1978, 41.

111. Shaw, "The Wilson Leprosy Center," 101.

112. Topple, "Lessons," 2.

113. Durham, interview, Jan. 1986.

114. Annual Report, 1975, 68.

115. Topple, *Lessons*, 7.

116. Ibid., 3–9.

117. Ibid., 11.

118. Ibid., 11–12.

119. *Wilson Leprosy Center Annual Report*, 1984.

PART III
Belgian Congo/Zaire

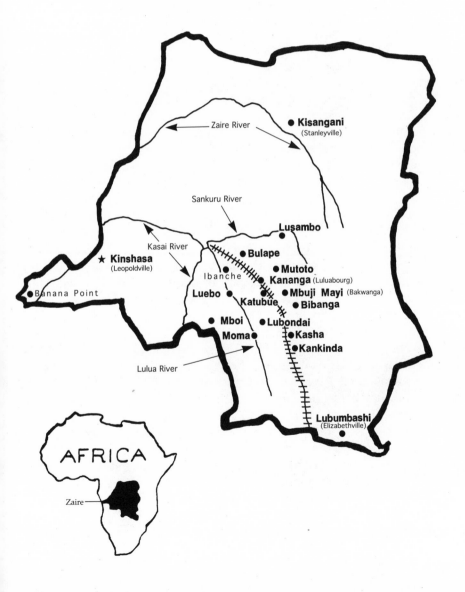

Chapter Seven

Belgian Congo (1906–1960)

Threte history of the PCUS in the Belgian Congo/Zaire divides into two distinct periods: one dominated by Belgian colonial power, the other under Zairian rule. The Belgian period began in 1885 and ended with "independence" in 1960; the Zairian, from 1960 to the present (1983). Technically the word *Zaire* did not come into general use until after President Mobutu Sese Seko came into power in 1971, but it is used in this history to mark the break from colonial to independent status.[1]

The Belgian Congo/Zaire occupies an area in central Africa about one-third the size of the United States. This area was virtually unknown to the people of the West until, between 1874 and 1877, Henry M. Stanley, the American journalist, made his exploratory journey down the mighty Congo River and gained fame for his classic greeting, "Dr. Livingston, I presume," when they finally met at Ujiji on the banks of Lake Tanganyika.

Stanley followed this second-longest river in Africa (fifth longest in the world, with a volume of flow per second exceeded only by the Amazon River) from its eastern origins until it roars off the continental shelf some 300 miles before reaching the Atlantic Ocean. Two hundred miles of cataracts, from Léopoldville (Kinshasa) to Matadi, hampered exploration of the interior and effectively protected the region from Western curiosity and exploitation.

Stanley's explorations created great interest and excitement in the West, nowhere more so than in the mind of King Leopold II of Belgium. King Leopold II, who reigned from 1865 to 1909, was determined that Belgium, like other European nations of the time, become a colonial power. Stanley entered the service of King

Leopold II in 1878 and continued his explorations until 1884. He launched steamers on the rivers, signed treaties with African chiefs, established the city of Léopoldville (Kinshasa), and surveyed a road around the cataracts. This road connected the estuary to what came to be called Stanley Pool where Léopoldville is located.

Congo Free State (1885–1908)

King Leopold II failed to gain support from the Belgian government or the Belgian people for his colonial adventures. He did, however, obtain authorization to act in a private capacity. The Berlin West African Conference, meeting in February 1885, recognized his International Association of the Congo (*Association Internationale du Congo*) as an independent state. In April 1885 the Belgian chambers authorized the king to become sovereign of this state on an exclusively personal basis and at his own expense.

In July 1885 the new state, King Leopold's private domain, took the name Congo Free State (*État Indépendant du Congo*). Its king and its administration remained in Brussels. King Leopold II pledged to abolish slavery, establish religious freedom, and encourage free trade. His administration eradicated the Arab slave trade (but not domestic slavery) and allowed Catholics and Protestants to establish mission work. Lacking adequate financial resources to develop a profitable economy, King Leopold leased large concessions to trading companies, which, in collusion with the government, scandalized international public opinion by using forced labor to harvest rubber and ivory. Outrage over this excessive brutality eventually forced the Belgian government to annex the colony. In November 1908 King Leopold II relinquished sovereignty, and the Congo Free State became the Belgian Congo (*Congo Belge*). Reforms were immediately initiated and, although years passed before the major abuses were stamped out, the Belgian Congo came to be considered one of the best governed colonies in Africa.[2]

Belgian Congo (1908–1960)

The Belgian system of colonial government was distinguished by two characteristics: (1) a high degree of centralization with administration based in Brussels, and (2) paternalism, viewed as a sensible, and indeed noble, concept best summed up in the phrase *dominer pour servir* (to dominate in order to serve).[3]

By the 1920s the Belgians no longer looked on the Congo "as a mere field of adventure and a country to be exploited, but as a land of primitive people to whom the government owed protection and care, a colony to be settled and developed."[4] The cruelties of the rubber and ivory trade disappeared; intertribal warfare was suppressed; slavery and cannibalism were abolished; human sacrifice and the poison ordeal (determination of guilt by the administration of the poison cup) were outlawed. Tribal chiefs continued to administer local affairs according to tribal custom.

The discovery of major deposits of copper, cobalt, tin, uranium, and industrial diamonds meant that mining replaced rubber and ivory as the principal sources of revenue. The colonial government regulated mining practices to protect the laborer from inhumane exploitation, but profits reverted largely to Belgian corporations or to the Belgian government.

Steamers plied the rivers. Transportation progressed from hammock (litter borne by muscular young men), to bicycle, to motorcycle, to auto and truck, to railway, to the airplane. Animal power (horses, donkeys, mules, or oxen) was not used because of sleeping sickness carried by the tsetse fly. A railroad was built around the cataracts from the port of Matadi to Léopoldville; another connected the Congo River system to the Cairo/Capetown railroad line; and a third crossed the southern Katanga Province to Lobito in Angola. Roads began to replace forest trails, bridges and ferries facilitated river crossings, and, in later years, air travel connected the larger towns. Electricity, radio, telegraph, and postal services were introduced.

The Belgians attempted to educate the whole population by starting with elementary school for all and then bringing in secondary schools and then university. This policy was adopted in an effort to avoid what was perceived as a British mistake in concentrating on the education of the upper classes.[5] Literacy on the elementary school level was outstanding among African colonies. However, few secondary schools existed before independence, and the first Congolese to receive a college degree graduated from a Belgian university in 1956. In 1954 the Catholics founded the first university, Lovanium University near Léopoldville; in 1955 the state opened a university in Elizabethville. At the time of independence, only a handful of Congolese (twelve to thirty, accounts vary) had university degrees.[6]

The Belgians adopted a colonial policy that envisaged the development of self-rule over a period of many years. Part of this policy was to withhold the vote from Congolese and European settlers alike until the Congolese could be trained in self-rule. No elected legislative council existed in the colony until 1957 when municipal elections were first held in the major towns.

The occupation of Belgium by Germany during World War II disrupted colonial policies in the Belgian Congo. The following decade (1948–58) was one of impressive progress and included new initiatives aimed at improving life for the Congolese: a ten-year plan (*Plan Décennal*) saw the investment of government funds in various economic projects; the Native Welfare Fund (*Fonds du Bien-Être Indigène* or FBEI) financed schools, hospitals, dispensaries, and agricultural projects; the King's Fund (*Le Fond du Roi*) assisted with housing; social welfare programs were expanded. As one of the missionaries wrote in 1971, "In the 1950s [Belgian Congo] possessed easily the most sophisticated economic and social-welfare structure to be found on the African continent and was generally viewed as a model colony."[7]

Unfortunately, the Belgian colonial policy in which everything was done *for* the Congolese *by* the Belgians did not meet the rising aspirations of the Congolese. The pace of nationalism in Africa failed to follow the timetable envisaged by the European colonials. By 1959 the Belgian government realized it was about to lose control of the colony and concluded that it would be fruitless to attempt to curb Congolese nationalism. On June 30, 1960, the Belgian parliament abruptly granted independence to the Belgian Congo.[8]

The PCUS in the Belgian Congo (1890–1960)

In 1861 the first General Assembly of the recently established Southern Presbyterian Church (PCUS) affirmed the goal of a missionary outreach and directed the church especially to Africa and South America as suitable fields for missionary endeavor. Dr. John Leighton Wilson, the first secretary of foreign missions (1861–77), had served in Africa (in Liberia and Gabon) for some twelve years and was eager to implement this directive. However, almost thirty years passed before the first missionaries embarked to establish the mission in Africa.

The Pioneers

In May 1890, twenty-three-year-old Samuel Norvell Lapsley and twenty-four-year-old William Henry Sheppard (the first of twelve black missionaries appointed during the pioneer period), landed at Banana Point at the mouth of the Congo River to begin what was to become the largest PCUS mission in the world. This mission was known as the American Presbyterian Congo Mission (APCM) and is here referred to in this way until the time of independence.

Samuel Lapsley, a descendent of a prosperous family of slave-owners in Anniston, Alabama, was an honor graduate of the University of Alabama. He received his B.D. in 1889 from McCormick Seminary in Chicago. William Sheppard, the son of former slaves, was born near Waynesboro, Virginia. He received his education at Hampton Institute in Hampton, Virginia, and Stillman Institute in Tuscaloosa, Alabama, where he graduated in 1884. After ordination, Sheppard served black churches in Montgomery, Alabama, and Atlanta, Georgia.

Twenty-two months after their arrival in Africa, Lapsley died from "bilious hematuric fever" (a severe form of *falciparum* malaria, also called "black water fever"). During those twenty-two months, however, this remarkable pair explored various options and selected the Kasai area for the PCUS missionary work. They obtained permission to open the first APCM mission station at Luebo, a remote trading post. After Lapsley's death, Sheppard continued his missionary service until 1910.

Rev. William Sheppard, with Rev. William Morrison, played a significant role in the campaign for reform that brought an end to the Congo Free State and brought Belgian colonial rule to the area. In the Kasai, the authorities had employed members of the Zappo Zapp, an aggressive cannibal group, to collect tribute and to force reluctant laborers to harvest the rubber. The Zappo Zapp resorted to cruel and inhumane practices that included murder, rape, pillage, chopping off hands, slave taking, and cannibalism. Sheppard and Morrison documented these events in articles, letters, and lectures that received international attention. In 1909 the two men were tried for libel against the *Compagnie du Kasai*. The trial, in which both men were vindicated, was widely publicized and contributed substantially to the reform movement.[9]

The Kasai and Its People

The Kasai area proved a wise choice for the location of the mission. The Kasai is on a high central plateau that is drained by the Kasai River, a major tributary of the Congo River. Tributaries of the river provide access into the region. With an altitude of 2,000 to 3,000 feet, the Kasai, although only a few degrees south of the equator, has pleasant weather. The mean temperature is in the mid-seventies, and the seasons vary from wet to dry rather than from hot to cold. Rain forests stretch across the northern Kasai and along the rivers; the south opens up to savanna land. Much of the area was as yet unexplored.

The choice of Luebo also proved to be fortunate. Located at the upper reaches of navigation some 900 miles from Léopoldville, Luebo became a river port providing access into the Kasai. A small Belgian trading post (*Compagnie du Kasai*) had recently been established on the southern bank of the river; the missionaries chose a site on a hill on the north bank.

More than 200 different ethnic groups populate the Belgian Congo. When carving out their colonies, European countries made no attempt to preserve ethnic integrity. For example, the Kongo tribe, from whom the country got its name, is to be found along the lower stretches of the Congo River and across northern Angola. Ethnic identities, language, and rivalries are very strong, and they remain an important element in the turbulent history of the region.

Sheppard estimated the population of the Kasai at about two million, one of the more densely populated areas of the Congo.[10] At first the APCM worked mostly with three ethnic groups: the Lulua, the Luba, and the Kuba and then with a number of smaller tribes including the Kete, the Bindi, and the Sala Mpasu (this last practiced cannibalism). Eventually the missionaries also contacted the Pygmies, who lived in the northern rain forests. The population was widely scattered in villages; there were no towns or cities.

The three main ethnic groups were very different. The *Lulua* were the most numerous and occupied the largest area. They were organized into clans but lacked a strong centralized government. Traditionally the men were hunters and warriors, while the women did agriculture. All were generally small in stature.

The *Luba* had flooded into Lulua territory in order to escape frequent raids by slave traders. They were tall, strong, intelligent, diligent, energetic, and ambitious; and they took advantage of the educational opportunities provided by the mission. Many found responsible positions in mission institutions, government, and trade. Both the Lulua and the Luba responded enthusiastically to the Christian gospel. Conflict between these two ethnic groups became a serious problem following independence.

The *Kuba* were a fascinating group who had a highly organized central government and ruled over many unrelated peoples. They were famous for their skills in ivory and wood carving, iron work, weaving, basketry, and embroidery. Proud and conservative, they had no desire to change their traditional customs. They tried to avoid contact with outsiders but were cruelly victimized during the Congo Free State period of forced labor. Their relationship with the APCM is discussed later.

The Tshiluba (che-lu-bah) language was relatively common among all the ethnic groups of the Kasai area. A major contribution of William Morrison was to put the Tshiluba language into writing, compile a dictionary and grammar, and, by 1903, begin translation of the Bible. Under Belgian rule, French became a necessary second language for the Congolese, as well as for the missionaries.

Black American Missionaries

It is interesting to note that eleven of the thirty-one missionaries appointed prior to 1908 were black. The Belgian government, after taking control, viewed them as potential troublemakers and subversives, and made it difficult for the black missionaries to get visas to enter the country. None were forced to leave, but, with one exception, no black missionaries were assigned to the Belgian Congo from 1908 until after World War II. Edna May Atkinson, the exception, entered the colony in 1923 to marry Rev. Adolphus A. Rochester.

During a time of racial inequality and discrimination in the United States, these black missionaries, despite some problems, received comparable pay, had an equal voice in mission affairs, and worked under the same rules as their white missionary counterparts. Their names follow:

William H. Sheppard, 1890–1910
Lucy Gantt Sheppard, 1894–1910
Henry P. Hawkins, 1894–1910

Maria Fearing, 1894–1915
Joseph E. Phipps, 1895–1908
Althea Brown (Mrs. Edmiston), 1902–37
L. A. DeYampert, 1902–18
Lillian Thomas (Mrs. DeYampert), 1894–18
Alonzo L. Edmiston, 1903–41
Adolphus A. Rochester, 1906–39
Annie Kate Taylor (Mrs. Rochester), 1906–14
Edna May Atkinson (Mrs. Rochester), 1923–39[11]

The American Presbyterian Congo Mission (APCM)

The American Presbyterian Congo Mission (APCM) was the largest of some forty Protestant missions serving in the Belgian Congo.[12] It was recognized in missionary circles as "one of the most successful missionary enterprises in Africa"[13] and as "one of the three great missions of Africa, judged either by the size or quality of the work being done."[14] Luebo, the "mother" station of the mission, remained the center of the APCM work until after World War II.

The first fifteen years in the Kasai were precarious, with death and disease taking a heavy toll of both the missionaries and their children; in fact, six out of twenty-four missionaries (25 percent) died. Moreover, by exposing the cruel labor practices of the rubber companies, the APCM missionaries incurred the government's hostility. Catholic missionaries also pressured the (predominantly Catholic) government officials to limit the activities of the Protestants.

The fact that the mission was concentrated in Luebo, however, proved beneficial in many ways. Luebo became a magnet for many Congolese, mainly from the Lulua and Luba ethnic groups. A village with a migratory but relatively stable population of some 10,000 persons grew up around the station. These villagers, who thronged the church sheds, schools, and catechumen classes, were eager to *learn* and soon expressed an eagerness to *teach*. As a result the mission emphasized the translation and printing of literature and the training of native evangelists. These evangelists became the primary messengers to far-flung villages, and their efforts promoted the formation of an indigenous church.

Until Belgian colonial rule was established, Luebo had been a center for the slave trade. The missionary community purchased the

A Legacy Remembered

freedom of many slave children and helped adult slaves obtain their freedom. Liberated slaves made up a large proportion of the village surrounding Luebo; many of the slaves were Luba.

In 1897 the APCM won reluctant permission from the Belgian authorities to open Ibanche station. Ibanche, some thirty-five miles from Luebo, bordered the territory of the elusive, mysterious Kuba people whom Lapsley and Sheppard sought to contact. Once established, Ibanche was, instead, flooded by the Lulua and the Luba.

By 1912 as relations with the Belgian colonial government improved, restrictions were eased and permission to open a number of new stations was granted. An influx of new missionaries and new financing ushered in a period of increased activity. A total of seven stations were founded (see Table 7-1).

Ibanche was replaced by Bulape in 1915, and Lusambo, a port city on the Sankuru River, was turned over to the Plymouth Brethren mission in 1925 so that Lubondai might be opened in a more central site. Mutoto and Lubondai were in traditional Lulua territory; Bibanga, far to the east, was in Luba country; Bulape served the Kuba. Luebo, because of its location as a trading center (including the slave trade), had a mixture of ethnic groups.

Each of the mission's stations resembled a self-contained village with its complement of schools for boys, for girls, and for evangelists, and a hospital with an outlying leprosy village. Trees, gardens, and tennis courts made the stations parklike oases in an undeveloped land. Each station acquired unique features depending on its location and on the personalities of its leaders. The ethnic makeup of the area was also a major influence.

In the 1920s the Belgians set up a Commission for the Protection of Africans, which was made up of civilians and included both Catholic and Protestant missionaries. Some APCM missionaries served on it.

Table 7-1			
APCM Stations			
Luebo	1891	Bulape	1915
Ibanche	1897–15	Bibanga	1917
Mutoto	1912	Lubondai	1925
Lusambo	1913–25		

The state expected the missions to act as partners in what was called "civilizing work" in the fields of education, science, and medicine. In the commission's view, the indigenous people had a "culture" but lacked "civilization."[15] Many missionaries came to support the aims of the Belgian regime, and some served in official capacities. Vernon Anderson served as school inspector of mission schools, and Dr. Eugene Kellersberger, one of the pioneer physicians, served as a district medical officer.

The Great Depression and World War II caused the mission to retrench. It became difficult to keep the mission adequately supplied with personnel and supplies during wartime. An outbreak of sleeping sickness and malaria among the missionaries further depleted the work force.

Post–World War II to Independence

The decade following World War II (1948–58) was for the APCM, as it was for the Belgian colonial government, a time of expansion, of ambitious long-range programs, and of great expectations.[16] The church in the United States experienced remarkable growth and renewed its interest in overseas missions. Funds became available for capital improvements, and an influx of young missionaries brought new ideas and energy.

Relations between the mission and the colonial government continued to improve, and tension between Catholics and Protestants eased. In 1946 state subsidies were granted to Protestant schools and hospitals. With the subsidies came the necessity of meeting government standards and regulations.

The Belgian government required educational and medical missionaries to spend time in Belgium before going to the Belgian Congo. In 1948 the Board of World Missions began to assign all new missionaries to a year in Belgium. Medical personnel took a course in tropical medicine. All studied French and received orientation in Belgian colonial policies and practices.[17]

Education remained a major focus for the mission. Secondary schools were established in Kakinda (1954) and, in cooperation with the Methodist Church, in Katubue (1957). Medical education advanced through the founding (1954) of the Institut Médical Chrétien du Kasai/Christian Medical Institute of the Kasai (IMCK). Plans for a Protestant university were under discussion.

In 1925 the capital of the Kasai moved from Lusambo to Luluabourg (Kananga), whose central location on the railroad provided easy access to the whole area. Luluabourg gradually replaced Luebo as the administrative center for the mission.

Communication and transportation improved immensely. By 1946 all the mission's stations were connected by radio transmitters. Ham radios provided regular contact with church leaders (and others) in the United States. Air service connected Luluabourg and Léopoldville. In the 1950s mission-piloted planes came into use. Each station had an airfield capable of handling the small planes.

Work expanded into a number of new locations. Kasha, Mboi, and Kankinda, which began as small "gospel centers," evolved into regular stations with day schools, homes for boys and girls, evangelistic schools, dispensaries, and missionary residences. At the request of the government, the APCM took over the well-built facilities at Moma from the Four Square Gospel Mission when that group closed operations in the Congo. Urban work, following the migration of the population to the cities, was begun in Luluabourg (Kananga), Bakwanga (Mbuji Mayi), and Léopoldville (Kinshasa). Katubwe became the site of the APCM's first senior high school.

Table 7-2 APCM Expands Its Work			
Kasha	1935	Kankinda	1948
Mboi	1937	Léopoldville	1955
Moma	1942	Bakwanga	1956
Luluaburg	1946	Katubwe	1957

Although the churches in the Kasai had been largely self-governing for some time, it was during the 1940s and 1950s that Congolese participation in mission, station, and departmental meetings and councils increased; Congolese served on the boards of institutions. The Presbyterian Church of the Kasai, as an entity independent of the APCM, had its birth on November 2, 1959.

The remarkable growth of the Christian faith in Africa is a major phenomenon of the twentieth century.[18] It is indeed surprising that, despite its close association with Western colonial power, the Christian religion should take root as it did. Christian missions in Africa have been harshly criticized for their ties to colonial regimes. Some of this criticism may be warranted, but final judgment will have to be made in the context of the history of the twentieth century.

Missionaries sought to improve the quality of life of the indigenous people. Life expectancy was low because of unhygienic living conditions, poor nutrition, tribal warfare, and traditional practices such as slavery, twin-murder, human sacrifice, cannibalism, and the administration of the poison cup to determine guilt. Education, modern medicine, and the introduction of Christian ethics were perceived as necessary ingredients for improvement.

Missionaries fought against the evils of colonialism and unbridled imperialism. Although they unashamedly identified European civilization with the Christian message and were generally unopposed to the underlying concepts of imperialism, they severely criticized colonial abuses. The APCM's exposure of the unprincipled labor practices of the Congo Free State reflected their commitment to basic justice for the Congolese.

Missionaries believed in the spiritual equality before God of peoples of all colors and races. By late twentieth century standards, some of the missionary attitudes might be judged racist but they differed significantly from the cultural norms of their time.

A number of missionaries became experts on various aspects of Congolese culture. Among the Ph.D. theses with African themes were Vernon Anderson's "Witchcraft in Africa, A Missionary Problem," and Kathryn Nelson's "Child Rearing Patterns in a Lulua Village of South Central Congo." Books by missionaries include: Winifred K. Vass, *In the Bantu Vernacular: Tshiluba of Zaire, Africa, The Bantu-Speaking Heritage of the United States, Doctor Not Afraid,* and (with Dr. Joseph Holloway), *The African Heritage of American English;* Virginia G. Pruitt and Winifred K. Vass, *A Textbook of the Tshiluba Language;* Conway T. Wharton, *The Leopard Hunts Alone;* David McLean, *Sons of Muntu;* Virginia Holladay (edited by Louise Crane), *Bantu Tales;* Winifred K. and Lachlan C. Vass III, *The Lapsley Saga.* Dr. John Miller's collection of snakes form the core of the Smithsonian Institution's collection of the snakes of Central Africa.

The PCUS Medical Program in the Belgian Congo (1906–1960)

The medical program of the APCM in the Belgian Congo prior to independence has four distinct periods: (1) the first eight years (1906–14) when Llewellyn J. Coppedge, M.D., was the only missionary physician in the Kasai area; (2) the five-hospital period (1914–30), during which hospitals were built in each of the mission's five stations; (3) stagnation and recession caused by the Great Depression and World War II (1930–45); and (4) a productive postwar period (1946–60) in which the medical work shared the mission's exuberant renewal in personnel, support, and initiatives.

The First Eight Years (1906–14)

The APCM medical program had a slow start in the Belgian Congo. Llewellyn J. Coppedge, M.D., arrived fifteen years after the landing of Sheppard and Lapsley. Dr. Coppedge has the distinction of pioneering the PCUS medical work in two countries: the Belgian Congo in 1906 and Mexico in 1920.

The pioneer APCM missionaries to the Congo responded to the plight of the sick and dying as best they could. Both Lapsley and Sheppard are reported to have shared their medicines with those in need. Rev. DeWitt Snyder (1892–1901), a pharmacist, operated a small dispensary in a thatched mud building in Luebo. Rev. Lucius DeYampert (1902–18), who had studied for two years with a doctor in Selma, Alabama, set up an isolation village for victims of smallpox. Althea Brown Edmiston (1902–37), a graduate of Fisk University who is remembered for her outstanding work in education and her compilation of a grammar and dictionary in the Kuba language, had charge of a dispensary in Ibanche. She later provided medical coverage in Bulape over a six-month period

Llewellyn Coppedge, M.D., pioneered the PCUS medical work in both the Belgian Congo (1906) and Mexico (1921) Photograph courtesy of Elsa Coppedge Thomas.

when there was no other medical person there and also assisted Dr. King in Mutoto.[19] Joseph G. Prichard (1909–13) is listed as a dentist, but apparently spent his time in administrative work, including a period as captain of the SS *Lapsley*, the mission's river steamer.

The primary motivation for starting medical work in the Belgian Congo stemmed from concern for the health of the missionaries in Africa's unhealthy environment. Although the APCM was located in the relatively healthful Kasai region, seven of the first eight missionaries died on duty or resigned for health reasons. This heavy toll is a shocking reminder of the dedication of the pioneers.

The toll among children was so high that most parents left their children with relatives or friends in the United States. A child born in the Congo would be left behind in the States after the next furlough. Dr. Thomas T. Stixrud, the fiercely independent physician who joined Dr. Coppedge in 1914, insisted on keeping his children with him, and, at their annual meetings, the missionaries whose children were in the States regularly took note of the continued robust health of the Stixrud children. The Stixrud children's health encouraged other families to keep their children with them, and in 1926 the mission opened a school to meet the needs of the growing number of missionary children.

Service in the Belgian Congo was limited to three years for the first term and four years thereafter—compared with terms of six, seven, and eight years in Asia. The short terms resulted in the reduction by one-fifth of the missionary force each year and created problems in maintaining coverage, especially in the institutions.

The health situation dramatically improved in 1919, when the Women of the Church of the PCUS undertook to provide better housing for the missionaries. Screened brick and concrete homes replaced the ones made of mud and sticks, permanent roofing took the place of thatch, and indoor plumbing and electricity were eventually installed. Cows (and sometimes goats) and gardens provided better nutrition. The famous Crosley "icy ball" refrigerator, an ingenious invention using heating and cooling ammonia in a pair of steel globes, was in use in the 1920s; later, the kerosene refrigerator gave excellent service.

The mental health of the missionaries was also at risk, partly because of the isolation of the stations, which were, on average, some 100 miles apart. For many years they could be reached only by days of travel on foot or hammock. Outside contact was rare and mail uncertain. The establishment in the mid-1920s of a rest and recreation retreat at a central location on the shores of beautiful Lake Munkamba contributed immeasurably to the physical and mental well-being of the missionary force.

At first, the Congolese were indifferent to Western medicine. Health problems were the domain of the village witch doctor, who was concerned with determining "who" rather than "what" was the cause of the problem. Illness, like other catastrophes, was thought to be caused by hostile spirits or by some hostile person. The witch doctor, after divining the cause, would recommend appropriate "magic." As previously noted, *Ngangabuka*, the title given missionary physicians, was the same as that for the witch doctor. As Jean Shive, R.N., expressed it, "Many felt the missionaries, like the witch doctor, had a 'magic' and could cure if they were only willing to."[20]

The missionary physician was always in competition with the local witch doctor, as Dr. William Rule pointed out:

> One cannot practice medicine in Central Africa . . . without feeling the proximity of the spirit world. Indeed one must deal with the practical aspects of such a world since it exists in the mind of one's patient, as well as in the minds of the African people. They generally accept the existence of a mighty God, the Creator, who is one person with dominion over everything, but he is distant and relatively inaccessible. The spirit world which is intimately about them is more meaningful and of practical import in their daily lives. The spirits are of the departed dead and they may be friendly and benevolent or capricious or often downright hostile and diabolical in their treatment. . . . The spirit world is in every rock and tree; in every event from harvesting manioc to a clap of thunder. The physician deals with this kind of atmosphere almost daily, in the minds and lives of the people he encounters.[21]

Dr. Coppedge arrived with little more than his black bag. Seven years passed before he was joined by Ethel Fair, R.N., the first nurse. His practice could be said to resemble that of the "horse and buggy doctor," except that he had no horse or buggy. He dealt as best he could with all who came to him for help.

As the only Western physician within 1,000 miles, Dr. Coppedge's practice included government officials, traders, and Catholic priests. In 1911 King Albert of Belgium honored Dr. Coppedge by making him a knight of the Royal Order of the Lion for his "devoted and distinguished service to His Majesty's subjects, both European and African." *The Missionary Survey* reported:

> Our first medical missionary to Africa was Dr. L. J. Coppedge who went out in 1906. His work was not so much needed there as a door-opener, for the doors were already open when he went. But it was desperately needed as a means of protecting the health of the missionaries. It has also been the means of revolutionizing the attitudes of the state officials, and the trading companies toward our work.[22]

The Five Hospitals Period

The five hospitals period (1914–1930) began when the Belgian colonial authorities finally granted permission for the mission to open a number of stations across the Kasai. Within a two-year period three missionary physicians were appointed: Thomas T. Stixrud in 1914, Robert R. King in 1915, and Eugene R. Kellersberger in 1916.

The hospitals that were eventually built in each of the five stations were one-doctor/one-nurse operations and were typical "bush hospitals": facilities were simple, equipment and supplies minimal, X-ray and laboratory help limited or nonexistent. The missionary doctor had a "solo" practice and encountered a host of medical challenges.

The term Super Nurse has been applied to many of the missionary nurses in the Belgian Congo, and it appears to be well deserved. The nurse was frequently left in charge of a hospital. Particularly during World War II when, for a while, only one doctor was in the Kasai, the nurses heroically kept the hospitals in operation.

An unusual feature of the APCM medical work, compared with the other PCUS missions, was its large number of medical couples. There were twelve doctor/nurse couples plus a doctor/medical technologist, a dentist/nurse, and a pharmacist/pharmacist couple.

Surgery was the most dramatic service and the one best accepted by the Congolese because the village practitioner did not attempt it. Complicated childbirth, hernias, burns, yaws, elephantiasis, and accidents were common. Huge cysts and tumors were sometimes astounding. Injuries from crocodile (*all* rivers were crocodile-infested), hippopotamus, leopard, and wild pig were encountered. There is no record, however, that any missionary or missionary child suffered an attack by a wild animal; some were bitten by snakes, none fatally.

Pioneer doctors of the "Five Hospital" period (1914–30). Left to right, back row: Jeff W. Chapman, J. Tinsley Smith, and Thomas T. Stixrud; front row: Eugene R. Kellersberger and George R. Cousar. Photograph courtesy of J. Tinsley Smith.

Three major tropical diseases infested the area: malignant malaria (*falciparum* malaria), sleeping sickness (trypanosomiasis), and amoebic dysentery. Missionaries and their children contracted all these diseases. Dr. Mark Poole claims to have survived all three.

Sleeping sickness caused by the trypanosome parasite and transmitted by the tsetse fly was, and is, endemic. The Belgian government, with some success, undertook to gain control by treatment of the disease and by the elimination of the breeding places of the tsetse fly (through the clearing of heavy undergrowth along the riverbanks at the regular river-crossings).[23] Experimental treatment carried out by Dr. Kellersberger was internationally recognized. Villages for the treatment of victims of trypanosomiasis, set up near each of the five hospitals, gradually disappeared as the disease came under control. During World War II and again following independence, when the tsetse fly controls were relaxed, sleeping sickness reappeared as a major epidemic.

Leprosy also was endemic in central Africa. Leprosy villages were established within a few miles of each of the hospitals. The Belgian government encouraged this work and provided some support, as did the American Leprosy Mission. Dr. Kellersberger also provided leadership in the control and treatment of this disease.

Concern for infants and small children remained an integral part of the medical work. Immunizations, well-baby clinics, and educational programs were conducted in each of the hospitals.

Training of medical personnel was at first informal; medical assistants trained in this manner became valued members on the hospital staff. Later a formal training program for nurse's aides was established at each hospital. Students who had completed fifth grade attended three years of lectures and underwent clinical training; after taking an examination, they received a certificate. In later years these programs met government standards, and graduates received government certificates. Graduates were in great demand in government and other institutions.

A major help to the medical work was the so-called industrial missionary. Central Africa lacked a skilled labor force, and the industrial missionary filled an important role in the construction and maintenance of mission buildings, including the medical institutions. He often went into the forest, selected the trees, and supervised the cutting and preparation of the lumber; bricks were made and burned on location. In later years the maintenance of vehicles and other equipment became part of his responsibility. The upkeep of property and equipment was time-consuming for all the missionaries; blessed was the missionary with some expertise in these matters.

Two nonmedical professionals played an important role in the story of PCUS medical missions in the Belgian Congo. In 1918–19 Rev. Hezekiah Methuselah Washburn was instrumental in controlling devastating outbreaks of dysentery and influenza among the Kuba people. His efforts resulted in the opening of this unfriendly tribe for missionary work. Rev. (Samuel) Hugh Wilds, although not a licensed dentist, took special training in dentistry while on furlough and provided satisfactory dental services to Westerners and Africans alike. The story of these two men is told later.

The Great Depression and World War II
The Great Depression and World War II (1930–45) created serious problems for the medical work. Budgets and salaries were severely cut; supplies became hard to get, travel restrictions caused by the war reduced personnel, and missionary health deteriorated as terms became extended without furloughs. At one time, twenty-four missionaries and their families (including Mark Poole, M.D., and Margaret Liston, R.N.) had sleeping sickness. In 1942 William Rule, M.D., was the only APCM physician in the Kasai.

Postwar to Independence

The medical program after World War II (1946–60) enjoyed a period of rejuvenation and growth. New personnel, fresh from advanced training, brought new ideas that encouraged new initiatives. The Program of Progress fund-raising campaign and the 1945 Birthday Offering of the Women of the Church (PCUS) "made possible," as one missionary put it, "the great forward surge which the work in the Congo experienced after World War II."[24] Life for the missionary was safe and even took on a gracious aspect.

Despite an undercurrent of nationalism that began to make itself felt (and culminated in independence in 1960), the Belgian colonial government seemed stable and fairly good.[25] Belgian doctors and a hospital were placed in each of the 150 territories into which the Congo was divided. Public health measures were improved and expanded. State grants in the form of drugs and supplies were awarded to Protestant as well as Catholic institutions. Funds from the Native Welfare Fund (FBEI) helped upgrade the mission's medical facilities. Mission hospitals were given semiofficial status.

A much improved transportation system reduced the isolation of the five stations and made it possible to establish dispensaries in newly opened stations. These dispensaries, staffed by a missionary nurse with Congolese assistants, emphasized child care and preventive health. Air dispensaries, regularly served by "flying doctors," brought modern medicine to remote areas. Radio transmitters improved medical consultation and treatment between the stations.

Newly appointed medical personnel were graduates with advanced training and experience. The APCM's first board-certified physician, L. Gladys Smithwick, M.D., anesthetist, was also its first woman physician (1955). The first licensed dentist (1948) and the first certified medical technologist (1950) joined the medical roster. Most nurses had their baccalaureate degrees in nursing.

The quality of medicine was upgraded by new buildings, modern equipment, and better supplies. Antibiotics, new antimalarials, and sulfa drugs changed the practice of medicine; many tropical conditions responded well to the new drugs. A uniform charting system in all the hospitals standardized the medical recordkeeping.

Surgery continued to be important. A partial list of surgical cases in one station (Bulape) illustrates the variety: emergency brain surgery due to trauma, mastoids, cataracts, huge thyroids, huge ovarian cysts, large uterine fibroids, intestinal obstruction, resections, cesarean sections, large hernias (sometimes extending to the knees), prostatectomies, club feet, chronic osteo, and burns. "Every operation started with prayer (as was the custom of the famous gynecologist Dr. Howard Kelly at Johns Hopkins) and we depended on the Lord."[26]

The training of Congolese medical personnel became a top priority. The teaching of the nurse's aides continued and a school for training midwives opened in Luebo. The establishment in 1954 of the Christian Medical Institute of the Kasai (IMCK) at Lubondai was a major accomplishment. This school trained nurses and dentists. As previously noted, a Christian medical school to be supported by a number of mission bodies was under discussion. The dream of training qualified Christian Congolese to supply the medical needs of their country seemed a real possibility.

The Belgian government continued to recognize the contribution of the medical missionaries by inducting most of those who served fifteen years or more into the Royal Order of the Lion. Among those who, in addition to Dr. Coppedge, received this honor were Dr. Thomas and Mrs. Mary Etta Stixrud, Dr. Eugene Kellersberger, Dr. Tinsley and Mrs. Catherine Smith, Dr. Mark Poole, and Rev. S. Hugh Wilds. Drs. Stixrud and Kellersberger were both decorated three times for their services to the Congo. Mary Porter Morrison, R.N., received the Gold Medal of the Lion.

In July 1986, twenty-six years after leaving the Congo, the Belgian government by royal decree presented Sara Day Poole (Mrs. Mark) the Golden Palms of the Order of the Crown. Because of her poor health, the Belgian Consul General stationed in Houston, Texas, went to the Poole home in Bay City, Texas, to present the beautiful medal in belated recognition of Sara Poole's services as a "Registered Nurse, Medical Missionary in the Belgian Congo, American Presbyterian Congo Mission."

McKowen Memorial Hospital
Luebo

Luebo, founded in 1891, was not only the first APCM station in the Kasai but, for twenty-one years, was virtually the *only* one except for Ibanche, a small outstation some thirty-five miles away. Luebo continued its dominant role in the affairs of the mission until after World War II.

A river port, Luebo was located on a high hill overlooking the rapids that marked the head of navigation on the Lulua River. For many years this river was the mission's only link to the outer world, and the mission-owned riverboat, named for Samuel N. Lapsley, was its primary means of communication. The interesting story of the SS *Lapsley* is appropriately included in a medical history of the APCM because the Lapsley Memorial Hospital in Bulape was built with money from its sale when, in 1930, the mission decided to get out of the riverboating business.

The Story of the SS *Lapsley*

A Sunday school class of boys in Lapsley's hometown first conceived the idea of raising money for a Presbyterian mission steamer. When word came of Lapsley's sudden death, the fund for "God's Steamer" for Africa snowballed. It became a special project for the children from all over the PCUS; even the children of Sunday schools in Luebo and Ibanche added their gifts. In a short time the sum of $18,000 was raised, and the William R. Trigg Company of Richmond, Virginia, commissioned to build the boat: a stern-wheeler, 70 feet in length with a 12-foot beam, 1 foot 1 inch draught, 1,420 cubic foot hold capacity, and a wood-burning steam engine capable of cruising at 10 knots.[27]

In 1901 the SS *Lapsley* arrived in crates, and the missionaries were faced with the daunting task of assembling, as well as of operating, the riverboat. Rev. Lachlan C. Vass Sr. put the boat together and became the first of a series of missionaries assigned to captain the SS *Lapsley*.

For eighteen months this first SS *Lapsley* made its way up and down the river before tragedy struck. Twenty-three people, including the newly arrived young missionary, Rev. Henry Slaymaker, drowned when the boat overturned in turbulent waters at the juncture of the Congo and Kasai rivers; twenty-two people survived. Captain Vass, a strong swimmer, climbed onto the overturned hull; Rev. Mott Martin, who could not swim, latched onto a wicker chair and floated to safety. Martin wrote a vivid account of the experience:

> The *Lapsley* appeared indeed a handsome boat. But while Mr. Vass pointed out her many good points, he warned us that she was better

suited for American rivers than for the Congo with its gigantic caul-
drons and whirlpools and deadly cross currents. . . . At seven A.M. on
November 16 [1903] we were one hour's steaming from the mouth
of the Kasai; here the waters of the two rivers unite, tremendous
whirlpools appear, the waters boiling up with tremendous force.
Our steamer, seized by this giant bubble, spun like a top; the helm
was thrown over, the engines reversed, everything done that he,
who is recognized here as the most efficient of captains, could do!
But our steamer is so narrow and answers her helm so slowly that
she careened—the current caught her lower deck—and in a flash we
were struggling with the awful current.[28]

The disaster brought a rapid reaction, and within six months more
than $24,000 was raised for a new steamer. The second SS *Lapsley*,
built on the Clyde River in Scotland, was carefully designed to meet
the special dangers of navigation on the Congo River. She was ninety
feet long with a nineteen-foot beam and was propelled by a paddle-
wheel at the stern that could navigate at a speed of nine knots through
the strongest currents. On Christmas Eve 1906 the new SS *Lapsley*
arrived at Luebo.

God's Steamer was well known up and down the river. It stopped
each night so that its crew could go out into the forest to chop wood
for the boilers; it stopped each Sunday for rest and worship; and a
signal with a white flag would bring it to a stop to minister to
someone who was sick or in special need. The SS *Lapsley*, with its
clean cabins and good food, not to mention the gracious hospitality of
the captain's lady, must have been welcome indeed to weary missionaries who may have ridden by hammock for up to three weeks from
a distant station.

All histories of these early days describe the excitement that
accompanied the arrival of the SS *Lapsley* at Luebo. As the distinct
two-toned horn sounded from down river, crowds streamed down
the steep hill from the mission. Joyous hymns rang out over the water
in welcome and were answered from those aboard the ship. On
departure the strains of "God Be with You 'Til We Meet Again"
echoed off the hills. The nostalgia of the missionaries for their SS
Lapsley is not surprising.

The SS *Lapsley* served the mission well for over twenty years and
continued in service on the river for more than seventy years. Belgian

riverboat captains are reported to have considered it "the finest stern-wheeler on the entire river system."[29]

Llewellyn J. Coppedge, M.D. (1906–1918)

Llewellyn J. Coppedge was twenty-four years old, single, and two years out of medical school (North Carolina Medical College, Charlotte) when he arrived at Luebo on December 24, 1906, on the second SS *Lapsley*'s maiden voyage into the Kasai. He wrote:

> The next day I went to the dispensary and, with a missionary inter-preter, prescribed for some cases. There were scores of cases of itch, caused by a microscopic parasite of the tick family. For this infection an ointment of sulphur is both cheap and efficacious. One gave the native a spoonful or two of sulphur which he mixed with palm oil and prepared his own ointment. For missionaries I added a small quantity of carbolic acid, camphor, and oils of cinnamon [and] nutmeg and helped disguise the odor of sulphur and allayed the intense itching, to which the Africans are less susceptible. Malaria, dysentery [usually the amoebic form], and various parasites were widely prevalent.[30]

An early history of the medical work states that Dr. Coppedge "removed medical work from the haphazard class, and placed it where it belongs in Foreign Missions, to the front, the forerunner of evangelistic work . . . "[31] He can be said to have made three significant contributions: he improved the health care of the missionaries and their children, he won the confidence of the Congolese, and by treating the ills in the European community he did much to overcome their hostility to the mission.

Medical service to the Congolese had a simple beginning compli-cated by the constant fight against superstition. The dispensary was a mud hut, and equipment consisted of a few bottles of pills. Dr. Coppedge performed his first operations outdoors in the presence of the patient's relatives, who were armed to the teeth. Elda Fair, R.N., APCM's first nurse to the Congo, did not arrive until 1913. She started an inpatient department in a shed built of sticks and roofed with palm leaves.

In addition to having medical responsibilities, Dr. Coppedge was given other assignments, a common practice in most PCUS mission stations. Because he was a single man without family obligations, he was sent to the outstations to examine candidates for baptism, arbitrate disputes between native Christians, and judge their fitness for baptism. He reported spending five weeks or more without seeing a white face or hearing a word of a European language.

> In the year 1910 I spent more than six months in the distant outstations doing work which properly belonged to a minister. On my return to the Homeland, I was urged to seek ordination as a special case, without the study of Hebrew and abstruse questions of theology half baked. This I declined to do as I thought proficiency in one profession was preferable.[32]

Over time the local people came to accept the strange ways of the missionary doctor. Another missionary doctor commented in 1916, "At times I think they have too much confidence in us. They expect us to do the impossible."[33]

Thomas T. Stixrud, M.D.

In 1914, when Thomas T. Stixrud arrived in Luebo, construction had finally begun on a hospital. Dr. Stixrud had a colorful background. He was born in Norway and went to sea at the age of fifteen in a three-masted sailing vessel. After three years on a variety of ships, he abandoned the life of a sailor while he was in the United States and decided to pursue his youthful ambition to become a missionary doctor. With money he had saved, he entered the North Carolina Medical College in Charlotte, North Carolina. When money ran low, he left school temporarily to work as a lumberman; time spent in this way provided experience that proved useful in his work in the Congo. Members of the Second Presbyterian Church in Charlotte, North Carolina, became interested in him and, with their assistance, he completed his studies, graduating in 1913.

Dr. Stixrud has been described by his fellow workers as vigorous and dynamic, physically strong, self-confident, and possessing a captivating personality[34]; a valuable man, jack-of-all-trades, and good at everything he undertakes[35]; and an outstanding abdominal surgeon.[36] During his first furlough he married Mary Etta Parks, R.N., one of Congo's Super Nurses.

Construction of the first PCUS hospital in the Congo, the McKowen Memorial Hospital in Luebo, was not easy. Funds ($5,500) were donated in 1914 by the McKowen family of Baton Rouge, Louisiana.[37] The master builder, as he was called, was W. Laurens Hillhouse, a man with many years of experience in construction in the United States that were an asset in the mission field. Many of the missionaries contributed time and energy to the project; at one point, Dr. Stixrud spent four days a week at the sawmill. The Congolese had to be taught what to do. *The Missionary Survey*, June 1916, tells the story:

> Mr. Hillhouse is, of course, the chief "contractor" on this job, as he has handled the construction of the hospital from the very first. At present he has the assistance of some of the missionaries, but there is a great deal of native labor in this building. Certainly this work is all new to the natives and they have to be shown and taught with a great deal of patience, but I find many of them exceptionally intelligent and all of them anxious to learn and serve . . . Only yesterday the chief of a neighboring village came in to see the wonderful building and stood gazing in wonder, with his hand over his mouth, and exclaimed, "A very strong house!"[38]

When the twenty-five-bed hospital was completed in 1916, it was one of only three hospitals in all of the Kasai, an area the size of France. The other two were the government hospital in Lusambo and a Catholic hospital in Mikalayi. In 1921 a wing of the hospital was destroyed by fire; the electric plant, laboratory equipment, and a year's supply of medicines was lost. The McKowens gave enough money not only to replace the burned wing and electric plant but to add a new wing, making the hospital a fifty-bed facility.

The McKowen Memorial Hospital in Luebo, completed in 1916, was the first PCUS hospital in the Congo. Photograph courtesy of John K. Miller.

The most common conditions seen by the earliest medical missionaries were sleeping sickness, malaria, leprosy, and yaws. The physical horrors resulting from these conditions were graphically described by Dr. Stixrud:

> The sleeping-sickness patient left outside the village to die or perhaps to be eaten alive by driver ants, the lepers dragging out a miserable existence with fingers and toes dropping off, enormous ulcers [yaws] dressed native fashion with stinking poultices . . . impressed on them [the APCM] the need for medical aid in their mission work.[39]

After a few dramatic successes, surgery became the primary drawing card. Dr. Stixrud wrote:

> Just about a year ago we performed our first intra-abdominal operation. Kabeya Lukenga, an elder in the native church, had for several years suffered from recurring attacks of pain in the right side. A diagnosis of chronic appendicitis was made, and I suggested operation. After consulting some of the older missionaries he consented to the operation, but the matter didn't end there. When he told his wife she started the death cry, and called in all their relatives. They told him he was crazy, and that we would kill him and make medicine of him, but he stuck it out. The operation was successful, and since that time he has been a walking advertisement for the medical department of the mission. On a recent trip we [found] him the center of large crowds of natives showing the scar and telling of the operation. "Nganga Buka Kanda Kanda killed me, cut out the pain and brought me back to life again, and I have never had any pain since," is his story.
>
> The result was at times embarrassing. People would come and say, "I have a pain here, please cut it out.". . . An old woman came to me and said: "Are you the man that cuts people?" When I answered in the affirmative, she lay down on the floor and said, "Cut me." After the first operation people began coming, slowly at first, later much faster than we could attend to them, as our quarters were very limited, till at last we had operations scheduled as much as two months in advance.[40]

During the 1920s and 1930s Luebo had an exceptionally competent group of nurses: Mary Etta Stixrud, Mary P. Morrison, Martha B.
Savels, and Jean S. Shive. All were married, and at one point all were
pregnant. Several of these nurses belong in the Super Nurse category.

Mary Morrison, who arrived in Luebo in 1921, described her experiences in the early years. Luebo had no electricity or refrigeration,
water was carried up one mile from the river, and transportation was
by hammock. Medical work was "a joy." The care of babies was a
major concern. Six to ten goats in her backyard supplied goat's milk
to as many as a dozen babies who were daily brought to her back
porch. The new medicines, such as the sulfas and antibiotics, made it
possible to accomplish "marvels" as compared to the early days.
Mary Morrison learned to do a number of laboratory procedures such
as malarial tests. Sometimes she accompanied her husband into the
country, where they lived in a trailer and she would treat the sick. She
always wished for more doctors and more equipment. The "White
Cross" supplies (linens from the PCUS Women of the Church) were a
"marvelous help."[41]

Mary Morrison's husband, Rev. John Morrison, a Scot who
became business manager for the APCM, commented:

> The medical work was run on a shoestring and was not adequately
> funded. From a business point of view the support seemed
> niggardly. I cannot understand why the church was not willing to
> do the job right with proper equipment and personnel as a business
> firm would do.[42]

In the mid-1930s, the hospital increased its emphasis on the maternity service. With a special grant from the United States, a training
program for midwives was started, and a maternity wing was built at
the hospital. Jean Shive, who considered training of Congolese the
most important contribution made by the missionaries, became very
active in this program. The students were older women, many of
whom were already practicing midwives. Their skills were upgraded
chiefly by teaching them what *not* to do.

Dr. Stixrud's missionary career came to an abrupt end in January
1942 when he suffered a heart attack while performing an operation.
In severe pain, with his wife by his side, he managed to complete the
surgery. He was furloughed to the United States and died that

December at the age of fifty-five. His death reduced to two the number of APCM doctors in the Congo at the beginning of World War II.

The work in Luebo suffered during the war years when missionary nurses struggled to hold things together. Dr. Robert King, the pioneer physician in Mutoto, arrived in 1944 and served until 1949.

After World War II to Independence (1946–1960)

After APCM business and administrative offices were moved to Luluabourg (Kananga) in 1946, Luebo lost its dominant position in the APCM community. Luebo, in the far west, was remote from the other stations, and its isolation increased as trains, cars, and trucks replaced river travel as the primary mode of transportation.

Luebo Hospital was in a sadly depressed state when Dr. John Knox Miller, a graduate of Tulane University (M.D., 1946), and his wife, Aurie Montgomery Miller, M.T., arrived in 1950. Buildings were in a badly run-down condition, and morale was low. An infusion of new personnel and monies revived the situation. The hospital was repaired and Aurie Miller began a training program for laboratory technicians.

John Miller, along with William Rule, M.D., and others, was committed to the dream of establishing a school that would further the medical education of the Congolese. After three years, the Millers were transferred from Luebo to Lubondai to establish the school for medical professionals.

Luebo next received three missionaries who had begun their missionary careers in China and transferred to the Belgian Congo when China fell to the Communists. These three, Henry S. Nelson, M.D., Katie W. Nelson, R.N., and (Laura) Gladys Smithwick, M.D., served in Luebo from 1953 until independence (see China: Taizhou and Xuzhou).

The Congolese were slow to accept Gladys Smithwick, a graduate of the Medical College of Virginia (M.D., 1925), as a genuine physician or *Ngangabuka* because she was a woman and she practiced no surgery. They had no appreciation of her distinction as one of America's first female board-certified anesthesiologists.

The medical program in Luebo improved over the next few years. The missionary staff was at an all-time high; in addition to the Nelsons and Dr. Smithwick, there were Jean Shive, R.N., Margaret

McMurry, R.N., and Mary Morrison, R.N. Moreover, Jean Baptiste Jung, D.D.S., practiced dentistry and gave clinical training to students from the dental school in Lubondai. Other people served for short periods of time.

The hospital expanded to 110 beds. A new building, completed just before independence, contained outpatient facilities, laboratory, an X ray, pharmacy, supply rooms, classrooms, and a large lobby that could be opened up for meetings.

The school for the training of nurse's aides admitted its first woman student. The training program for midwives was upgraded to a school for midwifery that met government requirements. The new school attracted young women who, upon graduation, received state certificates as *aides-accoucheuses*. The sense of accomplishment is reflected in this quotation from the 1957 annual report:

> Another landmark in mission medical history is indicated by the first effort to train Congolese girls in any phase of nursing. At the McKowen Memorial Hospital at Luebo, an initial class of seven eager and promising girls has started the first official course in midwifery offered by the Mission. This, too, promises the not-too-far-distant fulfillment of the dream of educating Congolese girls as full-fledged nurses![43]

GOLDSBY KING MEMORIAL HOSPITAL
Mutoto

Mutoto, 160 miles (five days by caravan) due east of Luebo, was opened in 1912 in response to the need for a station located near a rapidly growing Christian community. The beautiful site, in the midst of a great palm grove fronting a range of hills, was given Bertha Stebbins Morrison's Tshiluba name, *Mutoto*, meaning "a star." She died in 1910 soon after she and Dr. Morrison returned from a four-month exploratory search for a suitable location for the new station.

Mutoto station served a population consisting primarily of the Lulua ethnic group; many Luba and Zappo Zapp also lived in the area. Until World War II Mutoto occupied a strategic position and grew to be, for a time, the largest APCM station. Its importance as the center of activity for the mission gradually decreased as the population shifted once the railroad (some two hours away) was completed and Luluabourg (Kananga), some thirty-five miles away, became the capital of the Kasai.

Robert Rogers King, M.D. (1915–1931)

Robert King, a graduate of the University of Arkansas (M.D., 1915), arrived in the Congo in the fall of 1915 and was assigned to the newly opened station at Mutoto. In 1916 he married Marguerite Van Leancourt, R.N. She was one of a group of Belgian Protestants who joined the APCM when World War I disrupted their plans for opening a Belgian mission in the Congo.

Nina Lewis Farmer, R.N., arrived in 1920 and served until her death in Mutoto in 1931. Jean Setser Shive, R.N., served in Mutoto from 1922 to 1924 while her husband, Alexander Shive, oversaw construction of school buildings. Part of that time she worked without other medical help.

The hospital at Mutoto was one of three PCUS hospitals built in memory of Dr. Goldsby King of Selma, Alabama (see Zhengkiang, China, and Dourados, Brazil). Rev. Earl S. King Sr. supervised the construction of the buildings. Mutoto's three *Kings*—the physician, the builder, and the patron—were unrelated except in their Christian brotherhood of believers. Dr. and Mrs. King served in Mutoto until 1931 when her poor health forced them to return to the United States.

The Tinsley Smiths (1931–1962)

Catherine Minter, a graduate of Johns Hopkins School of Nursing (R.N., 1930), reached Mutoto in the summer of 1931 to find the station devastated by the death of Miss Farmer and the departure of the Kings. Additional support came in the fall with the arrival of (James) Tinsley Smith, a recent graduate of the University of Colorado (M.D., 1930). When they were married in 1934, the "Kit & Tin" team began a happy collaboration remembered by many for its grace and efficiency.

Catherine Smith oversaw the operation of the hospital; Tinsley Smith described his practice as consisting of the "skin and its contents." He set high standards—sterile technique, correct dosage, cleanliness—on which, as he put it, he "would not hedge."[44] A church executive once reported that the Mutoto Hospital was the only hospital he visited in the Congo that did not smell of latrines.[45] The treatment of acute cases limited the time available for public health work, but Dr. Smith did design a latrine for residential use, and Catherine Smith conducted a well-baby clinic. A major responsibility was looking after the health of the missionaries and of the students and staff in the many educational institutions of the station.

The efforts to eradicate sleeping sickness and control leprosy were rewarding. The hospital established a leprosy village some three miles away, where the staff cared for around 285 patients. A village for 100 to 150 cases of sleeping sickness gradually disappeared as this disease came under control.

Graduates of the training program for nurse's aides (male only) were recognized by the government. One graduate became minister of health of Zaire after independence.

The Congolese staff was well trained and loyal. The missionary staff operated on the philosophy, "Don't do anything a Congolese can do." Dr. Smith reported that at the close of his thirty-one years he still had the same house staff with which he had started except for two who had died and been replaced.

The outbreak of World War II found the Smiths on furlough in the United States. They, with their eighteen-month-old son and three PCUS missionaries including Lena Reynolds, R.N., were passengers on the ill-fated Egyptian ship, the SS *Zam Zam*, when it was attacked and sunk by a German "raider" in March 1941. Rescued by a German freighter, they eventually reached occupied France and were returned to the United States by way of Spain. They finally returned to Mutoto in July 1944.

Shortly after World War II the original hospital building was torn down and replaced with funds granted by the Native Welfare Fund (FBEI); a Belgian contractor supervised construction. This seventy-two-bed hospital with an additional twelve-bed maternity unit, was a practical plant well designed to meet the need of a small mission hospital. The addition of a utility unit, made possible by a $10,000 gift from the Independent Presbyterian Church of Savannah, Georgia, further increased its efficiency.

Dr. Smith, in commenting on his missionary medical experience, ruefully confessed to the tendency of most missionaries to write about the exotic, unusual events that occurred, whereas the real "nuts and bolts of the missionary existence," in his words, was the routine hard work.

The Mutoto Hospital, headed by the Smiths, was considered a smooth operation. Other missionary personnel served there for only short periods.

LAPSLEY HOSPITAL
Bulape

Bulape, founded in 1915 in hopes of reaching the proud Kuba people, is located some sixty miles northeast of Luebo on the edge of the equatorial rain forest. This forest, where tall trees reach for the sun and jungle animals (elephant, buffalo, monkey, and leopard) roamed, is home to a number of primitive peoples in addition to the Kuba. The Sankuru River flows into the Kasai River near Bulape.

Mission to the Kuba people was one of the motivating reasons that led Lapsley and Sheppard to select the Kasai region as the APCM area of work. Efforts to evangelize the Kuba, however, proved daunting.

William Sheppard, in particular, made it his goal to gain access to the Kuba. His first contacts were encouraging, as he was proclaimed to be a long-lost member of the royal clan and was welcomed into the capital city of Mushenge. When the friendly ruler died, however, a series of hostile kings made further efforts futile.

In 1897, as has been noted, Ibanche, the mission's first outstation, was built on the edge of Kuba territory some thirty-five miles from Luebo. Manned primarily by black American missionaries, Ibanche attracted large numbers of the Lulua and Luba ethnic groups but was shunned by the Kuba. In 1904, in a rebellion against the "white invader," the Kuba attacked and burned Ibanche; the missionaries and their followers barely escaped with their lives. The rebellion was soon quelled by Belgian authorities.

The Ibanche station was reopened for a time but continued unable to make significant contact with the Kuba people. In 1915 the mission got permission from the Belgian authorities to establish a station some twenty-five miles east of Mushenge, the Kuba capital, where the Kete (a subgroup of the Kuba), were friendly to the missionaries. The mission decided to make a ten-year effort to reach the Kuba from this new location. To further this effort they discouraged the presence of the Lulua and Luba while welcoming contact with the Kuba. The new station was given the name *Bulape*, the name of the first member of the royal family to become a Christian as well as the African name of Annie Tate Rochester (Mrs. Adolphus Augustus), a black American who died in 1914 after eight years of service spent chiefly in Ibanche.

Kubaland Receives the Missionary

The story of the APCM mission to the Kuba is a medical story, albeit the work of a nonmedical professional. Rev. Hezekiah M. Washburn, a Kentuckian described as having maintained a frontiersman's courage, independence, and ingenuity, is the hero of the story.[46]

Shortly after World War I, the Kasai, and the Kuba area in particular, was swept by two serious epidemics. The first was a dysentery brought by men who had been recruited as porters for Allied troops fighting the Germans in East Africa. The second was the pandemic influenza that killed millions around the world. Several APCM missionaries, including their beloved leader William Morrison, succumbed to influenza. In Luebo Dr. Stixrud was unable to leave his own patients to respond personally to Washburn's pleas for help, but he did send Elda Fair, R.N., with medicines and directions for quarantine, sanitation, and diet for people who had contracted the diseases. With the help of Elda Fair and his wife, Lillie, Washburn proceeded to implement these guidelines.

A great central quarantine camp, where strict sanitation was enforced, was set up not far from Bulape. The three missionaries and their helpers worked to the point of exhaustion. Washburn scoured the countryside in search of the sick, Elda Fair took charge of the camp and treated the people, and Lillie Washburn prepared large pots of gruel made of manioc-root flour, which were distributed several times a day. For two years the epidemics raged, claiming an estimated 600,000 victims in the Kasai region; some whole villages were wiped out. The death rate in the Bulape camp was a remarkably low four percent.[47]

Members of subgroups of the Kuba were the first to take advantage of the mission facilities. The Kuba, however, refused to have anything to do with the missionaries. Still bitterly antagonistic, King Mbope Mabinchi and his followers plunged deeper and deeper into the jungle in a futile attempt to escape infection. Finally, the queen mother, who carried ultimate authority, ordered her son to send for the help of the missionary. When he refused, she traveled some seventy-five miles to the king's camp, ordered a blacksmith to remove the heavy embossed brass anklet from his ankle, and sent this symbol of royal authority to Washburn in Bulape.[48]

Washburn had contracted a light case of influenza but, in response to the call, got up from bed and headed for Mushenge. There he was told, "As long as you hold that token, you are king in Mbope's stead; your word is law to us; speak your commands, only help us in our terrible need." Thus for some six weeks Hezekiah M. Washburn became virtual "King of the Kuba." Conway T. Wharton tells the story in his book, *The Leopard Hunts Alone.*

> With this assurance the missionary, with his helpers, now took up without delay the difficult task of rounding up the sick. Plunging into the forest, he searched out the stricken ones, even handling them with his own hands. Three he took from shallow graves who yet had the breath of life in them. Of these three, two actually survived. . . . The result of these heroic labours was a long line of sufferers slowly making their way toward Bulape and the hope of life. . . . Only pausing long enough to assure himself that there were no more victims within reach of his help, the missionary wearily mounted his wheel and pedalled back to the station ahead of the sufferers to help the trained nurse with the task of providing the necessary extra accommodations. For miles he passed group after group of those he had sent ahead. Some were walking, some being carried on the backs of others, some were actually crawling, and a few were lying still by the roadside. "Keep in the path, and keep coming!" he called as he passed; "If you can go no farther, stay in the path and we will try to send back for you; if you can just make it to Bulape we can help you!"[49]

In the meantime King Mbope became ill and, in panic, called for the missionary to come. Washburn hurried to his side but arrived too late; the king died in the arms of a native evangelist.

King Kuete Mabintshi, the next king of the Kuba, was an intelligent man who became a staunch friend of the missionary. Paralyzed in his youth (probably from polio), King Kuete Mabintshi was unable to walk and, in later years, barely able to move. He gained great weight and was an imposing figure who wielded great power during his twenty-five-year reign. King Kuete Mabintshi never joined the church but many of his harem (over 500 wives) became devout Christians.

Lapsley Hospital, Bulape. Note the tuberculosis village at the top of the picture. Each of the five hospitals had similar villages for patients with leprosy and with sleeping sickness, as well as tuberculosis. Photograph courtesy of Mark K. Poole.

As the epidemic slowly subsided, life returned to normal. Hezekiah Washburn was given a "Lifetime Seat in the (Ba)Kuba King's Tribal Council." With this honor—dramatically proclaimed at King Kuete Mabintshi's coronation—went permission to visit and preach in all the villages of the kingdom. The "taking of the eagle's feather," as it was called, occurred in April 1921, thirty years from the time Lapsley and Sheppard had first set foot in the Kasai. Tapping the leopard skin he carried on his left arm, King Kuete Mabintshi said:

> The elephants roam the jungles in herds; the monkeys pass through the tree-tops in bands; the driver ants travel in columns through the sand;—all the animals hunt in a pack—*But the leopard hunts alone*!

> I am the leopard, I hunt alone! Following my own will and judgment, I now pledge you, in my authority as King of the Bakuba, to friendship with the mission! Let them come and build their village at my capital! As the leopard tears his prey, so will I despoil those who refuse my commands![50]

Medical Work Established in Bulape

Bulape continued as the mission's principal station in Kubaland. Outstations were developed in Mushenge and other locations, and the church grew in a remarkable way.

Medical work, however, developed more slowly. Elda Fair, R.N., retired from mission service in 1921 and was succeeded by Emma Larson, R.N., who served until 1928. The decision in 1930 to sell the SS *Lapsley* and apply the money to the building of the Lapsley Memorial Hospital in Bulape encouraged the medical aspect of the work. Lena Reynolds, one of the mission's Super Nurses, arrived in 1927. Her organizational ability, excellent language, and good medical knowledge contributed greatly to the success of the medical program in Bulape. In addition she is remembered for her care and concern for sick children and for the "little people" (the Pygmies).

Lena Reynolds, R.N. (1928–62), one of Congo's Super Nurses. Photograph from First Presbyterian Church, Franklin, Tennessee.

Jeff Watson Chapman, a graduate of the South Carolina College of Medicine (M.D., 1928), was the first PCUS physician to be assigned to Bulape. He and his young wife, Mary Elizabeth Ayers Chapman, R.N., arrived in 1929 just as the Lapsley Memorial Hospital was nearing completion. Lawrence G. DeLand and William J. Anderson were the industrial missionaries who oversaw the construction of this hospital complex, which eventually developed into a 120-bed facility.

The high spirits with which the Chapmans began their assignment came crashing down in June 1930, when Mary Elizabeth Chapman died in childbirth; her infant lived only one month. Jeff Chapman became frighteningly depressed and was sent back to the United States. In December 1931 he married Rachel Crawford Chapman, R.N.

Medical ward at the Bulape
Hospital. Photograph courtesy
of Mark K. Poole.

They returned to Bulape in the spring of 1932. The Chapmans and
Lena Reynolds are recognized as the pioneers of the medical work in
Bulape. Unfortunately, Jeff Chapman contracted sleeping sickness
and had to resign from mission service in 1939.

Mark K. Poole, M.D. (1942–1960)

Mark K. Poole,[51] a tall, lanky Texan, was one of the more flam-
boyant members of the Congo Mission, with a penchant for practical
jokes. Under his leadership Bulape Hospital experienced its most
productive years until independence in 1960.

After graduating from Johns Hopkins (M.D., 1934), Dr. Poole
contracted endocarditis from a patient. This illness almost ended his
dream of going to Africa as a medical missionary, but he persuaded
the Board of World Missions to appoint him on a one-year trial basis
at no expense to the board. He left in 1936 for a year's study of tropical medicine in London. Here he was joined by Sara Amelia Day, a
graduate of the Johns Hopkins School of Nursing (R.N., 1935). They
were married in Westminster Chapel by the famed evangelist Dr. G.
Campbell Morgan. Her husband describes Sara Poole as "one of the
best surgical assistants I ever had."

Dr. Poole's first assignment was to cover for mission doctors on
furlough. He went to Bulape in 1936 and by 1942 had served in each
of the other four mission hospitals at Luebo, Mutoto, Lubondai, and
Bibanga. In 1942 Bulape became his permanent assignment.

Shortly after he arrived in the Congo in 1937, Dr. Poole took an
adventurous nine-day trip into the jungle area north of Bulape where
only six other white people were said to have penetrated. The
journey—75 miles by car and 140 miles by dugout canoe, hammock,
and walking—revealed the plight of the primitive peoples (some
were Pygmies, some cannibals) who were hidden in the forests, and
he decided to respond to their need for medical assistance.

As a consequence, Dr. Poole, during his first furlough in 1940 and with the encouragement of Dr. C. Darby Fulton, executive secretary of the Board of World Missions, took flying lessons at the Dallas Aviation School. He augmented this training with aerobatic instruction and instrument training, and eventually acquired a pilot's license in the Congo and an instructor's rating so that he could legally teach others.

The APCM was slow in accepting the use of planes. It was not until 1951 that a Piper Tri-Pacer was donated by members of the Shenandoah Presbyterian Church of Miami, Florida, in honor of Maj. Daniel Iverson, hero of Wake Island and a casualty of World War II. (Iverson was the brother of Lalla Iverson, M.D., of the China Mission.) A second plane, donated by Dr. Poole's brother, was acquired in 1957 when former U.S. Air Force Maj. John Davis joined the mission. In due time, plane service became well established and, at the time of independence, proved crucial in the evacuation of mission and other personnel. Dr. Poole himself enjoyed a notable reputation as the "Flying Doctor of the Congo."

The airstrip at Bulape took four years to build by hand at a cost of about $1,300 in salt, meat, and cash. Some days as many as 700 people worked on it.

One day a small man from Batua, the Pygmy village some seventy-five miles from Bulape, appeared at the hospital and begged Dr. Poole to come immediately by plane to treat a man who had fallen out of a tree. When Dr. Poole demurred, the man insisted there was

Mark Poole's Piper Tri-Pacer. Dr. and Mrs. Poole stand at the far left. Photograph courtesy of J. K. Miller.

now an airstrip on which the plane could land. Somewhat skeptically, Dr. Poole took off to investigate and found to his astonishment that, on their own initiative, this Pygmy group had constructed a very acceptable airstrip. A few Batua had secretly traveled down to Bulape, looked over the airstrip, and returned to tell the others about it. With no tools other than sticks, they had moved the earth and packed it hard by dancing on it. Needless to say, the Batua were ecstatic when the plane set down on their airstrip.[52]

Each of the air dispensaries of Bulape Hospital (at Bambuya, Shongamba, and Batua), had its own airstrip, and airstrips were eventually built at each of the mission's stations. The planes were instrumental in bringing care to people scattered over an area of roughly 5,000 square miles in the jungle. Because of the isolation, poor roads, and many rivers, it was next to impossible to reach many by the ground route. Thanks to the air dispensaries, thousands of Africans received medical care and the gospel message; teachers and evangelists were willing and able to stay in isolated areas; and very ill patients were transported to the hospital for surgery and care that they could not obtain in the deep bush.

The planes were also helpful in moving missionaries from place to place and the mission's children to and from their school in Lubondai. "The planes," said Dr. Poole, "allowed us to operate far more efficiently and enabled us to expand the work greatly."

The mission allotment for operation of the planes was the same as that for cars and proved adequate to enable the operation to stay on the credit side. Dr. Poole's meticulous care of his plane was legendary: he strained the gas and oil himself before filling the tanks, and the engine looked new after years of heavy duty. No major mishap occurred in connection with the APCM planes.[53]

Under Dr. Poole's direction, the 120-bed Lapsley Memorial Hospital became a well-known and respected mission hospital. A modern operating room, an X ray, and a laboratory made it possible to sustain a relatively high level of practice; outpatient services included the three dispensaries served by air; villages were maintained for the treatment of chronic conditions (tuberculosis, sleeping sickness, and leprosy). A formal three-year program trained students to the nurse's aide level, and a less formal, apprentice system produced skilled assistants. Dr. Poole's reputation as a surgeon, combined with an influx (after World War II) of Belgian nationals to the Congo, brought a number of European patients to the facility.

Ruth Worth, M.T., transferred from the defunct China Mission in 1952 and introduced laboratory skills to Bulape. Ruth Worth had originally applied to the Congo Mission for service in 1932 after completing her training as a medical technologist at the University of Virginia. At that time she was told that there was no need for medical technologists in the Congo because locally trained personnel were adequate for the simple tests that were required. She then applied and went to the China Mission (see Jiangyin). In 1954, the Presbyterians of Wilmington, North Carolina, followed her to the Congo and built the new laboratory/outpatient dispensary there as a memorial to her father, George C. Worth, M.D., whose work they had supported in China.[54]

For two years during World War II the Bulape Hospital participated in a research project under Dr. Harry Eagle, chief of Microbiology, U.S. Public Health Service, Bethesda, Maryland. It was feared that U.S. armed forces might be exposed to sleeping sickness (trypanosomiasis), and Bulape became one of five sites for testing the use of 70 A (para-arsenico-phenyl-butyric acid) for the treatment of sleeping sickness. This drug, with little or no toxicity, was found to be effective in reducing the time of treatment from three months to seven days.

Capital improvements during the 1950s upgraded the hospital, although it continued to contain an interesting mixture of tin-roofed brick and thatched mud/stick buildings. The chapel and some surgical buildings were built by members of Dr. Poole's family. The obstetrical building was constructed with a grant from the Native Welfare Fund (FBEI) under the supervision of Belgian contractors rather than the mission's industrial missionary.

In 1959 the annual budget of approximately $12,000 came from three sources: one-third from the APCM, one-third from the Belgian colonial government, and one-third from the patients. It was found that paying patients were more cooperative and more likely to follow through on prolonged treatment, but no one was turned away for failure to pay.

Relations between the Kuba people and the APCM continued to be good. King Kuete Mabintshi chose Kuba names for each member of the Poole family: Dr. Poole received the name of a former king,

Kuete Mingashanga, Mrs. Poole became *Mbawota*, and Amelia was named *Mabintshi*. When daughters were born to the king and to the Pooles on the same day, the king gave his daughter's Kuba name, *Mbomantshela* meaning "Happiness," to Elizabeth and took Elizabeth for his daughter's English name.

Interest in the Kuba people intrigued many, and a number of scholars, anthropologists, and artists came to study their culture. Of special interest is the study done by E. Torday and T. Joyce, *Notes Ethnographiques sur les peuples communement appelés Bakuba ainsi que les peuplades apparentees. Les Bushongo*, (Brussels, 1910). Torday was a Hungarian explorer sent out by the British Museum in 1907 to make an ethnographical study of Central African ethnic groups.[55]

Edna Kellersberger Memorial Hospital
Bibanga

Bibanga, founded in 1917, was both the most isolated and, in the opinion of some, the most beautiful of the APCM stations in the Congo. Its location on a hilltop with an elevation of some 3,000 feet provided a spectacular view of the lush valley where two large rivers, the Lubilashi and the Mbujimayi, joined to form the Sankuru.

These two rivers, when in flood, further compounded the isolation that can best be described not in miles (300 from Luebo, 100 from Mutoto, 150 from Lusambo), but in travel time depending on weather and road conditions. In 1921 the Kellersbergers (in order to catch a riverboat) chose the eight-day hammock trip to Lusambo instead of the three-week overland journey to Luebo. On another occasion, however, Dr. Kellersberger made the trip from Lusambo to Bibanga in four consecutive days of tough bicycling; in 1923, in response to a medical emergency, he reached Luebo in two days riding on the back of a motorcycle driven by another missionary.[56]

Bibanga was situated in the heart of Luba country. This ethnic group had been receptive to the Christian gospel since early days. "The Luba have been eager to accept the advanced education as offered by the government and the missions, and they have naturally assumed positions of leadership in both church and civil communities."[57] During the days of the slave trade, the Luba were prime targets and hence were to be found in all parts of the Kasai.

Eugene Roland Kellersberger, M.D. (1916–1940)

The story of the medical work in Bibanga up to 1940 is basically the story of Eugene R. Kellersberger (Washington University, M.D., 1916), and is shaped by the personal tragedies and triumphs of his twenty-four years of service in the Congo. He and Edna Bosche Kellersberger, who had the same birthday, were twenty-eight years old when they arrived in the Congo in 1916.

The Kellersbergers' first assignment was to Lusambo, a river port on the Sankuru River, a major branch of the Kasai River north of the Lulua River on which Luebo is located. The Lusambo station provided support to members of other mission bodies (Methodists and Plymouth Brethren) as well as for the inland APCM stations (Mutoto and Bibanga); the SS *Lapsley* made regular calls with personnel and supplies.

Dr. Kellersberger's months at Lusambo served to introduce him to the new culture and to the practice of medicine in primitive conditions. His first clinic was a twelve-by-twelve-foot open shed with a grass roof, which he shared with the station carpenter; a carpenter's bench served as his examining and operating table, and a five-gallon kerosene drum was his only sterilizer.[58] In 1918, soon after the construction of a neat three-room dispensary, the Kellersbergers were assigned to the newly established station at Bibanga.

Medical work in Bibanga began simply; the first operation was performed under a large diwole tree with sheets tied in the branches to prevent debris from falling into the incision. The Kellersbergers then chose to use two rooms of their four-room house as the clinic and operating room until furlough in a few months. Dr. Kellersberger also spent considerable time answering medical emergencies in other places. A month's journey to a Methodist post some 135 miles away took him through unexplored territory.

While on furlough in 1920 Dr. Kellersberger received permission to go to England for three months to take a "certificate course" in tropical medicine and hygiene at the London School of Tropical Medicine. This decision was to prove highly significant after the couple's return to the Congo.

Trouble began on the voyage up the Congo River when Edna Kellersberger was bitten by an infected tsetse fly; by the time they arrived in Bibanga she was quite ill with sleeping sickness. It took from August to December (1921) for the Kellersbergers and their two little girls to wend their way back to London. Edna Kellersberger was put in the care of eminent authorities on the staff of the London School of Tropical Medicine. They decided to give her a German drug, Bayer 205 (Germanine), which had recently been developed specifically for the treatment of African sleeping sickness. The experimental administration of this drug proved successful, and she was dismissed in July 1922 as cured. Her case was reported in the literature as one of seven patients "infected with *Trypanosomiasis gambiensi* who made what appears to be rapid and complete recovery by being treated with Bayer 205."[59]

During Edna Kellersberger's convalescence, the two little girls were taken to the United States, and Dr. Kellersberger again took up medical studies in London. He received his "Diploma in Tropical Medicine and Hygiene" from the London School of Tropical Medicine and the "Diploma in Surgery" from the Royal College of Physicians and Surgeons. These degrees were to greatly enhance his contribution to the medical scene in the Congo.

On the advice of the medical professionals it was decided that Edna Kellersberger (and her daughters) would stay in the United States for two years to recover fully from her illness, while Dr. Kellersberger would return to the Congo. En route he stopped in London, where he learned of the continued success with the use of Bayer 205; in Germany, where he spent a week in the laboratories of Faben Fabriken, the manufacturers of Bayer 205; and in Brussels, where an important conference with the *Médecin en Chef* produced letters of introduction to medical officers in the Congo.

The return trip by ship to South Africa and train to the Congo included a three-month stopover in Elizabethville. There Dr. Kellersberger contacted public health officials, carried out research on tsetse fly distribution, and gained experience in government and mining company hospitals. At the end of the three-month period, in April 1923, he was appointed *Médecin Agree*, and became a Belgian colonial medical service doctor. He wrote his wife:

I am now an officially recognized government doctor and will have the entire Lubilashi Valley as my territory. I now have the right to practice medicine and to charge as well as treat government personnel at a fixed price. I have the power to summon the native population for public health purposes when necessary, to examine them or give preventive measures. I have been given supplies of smallpox and typhoid vaccine, as well as a brand new microscope and the other drugs which I requested, with the promise of more as I need them.[60]

Back at last in Bibanga, Dr. Kellersberger plunged into a hectic schedule. The first unit of a permanent hospital building was nearing completion. Funds ($10,000) had been given by Charles Lukens Huston of Coatesville, Pennsylvania, a steel magnate, in gratitude for Dr. Kellersberger's treatment (while on furlough) of his son. Rev. J. Hershey Longenecker supervised the construction.

An account condensed from Longenecker's autobiography, *Memories of Congo*, describes some of the difficulties faced in the construction:

I needed lumber, and trees were scarce. Lumber from the small clusters of forest trees was not usable because the termites destroyed it so readily. The *nsanga* tree was practically termite proof but they were few and far between. About six miles east of Bibanga we spotted a tree that stood all alone. It seemed impossibly big, something like looking for a cow and finding an elephant. The tree had a solid diameter of six feet and stretched up some seventy feet from the ground to the first branches. It looked as if that tremendous tree could not possibly be cut down and turned into lumber with the tools we had at Bibanga. But to our God all things are possible and it was decided to undertake the impossible task.

However, the axemen, believing the tree to be full of *Mihongo* [evil spirits or devils], refused to cut down the tree. After considerable "palaver," ten men, one native pastor, and one missionary went out one morning through the high grass to the tall tree that dominated the landscape for miles around. The pastor and I led in prayer and thanked God for putting the tree there for building the hospital and asked His protection for the men. Then I took an axe and began to chop. Church officers took turns staying with the men every day while they chopped and, at last, I was happy to see the giant fall with a mighty crash to the ground.

Victory to the *Mihongo* threatened when major problems developed in handling the huge log and in bringing down a second *lusanga* tree [singular is *lusanga*, plural *nsanga*]. In the end I count it nothing less than a wonderful answer to prayer that in the eleven months required to cut those two great trees into lumber none of the men were injured. For it is quite clear that any serious mishap would be credited to the vindicative power of the *Mihongo*.[61]

The volume of patients in the new hospital exceeded 1,000 during the first month. Repair of a broken sterilizer, the preparation of intra-venous injections, and surgery in the newly tiled operating room were notable events. Patients were treated with Bayer 205, and careful records were kept. Dr. Kellersberger wrote, "I am going about my work in a scientific way now, because of the training I received in London. My blood and lab work are easy now and I enjoy it. . . . Sleeping sickness is definitely on the increase right here at Bibanga."[62]

Medical emergencies required trips to other mission stations. In August, after Dr. Stixrud developed sleeping sickness, Dr. Kellersberger wrote his wife:

> Your illness, and the training I received because of it, has made it possible for me alone to have a supply of Bayer 205 on hand! Only through your suffering has help come to Mrs. Vinson and Dr. Stixrud, as I was able to provide them both with enough medicine for a course of treatment.[63]

Six months after Dr. Kellersberger's return to Bibanga, however, tragedy struck again. Back on a ranch near Kopperl, Texas, on October 23, 1923, Edna Kellersberger was shot and killed in the pres-ence of her daughters by her stepmother, who was estranged from her father. The depth of faith, the strength of character, and the quality of spirit that carried Eugene Kellersberger through the months that followed can be seen in words written to his parents, "God must love me to permit all this. 'Whom the Lord LOVES He chastens!' . . . God be merciful to me! Pray for me."[64]

September 1924 found Dr. Kellersberger back in Bibanga, the two little girls with relatives in Kansas City, Missouri. The next four years were incredibly difficult. He called them his "acid test," a time of brutal spiritual and physical testing. It was also a time of great accomplishment. In addition to the crowded clinics, heavy surgical load, and the trips to meet emergency calls, his work on sleeping sickness contributed significantly to the treatment and control of that dread disease.[65]

The story of the fight against sleeping sickness is many faceted. Dr. Kellersberger's official position as the *Médecin Agrée* for the Lomami District made it possible for him to survey the population of the Lubilashi Valley for which he was responsible. Experimental treatment helped determine that Tryparsamide, developed by the Rockefeller Institute, was the drug of choice, and it replaced the use of Bayer 205 which proved useful primarily in early cases. Treatment by Tryparsamide generally required just eight injections and was well received, as patients soon saw improvement in their condition. Villages of grass huts were constructed in each of the five

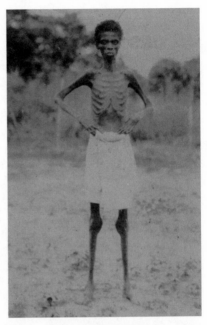

One of Dr. Kellersberger's patients with sleeping sickness. Photograph by Eugene R. Kellersberger.

mission stations to house victims of the disease during treatment. The gradual disappearance of these villages attested to the success of the vigorous efforts of government and medical professionals in the control of sleeping sickness in the Belgian Congo.[66]

A valuable store of information on trypanosomiasis was accumulated at Bibanga by careful recordkeeping, photography, and follow-up. From this material Dr. Kellersberger published a number of articles in American, British, and Belgian medical journals, and the Blakiston Medical Publishing House commissioned him to write the definitive chapter on "African Trypanosomiasis" in Stitt's classic medical textbook, *Diagnosis, Prevention and Treatment of Tropical Diseases*, volume 1, chapter III.[67]

Dr. Kellersberger's final ten years of service in Bibanga were happily different from those that preceded it. His second wife, Julia Lake Skinner Kellersberger, lived up to her Tshiluba name *Musankisha*, meaning "The One Who Makes Happy." In addition to continued surgical and clinical work in what was named the Edna Kellersberger Memorial Hospital, a number of significant medical developments should be noted.

First, the hospital had the reputation of a well-run institution with a high level of discipline and efficiency. Graduates of the school for nurse's aides were in great demand in government medical service.

Second, during the years of the Great Depression, when mission budgets were drastically reduced, Dr. Kellersberger withdrew the Bibanga medical program from the working budget of the APCM and operated entirely on receipts generated locally. These included government subsidies, drug grants, fees from Congolese and white patients, and his salary as a *Médecin Agrée* of the Belgian Congo government. The Bibanga appropriation from the APCM was divided among the other four hospitals of the mission.

Third, a surprising number of researchers found their way to Bibanga as a result of Dr. Kellersberger's reputation in tropical medicine circles. Memorable were Dr. Van den Berge's research on *Schistosoma* (liver flukes) and Dr. R. P. Strong's lecture on *Onchocerca* (nematode-causing blindness).

Finally, public health responsibilities for the Lomami District continued with a significant new development. With sleeping sickness somewhat under control, Dr. Kellersberger became concerned about the plight of people with leprosy. He concentrated on the treatment and management of leprosy in these latter years.

In 1930 work began on a leprosy village some three miles from the hospital. A church, dispensary, and neat rows of mud-dried brick homes provided an attractive refuge for 300 to 500 leprosy patients and their families. By 1937 leprosy villages had become an integral part, as well, of the other mission hospitals at Luebo, Mutoto, Bulape, and Lubondai. The leprosy work received substantial support from the Belgian colonial government and from the American Leprosy Mission. Dr. Kellersberger wrote in 1939:

We get the best results with the fresh, whole chaulmoogra oil, with 5 percent creosote added, two injections given weekly, from 1 up to 10 c.c. per injection. A special feature of our colony is our thriving 1,200–tree plantation of chaulmoogra oil trees [*Hydnocarpus anthelmintica*]. The trees [the seeds for planting were sent from Ceylon] are now nine years old and have been bearing for four years. We have made about five gallons of the fresh oil ourselves in our press, and are getting even better results than with the oil shipped from Siam . . .

We believe that leprosy can be cured, can be aborted, can be arrested and made inactive. One of the best methods is by an agricultural colony which combines healthy, wholesome, loving influences with careful, detailed scientific study and management. We need to give the loving human touch that makes life worth living again to these, the most despised and feared of all on earth![68]

Dr. Kellersberger's accomplishments in the field of leprosy were well known internationally and led to his resignation in 1940 from the APCM mission in order to accept the position of general secretary of the American Leprosy Mission, with headquarters in New York City. His fifteen years of service with the American Leprosy Mission were a fitting cap to a distinguished missionary career.

Dr. Kellersberger received many honors for his outstanding accomplishments. Among these were three awards from the Belgian government: he was made a knight of the Royal Order of the Lion, (1936), a knight of the Royal Order of the Crown, and, the highest honor, an officer of the Royal Order of the Crown (in 1957).

Those who worked with Dr. Kellersberger included a staff of capable Congolese who received on-the-job training and became remarkably effective in carrying out routine procedures. Ruby Rogers, R.N. (1919–36), a Texan and first cousin of Dr. Robert R. King of Mutoto, was Dr. Kellersberger's chief nurse. She was twenty-four years old on arrival in the Congo and has been described as a practical, no-nonsense woman. She served as anesthesiologist, held child care classes, and conducted a "thriving" well-baby clinic. Effie Lucille Dale, R.N., however, was overwhelmed by the conditions under which she worked and she committed suicide in 1937 after only five months in Africa. The last page of her diary contained these words, "O! Those dark wards! Those dark wards!"[69]

1940–1960

The medical program in Bibanga, following Dr. Kellersberger's resignation, suffered from a lack of missionary leadership during the World War II years. Mark Poole, M.D., served for two years (1940–42).

Blanche Amanda Sawyer, R.N. (1939–55), carried major responsibilities and rendered valiant service with the aid of the dedicated Congolese staff.

With the arrival of William Rule, M.D., in 1946, the Bibanga program took on new life. Bill Rule, who deeply admired Dr. Kellersberger's work, found working in "Dr. Kelly's" hospital inspirational. Dr. Rule described the Edna Kellersberger Memorial Hospital in 1946:

> The modest complex was composed of six brick buildings with metal roofs, an adjoining group of native huts with thatch roofing for patients and their families while under treatment, and an open shed for worship. The buildings included a surgical section with operating room and adjunctive areas for sterilization and surgical supplies, a men's ward, a women's ward, and an out-patient dispensary. The two remaining buildings were given over to a clinical laboratory, a class and assembly room, several isolation units and storage space. The total capacity was a little over 50 beds. The Bibanga leprosy camp was five miles away where 500 victims of the disease were under treatment.[70]

These facilities were enlarged and upgraded with Program of Progress funds from the church in America and with grants from the Native Welfare Fund (FBEI). Two buildings were constructed: a maternity ward with labor and delivery rooms and an administration building with doctor's offices, pharmacy, classrooms, and storage area; other buildings were enlarged. New equipment included the *first* X ray, an hydraulic operating table, surgical instruments, a new microscope, electric suction apparatus, and high-frequency cautery. In 1952 the arrival of Elizabeth Templeton, M.T., a medical technologist with certification as an X-ray technician, raised the level of medical practice in Bibanga.

A bonanza for all the mission's hospitals came in 1958 when the General Hospital in Knoxville, Tennessee, moved into new modern facilities. Friends in Knoxville, which was Dr. Rule's hometown, acquired much of the old hospital's equipment for the medical work in the Congo. The arrival of this equipment in four wooden cases, each "large enough to hold an automobile," was, as Dr. Rule wrote, "like Christmas."[71]

In addition to the usual tropical diseases, Dr. Rule found himself dealing, for the first time, with persons suffering from intestinal and hepatic schistosomiasis. Tuberculosis also had become a major health problem.

The greatest challenge, however, and the one that was to consume Dr. Rule's energies for the duration of his mission service, was the need for formal medical education for the Congolese. In the APCM, as in other missions, the missionaries disagreed over (1) whether to distribute limited medical resources as widely as possible or (2) whether to concentrate personnel and equipment in order to teach Congolese and, secondarily, to practice a higher level of medicine.

At the 1946 meeting of the mission, Dr. Rule obtained permission to experiment with a class for medical assistants. With great enthusiasm a class was selected by entrance examinations held in all the mission stations. Margaret Liston, R.N., a senior nurse from Lubondai, was assigned to assist in instruction. Although after only one year, the mission was not able or willing to continue the teaching experiment, the seed was planted, and six years later, in Dr. Rule's words, "sentiments changed to allow our medical department to expand to the point of making higher medical education a valid project."[72]

This change in sentiment occurred in 1953, and Lubondai was selected for the site of a school for *infirmiers* (nurses). Dr. Rule was moved to Lubondai to be director of the school, and Dr. George Cousar took charge of the Bibanga Hospital. In 1959, just before independence, Dr. Cousar left on furlough and Hugh L. Farrior, M.D., the son of PCUS missionaries to China and a graduate of the Medical College of Virginia (M.D., 1953), took charge of the hospital complex in Bibanga.

LUBONDAI HOSPITAL
Lubondai

Lubondai station was established in 1925 in order to better reach the peoples in the southern area of the Kasai. The land for the station, some sixty-five acres, was ceded to the mission by Chief Ntolo, the friendly paramount chief of a nearby complex of villages. He remained a staunch supporter of the mission throughout his life. The name Lubondai was taken from the name of a nearby stream.

William Anderson, profiting from the building experience in the other stations, planned a well-designed layout for Lubondai: a church, school, hospital, and missionary homes of red brick were connected by well-maintained pathways; a grassy campus bordered by tropical trees and flowering shrubs gave a parklike appearance. George R. Cousar, a graduate of Johns Hopkins University (M.D., 1922), and Margaret Lapsley Liston, R.N., great-niece of the pioneer, Samuel N. Lapsley, were assigned to the new station to open the medical work.

George R. Cousar, M.D. and Margaret Liston, R.N.
The medical work in Lubondai had a slow start, and Dr. Cousar is remembered as the doctor who sat under a tree and nobody came. The people were fearful of the foreign medicine man and were aghast when the son of one of the chiefs announced he was going to go to the new doctor and ask for a job. This young man, Mashondo Pierre, became the chief medical assistant at Lubondai and served with distinction until his death from cancer some twenty years later. Lukusa, another medical assistant, had this to say:

> At first the sick were scared of the hospital and would not come. They were enticed by gifts of salt, soap, medicine, food, and even cash. New babies were given baby clothes. Now [1985] people are not only willing to come but are willing to pay for hospital care. However, many are too poor to pay.[73]

In 1927 Lubondai became the site for Central School, the school for missionary's children. Up to sixty young people from a number of mission bodies attended this school in grades four through twelve. They were given instruction in English and prepared for higher education in American schools. A resident physician was assigned to Lubondai at all times to provide medical coverage for these young people.

The forty-bed hospital consisted of a central core with two large wards (one for men and one for women), an isolation ward, an operating room, and a work room. An adjoining dispensary housed a record room, pharmacy, and clinical laboratory. A steam boiler, fired with logs cut from the forest, provided steam for sterilization and for a generator that produced some electricity. Running water came from rain water collected in a large cistern and pumped to an elevated reservoir.

The leprosy camp, some five miles away, contained a dispensary, chapel, and housing for two medical assistants; many rows of mud-and-stick huts housed the 300 to 400 patients. This camp was later merged with one not far away, which was operated by the government under Catholic supervision.

Dr. Cousar was detained in the United States during World War II. William Rule, a graduate of the University of Pennsylvania (M.D., 1936) and newly arrived in 1940, served his first term in Lubondai. As previously noted, he was at one time the only APCM physician on the field. Dr. Rule called these his "traveling years" and estimated that in 1942 he was on the road a total of 192 days.[74]

The war years were not without their accomplishments. The hospital, now enlarged to 90 to 100 beds and staffed with male nurse's aides, was a busy place. Pathology was varied and interesting. Blood transfusions were administered for the first time. A maternity ward, with delivery room and a dozen obstetrical beds, was constructed with funds donated by a Belgian firm (*Compagnie Cotonnière Congolaise*). A prenatal clinic was established and became well accepted. Some ten students (with a minimum of six years' education) were enrolled in a two-year training program and became licensed nurse's aides after passing a government examination.

Dr. Rule laughingly commented that perhaps his greatest surgical operation, and one of which he was proud, was the repair of the steam boiler. He was also proud of improving sanitation in the hospital by prohibiting patients' families from moving into the wards with the

Barrels of white cross supplies (gift of the PCUS Women of the Church) being unloaded at the hospital in Lubondai. Photograph courtesy of Margaret Liston.

patients, by requiring that food be prepared outside the building rather than by the patients' bedside, and by putting sheets on the beds.[75]

Dr. Cousar returned to Lubondai in 1944, and the Rules were assigned to Bibanga. Lubondai profited in several ways from the revitalization of the postwar years. Buildings were upgraded and, best of all, a hydroelectric plant that delivered round-the-clock electricity to the station was installed.

Dental Program

Sandy C. Marks, a graduate of the Atlanta Southern Dental College (D.D.S., 1933), was thirty-eight years old when, after fifteen years of private practice in Wilmington, North Carolina, he decided in 1948 to become a missionary/dentist of the APCM in the Congo. Accompanied by his wife, Katherine, R.N., and three children, he was assigned to Lubondai.

Before 1948 (for some twenty-five years), the dental needs of the mission had been met by a most unusual person, Rev. (Samuel) Hugh Wilds. Described by Dr. Marks as a "multi-talented evangelistic missionary," Wilds served, for a while, as captain of the SS *Lapsley*. During a furlough year he studied dentistry with a dentist in Richmond, Virginia, and returned to make this his vocation in the Kasai region. Luebo was his home station, but for much of the year he made rounds of the stations with his truck full of instruments and a portable (foot-pedaled) drill to look after the needs of the missionary families and others who sought his care. He established an office at Lake Munkamba where vacationers were prevailed upon to get their teeth checked. Wilds was able to keep the mission in acceptable dental health.

Wilds was once called upon to treat Prince Leopold of Belgium (subsequently King Leopold III), who was touring the Congo. In later years, when government officials questioned whether, since he held no degree from a dental school, Wilds should be allowed to continue his practice, this successful treatment of the young prince proved decisive. Because Wilds was judged competent enough to treat royalty, he should be allowed to continue treating others as well.

In addition to his practice among the missionary (and European) population, Wilds engaged in what Dr. Marks called "evangelistic extractions."[76] Churches in villages visited by Wilds invariably received an influx of new members. Other evangelistic missionaries, notably Rev. A. Hoyt Miller and Rev. Carroll R. Stegall, regularly engaged in this practice as well; dental forceps became part of their armamentarium.

Dr. Marks felt "called" to the mission field for two specific purposes: to care for the dental needs of the 160 APCM missionaries and their children and to establish a dental school to train Congolese in dentistry.

The first of these two purposes was soon implemented and quickly expanded into a very active dental practice among the Europeans who were settling in the Congo in ever increasing numbers. Dr. Marks wrote:

> It was not our purpose in going to Africa to build up a large European clientele. At the same time, we could not satisfy a Christian conscience by refusing to help people suffering from toothache. We did our best to help all who came and collected professional fees for the work done on patients outside of our mission. With the profits made from this work we were able to finance the construction of some of the buildings for our dental school and buy a limited amount of equipment. [Free dental care was provided to the mission's Congolese employees.][77]

Establishing a dental school (the first in the country), which took place in conjunction with the establishment of the training school for nurses, took seven years to accomplish. During the intervening years, plans were made for the construction of the dental buildings, curriculum was worked out in consultation with Belgian officials, and two dentists, Jean B. Jung (D.D.S. in 1936 from the Loyola University

J. B. Jung, D.D.S., and Sandy C. Marks, D.D.S., with their first class of IMCK dental students. Photograph courtesy of Sandy C. Marks.

of the South, New Orleans) and Bernard G. Jackson (D.D.S. in 1956 from Northwestern University) were recruited so that the school would be staffed by two dentists at all times.

Institut Médical Chrétien du Kasai (IMCK)

The founding in 1953 of the IMCK, a training program for nurses and dentists, represented a new dimension in medical work for the APCM. A determining factor in locating the IMCK in Lubondai was the presence of the Central School and its need for medical coverage.

After World War II William Rule, M.D. (and others of the newer medical missionaries), had become convinced that the time had come for the mission to expand its medical program to include training that would help provide a Christian medical profession for the Congo. While studying at the Tulane School of Tropical Medicine during his first furlough (1946), Dr. Rule met John K. Miller, a medical student and son of Congo missionaries, who was preparing to return to the Congo. These two found that they had a similar vision for the future of the medical program. Drs. Rule and Miller, along with Dr. Sandy Marks, are the recognized founders of the IMCK.

Drs. Bill Rule and John K. Miller were recognized as founders of the Institute Médical Chrétien du Kasai (IMCK). Photographs courtesy of John K. Miller.

The need was for Congolese doctors, but because the level of education was low, the beginning was made on the paramedical level with the training of nurses. The mission's first high school was not established until 1954 (in Kankinda) and its highest educational institution, the *École Secondaire Unie* (senior high school) in 1957 (in Katubwe).

The concept of an institution specializing in medical education was not readily accepted by missionaries, government officials, or the people. As noted, the experiment in training nurses on the *infirmier* (R.N.) level that was initiated by Dr. Rule in Bibanga in 1946 was aborted after one year. Not until 1953 did the mission vote to establish the school for *infirmiers* in Lubondai. This decision meant the reassignment of missionaries: Rules, Millers, Margaret Liston, and Alice Longenecker to Lubondai; the Cousars to Bibanga; and the Nelsons to Luebo. Start-up funds were provided by the mission's Program of Progress and by the Belgian government's Native Welfare Fund (FBEI).

IMCK opened in January 1954 with eight students, all males who had completed the seventh grade; entrance was by examination. To earn the coveted nursing degree, students had to complete a five-year course and pass an examination given by Belgian officials. Ten nurses graduated from IMCK prior to independence.[78]

The original plan to train *infirmiers* expanded in 1955 to include the training of dentists. Many of the basic courses could be taught

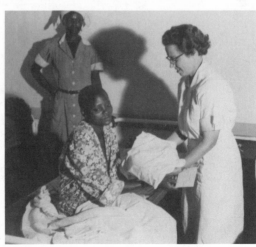

Alice Longenecker, R.N., gives a young mother a layette sent by the Women of the Church. Photograph courtesy of John K. Miller.

Dormitories at IMCK, Lubondai. Photograph courtesy of John K. Miller.

together. The courses were designed to meet standards set by the government and were conducted in the French language. Because no teaching materials were available, lessons were written out and mimeographed for distribution to the students.

Nine students entered the first dental class in 1955. All these students also were male and had completed the seventh grade. The dental course took five years—three years of study followed by two years of clinical training. Six of the first-year class completed the course and, by independence, a total of ten dentists had graduated and received their diplomas. Each graduate was given dental supplies sufficient for one year.

The first faculty consisted of two doctors (William Rule, director, and John Miller, associate director), one dentist (Sandy Marks), three nurses (Margaret Liston, Alice Longenecker, Katherine Marks), and one medical technologist (Aurie M. Miller). Others who taught at IMCK prior to independence include Hugh English, M.D., Robert Dunn, M.D., Jean Baptiste Jung, D.D.S., Bernard Jackson, D.D.S., Julia Hampton, R.N., Lucille McElroy, R.N., and Nolie McDonald, X-ray technician.

The IMCK was off to a good start with a bright future when independence brought an end to this first phase of the story.

THE OUTSTATIONS
1913–1960

The APCM, as previously noted, undertook medical work in a number of places outside the five main stations. The first of these was Lusambo, the river port on the Sankuru River, which served as a mission station from 1913 to 1925. Despite the depression, in the 1930s the APCM decided to open a number of "small stations devoted entirely to evangelistic work . . . without the usual large physical equipment of a main station." These "Gospel Centers" quickly grew, and by the 1940s there was a vastly more effective mission of ten stations. In the 1950s new work was begun in three more locations making a total of thirteen APCM stations.

The APCM undertook no medical work in three of the new stations that were in urban areas where well-developed medical facilities existed: Luluabourg (Kananga), Léopoldville (Kinshasa), and Bakwagna (Mbujimayi). The medical work in Kasha, Mboi, Moma, Kakinda, and Katubwe remained on the dispensary level, although a hospital was built in Moma just before independence. Staffing of these dispensaries was primarily by missionary nurses assisted by male nurse's aides trained in the mission's hospitals; physicians were assigned to Mboi and Moma for short periods of time.

Regular support for the dispensaries was provided by the nearest mission hospital: to Kasha and Kakinda from Bibanga, to Katubwe and Moma from Lubondai, and to Mboi from Lubondai and Luebo. In later years airstrips facilitated these visits.

Lusambo

Lusambo was the capital of the Kasai at the time the APCM maintained a station there; a Belgian government hospital with Belgian doctors provided adequate medical coverage. However, a small dispensary was constructed as part of the APCM facilities and two APCM medical personnel were assigned there for short periods of time. Eugene Kellersberger, M.D., spent his first two years (1916–18) at Lusambo before going to Bibanga. Jean Setser, R.N. (1920–21), was in Lusambo before her marriage to Alexander Shive, the industrial missionary whose skill as a builder took the Shives to several stations (Mutoto, Luebo, and Lubondai). As reported earlier, the APCM discontinued work at Lusambo in order to open the Lubondai station.

Kasha

Kasha, the first of the new stations, was opened in 1935 near the railroad. Orcelia Bissett King (Mrs. Earl S. King Sr.) operated a clinic and, though not a trained nurse, energetically cared for many sick people. Regular visits by the physician at Bibanga provided supervision and support. Margaret Moore, R.N. (1943–45), was the first registered nurse to serve in Kasha.

Mary Etta Stixrud, R.N., the widow of Dr. Stixrud, went to Kasha in 1947 and married Rev. W. Frank McElroy in 1953. The McElroys served in Kasha until their retirement in 1956. Mary Etta Stixrud McElroy operated a very successful, and indeed booming, clinic concentrating on the welfare of women and children. Blanche Sawyer, R.N., served in Kasha for one year (1956–57).

Mboi

Mboi was established in 1937 among the (Ba)Bindi people in a remote area to the southwest almost equidistant from Luebo and Lubondai. Missionary nurses at Mboi were Bessie Hancock Wilson (1946), Julia Hampton (1946–54) until assigned to teach at IMCK, Nannette Fulson (1955–56), Margaret McMurry (1958–60) and Virginia King (Mrs. Earl King Jr.) (1954–60). Gladys Smithwick, M.D., a board-certified anesthesiologist, was inexplicably assigned to the clinic at Mboi for one year (1953–54).

Virginia King, whose husband was the evangelist and builder of the school in Mboi, was assisted by three male nurses and two midwives (village women who were given special training) in the dispensary and sixteen-bed maternity unit. A Belgian government doctor, twenty miles away, could be called on for emergencies. Mission doctors at Lubondai and Luebo visited regularly.

Virginia King reported that she enjoyed the curative aspect of the dispensary work and the work with babies, but felt that her most valuable contribution was in training and teaching. Most of the training went to the Luba people, who aggressively sought the opportunity to learn. In retrospect, she wishes she had tried harder to teach the local (Ba)Bindi who were a primitive people. She was grateful for the help of good Congolese nurses, and added that the most difficult part of this work was the responsibility resulting from isolation from a doctor.[79]

Moma

Moma, some eighty-five miles south of Lubondai, became an APCM station in 1942 at the request of the Belgian government officials. Moma was established by the Four Square Gospel Mission, which was founded by the famous woman evangelist Aimee Semple McPherson. The property was well developed with a church, schools, and residences, but the Four Square Gospel Mission personnel were not successful and eventually left the country.

Moma, the name meaning python, was located in an area where elephants roamed and leopards prowled. The Sala Mpasu people were cannibals and the most primitive of any with whom the APCM worked.[80]

Dr. Rule, in Lubondai at the time, was asked to recruit a trained medical assistant to help run a small dispensary at Moma. This was not easy, as one of the mission's Congolese evangelists had recently fallen victim to the cannibals. Dr. Rule chose Muwaya Simon, a good man with several years' experience, and offered him the job. Muwaya at first demurred but finally agreed and worked successfully in Moma for thirteen years.[81]

John Morrison and his wife, Mary, R.N., left Luebo in order to help open the work in Moma, where they served for two years (1943–45). Lucille Stone McElroy, R.N., a capable nurse with excellent native language skills, having grown up in the Congo, then ran the clinic from 1947 to 1956; she left to help with the teaching program at the IMCK in Lubondai. Dr. Robert King, the pioneer physician of Mutoto and Luebo, completed his missionary career at Moma (1951–55). Melford S. Dickerson, a graduate of Baylor University (M.D., 1939), and his wife Mary Frances, R.N., arrived in Moma in 1956 and served until independence in 1960.

In 1958, with support from the mission and the enthusiastic collaboration of Rev. Joseph H. Spooner, Dr. Dickerson constructed a small, sturdy hospital of gray fieldstone. It contained a forty-bed ward, operating and sterilizing rooms, a pharmacy, and an X ray. Unfortunately, the work of this hospital was closed by the events surrounding independence.

Kakinda

Kakinda, near the railroad south of Luluabourg, was founded in 1948 and became, in 1954, the site of the first high school (normal school) to be run by the APCM. Alice Longenecker, R.N., was the first medical missionary assigned to Kakinda in 1951 and served until 1954, when she was asked to join the faculty of the IMCK. She was followed by Elizabeth Miller (1954–60), who graduated from the John Hopkins School of Nursing in 1929.

Elizabeth Miller's description of her work at Kakinda gives a good picture of the heroic work carried on in the "outstations" by the mission's nurses. The Kakinda dispensary had a simple laboratory and a ward for twenty to thirty patients. Elizabeth Miller also had medical responsibility for students in the high school and taught classes in hygiene at the school. Dr. Cousar came from Bibanga regularly. A Belgian-run *Formulac* Hospital, some thirty miles away, had two doctors and a number of nurses who provided support as necessary. Common cases included snake bite, burns, hysteria, fractures, always malaria, malnutrition, and complicated pregnancies. A patient with a severe crocodile bite was sent to *Formulac*.

Elizabeth Miller remembers two cases for which, she says, "I must give the Lord all the credit." One was a case of smallpox that was sent to *Formulac* but was sent back because that hospital's isolation ward was full. She fixed up an isolation room and commandeered the help of a cousin of the patient by locking up his bicycle. Together they managed to pull the patient through. On another occasion a two-pound premature infant also survived after his young parents walked for two days to bring him to the clinic.[82]

Kakinda station was badly damaged during the Luba/Lulua wars at the time of independence.

Katubwe

Katubwe, located on the railroad south of Luluabourg, was the site of the *senior* high school founded in 1957 with the Methodist mission. A clinic at the high school was staffed by Bessie Wilson, R.N. (1958–60), whose husband, Robert, was a teacher in the school. Although a Belgian-operated hospital was accessible, many local people sought the services of the clinic and were not turned away.

Notes

1. After independence many place-names were changed from European to traditional African names. In general, the names used herein reflect the time when they are used; an alternate name appears in parentheses when needed to clarify the text.

2. Ethel Taylor Wharton, *Led In Triumph* (Nashville, Tenn.: Board of World Missions, Presbyterian Church, U.S., 1952), 74.

3. Virginia Gray Pruitt, "New Nation, New Church: Congo 1960–1970," typescript, 1972, 6.

4. Wharton, *Led in Triumph*, 119.

5. Vernon Anderson, interview, Feb. 1984.

6. David Lamb, *The Africans* (New York: Vintage Books, 1984), 139; Pruitt, "New Nation, New Church," 62.

7. Pruitt, "New Nation, New Church," 6.

8. *Encyclopedia Britannica*, vol. 3, 1969, 414–16.

9. Stanley Shaloff, *Reform in Leopold's Congo* (Richmond, Va.: John Knox Press, 1970), 74–127.

10. William E. Phipps, *The Sheppards and Lapsley: Pioneer Presbyterians in the Congo* (Louisville, Ky.: Presbyterian Church (USA), 1991), 32.

11. Stanley Shaloff, *Reform in Leopold's Congo*, 47–52.

12. Pruitt, "New Nation, New Church," 26.

13. Shaloff, *Reform in Leopold's Congo*, 178, quoting J. Du Plessis, *The Evangelisation of Pagan Africa* (Capetown: 1929), 219.

14. Ibid., 178, quoting Thomas Ellis Reeve, *In Wembo-Nyama's Land* (Nashville Tenn.: 1921), 126.

15. Anderson, interview.

16. Pruitt, "New Nation, New Church," 26.

17. Vernon Anderson, *Still Led in Triumph* (Nashville, Tenn.: Board of World Missions, PCUS, 1959), 31.

18. David B. Barrett, *World Christian Encyclopedia* (London: Oxford University Press, 1982), 758.

19. Mary Dabney, *Light in Darkness* (Knoxville, Tenn., by Martha Reid Bedinger, 1971), 35.

20. Jean S. Shive, R.N., interview, Feb. 1984.

21. William Rule, M.D., "Milestones in Mission" (Knoxville, Tenn., 1991), 199–200.

22. *The Missionary Survey*, Aug. 1916, 595.

23. Winifred K. Vass, interview, September 1997.

24. Patricia Houck Sprinkle, *The Birthday Book: First Fifty Years* (Atlanta, Ga.: Board of Women's Work, PCUS, 1972), 16.

25. J. Tinsley Smith, M.D., interview, Feb. 1984.

26. Mark K. Poole, M.D., interview, Jan. 1984.

27. Winifred K. and Lachlan C. Vass III, *The Lapsley Saga* (Franklin, Tenn.: Providence House Publishers, 1997), 68–71.

28. Motte Martin, *Kasai Herald*, Jan. 1904.

29. Winifred K. Vass, *Doctor Not Afraid: E. R. Kellersberger, M.D.* (Austin, Tex.: Nortex Press, 1986), 102–06.

30. Llewellyn J. Coppedge, M.D., "Twelve Years in Congoland," typescript at the Department of History, Montreat, N.C..

31. Thomas T. Stixrud, M.D., "History of Medical Work at Luebo," *Presbyterian Survey*, April 1924, 278.

32. Coppedge, "Twelve Years in Congoland," 10–11.

33. Thomas T. Stixrud, M.D., "Medical Work in the Congo. Does it Pay?" *Missionary Survey*, June 1916, 435.

34. William Rule, M.D., "Milestones in Mission," 78–79.

35. Carroll R. Stegall, "Industrial Department," *Missionary Survey*, June 1916, 437.

36. Mark Poole, M.D., interview, Dec. 1984.

37. In 1914 the McKowens also donated funds for the hospital in Chonju, Korea.

38. Carroll R. Stegall, "Industrial Department," 437.

39. Stixrud, "History," 278.

40. Stixrud, "Medical Work," 435.

41. Mary Morrison, R.N., interview, Nov. 1984.

42. John Morrison, interview, Nov. 1984.

43. Annual Report (Minutes, PCUS General Assembly), 1957, 31.

44. J. Tinsley Smith, M.D., interview, Feb. 1984.

45. Rev. Eugene Daniel, conversation, 1985.

46. Conway T. Wharton, *The Leopard Hunts Alone* (New York: Fleming H. Revell Co., 1927), 108.

47. Hezekiah M. Washburn, *Knight of the Congo: God's Ambassador in Three Continents* (Bassett, Va.: privately published, 1972), 127–30.

48. Ibid., 130.

49. Wharton, *The Leopard Hunts Alone*, 123–24.

50. Wharton, *The Leopard Hunts Alone*, 138.

51. Mark Poole, M.D., interview, Dec. 1984.

52. George Kent, "20 Years of Eventful Days in the Congo," condensed from *Presbyterian Life* (June 9, 1956); printed in *Reader's Digest* (July 1956).

53. John K. Miller, M.D., interview, June 1985.

54. Ruth Worth, M.T., interview, 1984.

55. Wharton,*The Leopard Hunts Alone*, 16.

56. Vass, *Doctor Not Afraid*, 172, 203, 233.

57. Rule, "Milestones in Mission," 166.

58. Vass, *Dr. Not Afraid*, 115.

59. Ibid., 188.

60. Ibid., 194.

61. J. Hershey Longenecker, *Memories of Congo* (Johnson City, Tenn.: Royal Publishers, 1964), 48–60.

62. Vass, *Dr. Not Afraid*, 200.

63. Ibid., 203.

64. Ibid., 215–16.

65. Ibid., 221.

66. Ibid., 243.

67. Ibid., 348, 350.

68. Ibid., 265–66.

69. Ibid., 266–67.

70. Rule, "Milestones in Mission," 166.

71. Ibid., 171.

72. Ibid., 169–70.

73. Lukusa, interview, June 1985.

74. Rule, "Milestones in Mission," 118.

75. Rule, interview, Sept. 1984.

76. Sandy C. Marks, D.D.S., "Dentistry on the Mission Field," paper presented at the annual meeting of the N.C. Dental Society, May 3, 1959; reprinted in the *North Carolina Dental Society Journal*, 1959, 302.

77. Ibid., 302–03.

78. Rule, interview, 1984.

79. Virginia King, interview, June 1985.

80. John Morrison, *Mission to Africa* (Nashville, Tenn.: privately published, 1979), 211–12.

81. Rule, "Milestones in Mission," 96–99.

82. Elizabeth Miller, R.N., interview, March 1984.

— Chapter Eight —

Congo/Zaire (1960–1965)

Independence!

The year 1960 proved to be pivotal in the history of Congo/Zaire. As Virginia Gray Pruitt, a veteran PCUS missionary, put it, "Congo history hinges on the year 1960; everything is viewed in the perspective of pre- or postindependence."[1] Her monograph, "New Nation, New Church: Congo 1960–1970" is a concise account and is the primary source of the historical events presented here.

The political history of the first five years of independence can be divided into four distinct periods:

1. Independence from Belgium on June 30, 1960, followed by ten days of turmoil;
2. United Nations presence, which maintained the peace for four years until June 30, 1964;
3. Mulelist/Simba rebellion, 1964–65, which simmered underground and burst into bloody guerrilla warfare after the departure of the UN peacekeeping force; and
4. A bloodless coup d'état by General Mobutu Sese Seko on November 24, 1965, and his establishment of a military dictatorship.

Independence from Belgium (June 30, 1960)

The Congo that the Belgian government released to independence in 1960 was vastly different from the one it had reluctantly taken over from King Leopold in 1908. While admittedly profiting from its status as a colonial power, the Belgian government took seriously its responsibility to bring modern civilization to the Congolese; what was

272

accomplished within fifty-two years in an immense, totally undeveloped, and only partially explored country was remarkable. However the Belgian's paternalistic policy encouraged Congolese dependency and stifled initiative and responsibility. This approach also fostered a superiority complex on the part of *Europeans* (a term used for all "whites"), convincing them that they knew better what was good for the Congolese and how their future should be planned. Economic development and generous social welfare benefits expanded enormously in the 1950s, but little was done to train the Congolese for leadership in the political or any other arena.

Life for the Congolese had changed radically under the Belgians. Railroads and industry had contributed toward urbanization; schooling (elementary level) had produced what was considered by some observers to be the best literacy rate in Africa; a small middle class made up of teachers, clergy, medical assistants, and white-collar clerks slowly began to emerge. This young elite group resented their lower living standard, unequal pay, and lack of social acceptance by the colonials. The isolation that the Belgian government had sought to maintain began to erode as the Congolese took part in World War II and experienced a limited amount of travel and education abroad.

Two events in 1958 opened the eyes of the emerging young leaders of the Congo to the rising tide of nationalism and anticolonialism in the rest of the world.

1. Hundreds of Congolese attended the International Exposition in Brussels, in which many musicians, dancers, and artisans participated. Not only did they experience the outside world for the first time, but the elite from wide-apart Congo cities had an opportunity to meet and share ideas and aspirations.

2. Patrice Lumumba, an emerging leader of the independence movement, attended the first All-African People's Conference in December, which was held in Ghana (in 1956 black Africa's first independent country). He returned to inflame a mass meeting in Léopoldville, and in January 1959 bloody riots swept the city.

These riots profoundly shocked the Belgians who were bewildered by the resentment thus revealed, which they saw as biting the "hand that fed."[2] They were also stunned at their inability to control the leadership and the masses, and realized that the time had come for drastic new measures. Either they would have to rule by force or they would have to find a way to accommodate the nationalistic aspirations of the Congolese. Also in 1959, for the first time, expenditures in the Belgian Congo exceeded profits.

On January 13, 1959, King Baudouin of Belgium issued a declaration of Congo independence, "We are today resolved to lead, without fatal evasions but also without imprudent haste, the Congo populations to independence in prosperity and peace."[3] The Belgians envisioned a transition period in which to build a Congolese state closely aligned to its former colonial ruler; they expected that their decades of concern for the welfare of Congo and their generous offer of independence would contribute to a cooperative relationship. They misjudged the temper of the times and were to lose disastrously in what came to be spoken of as the Congo "gamble."

On June 30, 1960, in a colorful ceremony in Léopoldville (Kinshasa), King Baudouin formally bestowed independence on the colony that Belgium had ruled for fifty-two years. Much to everyone's relief, all went well and the independent Republic of Congo was launched.

Euphoria was to prove short-lived. Four days later, on July 4, the Congolese *Force Publique* (army and police) mutinied against their Belgian officers. All over the Congo, a trigger-happy drunken mob ran amok in the streets. Belgians were hauled from their homes, beaten, and humiliated; women were raped. Congolese, as well as Europeans, were victimized by a leaderless and lawless mob rule. Few were killed, but the malicious glee of the mob was terrifying, and the result was a headlong departure of "whites" from the country. Belgian paratroopers assisted in the evacuation from remote areas. The participation of the Belgian troops exacerbated an already volatile situation because it was misinterpreted by many Congolese as a Belgian attempt to repossess the country. Relations between the Belgians and the Congolese were irrevocably ruptured; any hope of a peaceful cooperative period of nation building vanished.

Independence fever, as it was called, raged throughout the country with an excess of totally unrealistic expectations. Power struggles for domination in the new government ignited ethnic conflicts. A secessionist movement threatened to split the country: in Shaba (Katanga) Province, the rich mining province to the southeast, relations with the Belgians remained good and a separatist movement gained popular support; in the Kasai, where open warfare had broken out, the Lulua and the Luba each sought to form their own government.

United Nations Troops Keep the Peace (1960–1964)

On July 12 Congolese government officials made an urgent appeal to the United Nations for help. In a remarkably speedy response, United Nations peacekeeping troops were in the country by July 18; they remained for four years, until June 30, 1964. The UN mandate was fourfold:

1. To replace Belgian troops and maintain the peace until the Congolese police could be rehabilitated;
2. To keep down ethnic strife and prevent the splitting of the country into separate entities;
3. To ward off cold-war manipulations; and
4. To provide technical skills no longer available after the departure of the Belgians.

As Virginia Pruitt wrote, "By and large the UN forces comported themselves well, commanded the respect and gratitude of the Congolese, and fulfilled their duties as called upon. Without their deterring presence, tribal and regional conflicts would no doubt have torn the Congo to pieces."[4]

The threatened secession of the rich Shaba (Katanga) Province, on which the newly formed republic based its economic survival, continued to fester. Dag Hammarskjöld, secretary general of the United Nations, died in 1961 when his plane crashed while on a peacemaking mission to Elizabethville (Lubumbashi), the Shaba capital. In January 1963 the UN troops defeated the Shaba militia, thus preventing division of the fledgling nation.

Mulelist/Simba Rebellion (1964–1965)

In the meantime the Congolese government struggled to provide stable leadership, and the mood in early 1964 was generally optimistic. A constitution based on the principles and values of Western democracy was drafted. Lessons in self-government that had not been offered by the Belgians were being learned in the hard school of experience; a willingness to get on with the serious business of nation building was evident. However, a rebellion that would prove to be more bloody and devastating than anything that had gone before was in the making.

The Mulelist/Simba rebels emerged after the departure of the UN peacekeeping troops and established their headquarters in Stanleyville (Kisangani). Fed by fires of ethnic rivalries and general discontent, the rebellion was a leftist movement and, with the emergence of Pierre Mulele as leader, took on the terminology and tactics of Maoism with African adaptations. These adaptations included witchcraft, traditional ceremonials, war dress, and war paint. Following the patterns found wherever Communists have taken power (in Korea, Cambodia, Peru, China), a fanatically cruel guerrilla war was unleashed against the "reactionaries," "exploiters," and "neocolonialists"; many innocents were caught in the fray. Untold numbers of the most promising leaders and best-educated Congolese (politicians, teachers, religious leaders, civil servants, soldiers, police) were ruthlessly killed. The movement was not at first directed against the whites, but before it was over it became explicitly antiwhite; many Europeans were killed or held hostage.

The rebellion was finally brought under control in November 1965 with the assistance of South African mercenaries and international soldiers of fortune. Belgian paratroopers ferried by U.S. planes rescued Europeans held hostage in Stanleyville. The fighting was merciless on both sides. Sporadic outbreaks continued through 1967.

A particularly tragic aspect of the movement was the recruitment and indoctrination of young men, many in their teens, who were called the *Simba*, a defiant title meaning lion. These youthful warriors turned ruthless. They were encouraged to smoke hemp (marijuana) and sent into battle believing they were invulnerable. They were to die by the hundreds.

The tragic consequences of this Mulelist/Simba rebellion have been described as threefold: (1) the decimation in rebel-occupied areas of the most promising Congolese leaders (at least 20,000 Congolese were killed); (2) the cynical manipulation and indoctrination of the young Simba; and (3) the slaughter of the whites, including 150 Catholic and 29 Protestant missionaries.[5]

General Mobutu's Coup d'État

The final chapter in the Congo's quest for independence was the bloodless coup d'état of November 24, 1965, in which Gen. Mobutu Sese Seko took over and established the military dictatorship of the country. As in so many African countries, the idealistic search for freedom and independence was destroyed by chaos that made a military dictatorship seem a reasonable solution to an unmanageable situation.

Independence and the APCM

The APCM, in contrast to other mission bodies in the Congo, suffered no deaths during the years of chaos that followed independence in 1960. Four PCUS missionaries were injured; harassment, threats, and unpleasant incidents were common. Danger was real, and fear was an ever present fact of life. A number of Congolese colleagues were killed and injured.

Five historical events affected the work of the APCM:

1. Ethnic warfare between the Luba and the Lulua (1959–62);
2. Evacuation of the mission personnel (July 1960);
3. Return of the missionaries and resumption of work (August 1960);
4. Mulelist/Simba rebels' advance on Luluabourg repulsed (August 1964); and
5. General Mobutu's assumption of power (November 1965) and formation of a military dictatorship.

Luba/Lulua Conflict (1959–1960)

The rising tide of nationalism was hardly to be discerned in the hinterland of the Kasai until 1959, when the Belgians announced the date for the end of their colonial rule. Jockeying for power in the new government broke out all over the country. The power struggle was nowhere more violent than in the Kasai between the Luba and the Lulua peoples.

The Lulua, the more numerous, occupied most of the western portion of the Kasai. The Luba, whose traditional home was in the east, were scattered all over the Kasai. As has been noted, this scattering first occurred as the slave traders preyed upon the Luba; later the Luba took advantage of educational opportunities and secured prestigious employment in government, industry, and church circles. The Lulua reacted violently to the realization that, in the new regime, they would probably be subordinate to their former slaves; they were determined to force the Luba back to their homeland in the east.

Enmity escalated and in 1959 broke into open warfare, which was traditional in form, accompanied by war dances, war paint, war cries, witchcraft, and fetishes. Weapons included machetes, spears, bows and arrows, and ancient muzzle-loading guns; arson and destruction of property were common.

This ethnic violence took the APCM personnel by surprise. Within church circles, ethnic differences had been ignored, and most missionaries were not even aware of the ethnic background of their Congolese colleagues. In the midst of conflict, the missionaries tried to be impartial and act as peacemakers, but with little success. They cared for the wounded, offered sanctuary to refugees, and hauled truckloads of Luba families to Luba country.

In early 1960 Belgian authorities attempted to mediate a solution by ordering the repatriation of 100,000 Luba from Lulua country to their homeland in the east. UN peacekeeping troops later assisted in the transfer of the Luba. This transfer of peoples was accompanied by bitterness, anger, retaliation, and suffering. A casualty of the Luba/Lulua conflict was the mission's vacation/conference center on Lake Munkamba. Located on the border where fighting surged back and forth, the center was completely destroyed.

The concentration of the Luba in the eastern part of Kasai Province led the Luba to attempt, unsuccessfully, to form the independent nation of "South Kasai." It also led to the division of the province into West Kasai, with its capital Luluabourg (Kananga), and East Kasai, with Bakwanga (Mbuji Mayi) as its capital. The church, too, separated into two "synods," the Synods of East and West Kasai. The two synods were linked under a single General Assembly of the Presbyterian Church of the Kasai, which was eventually renamed the Presbyterian Church of Zaire (CPZ).

Evacuation of APCM Personnel (July 12, 1960)

Before the ceremonial declaration of independence on June 30, 1960, the American embassy and the church offices in the United States alerted APCM personnel to possible peril. Contingency plans for evacuation were made. Airstrips were completed in each of the mission's stations, and daily radio communication was maintained. The mission's two planes were kept in flying condition, and the three pilots, Mark Poole, M.D., John Davis (former U.S. Air Force major) and John Miller, M.D., were at the ready.

The APCM hoped to be able to stay in place and participate with their friends in the joys of independence. The great day passed in peace and was celebrated in churches in all the mission's stations. However, the mutiny of the *Force Publique* and the rampaging of the drunken mob that targeted white people changed the picture. In

Luluabourg (Kananga) the Belgians were attacked and raped; their homes and property destroyed. Many Belgians gathered in the the upper floors of a large apartment complex from which they sent the SOS that brought Belgian paratroopers to their aid.

APCM personnel communicated with each other by radio and, although many were reluctant to leave, decided to follow the advice of the American embassy. The plan of evacuation called for the missionaries to congregate at the airport in Luluabourg. They would then be ferried first to the Belgian airbase at Kamina in Shaba (Katanga) Province and then to Salisbury (Harare) in Southern Rhodesia (Zimbabwe). Dr. Mark Poole tells the dramatic story:

> In four days, with little rest for the planes or the pilots, some 182 persons [missionaries and their families and some Belgians] were airlifted, three or more at a time, in the two small planes. The 182 count is probably not entirely correct as some were double lifted and some managed to move by car. For instance, I flew the Blount family from Bulape to Luluabourg on the first flight of the lift and found Luluabourg still held by rebel soldiers. A local friendly soldier tore out to the runway and warned me. I took off from the taxiway without stopping the motor and dropped them at Lubondai. Later they were airlifted back to Luluabourg by John Davis, I think. I returned to Bulape for another load and returned to Luluabourg where I could see the strip was under control of Belgian paratroopers. Three hundred of the top Belgian paratroopers from Kamina airbase to the south had made their drop on Luluabourg in the meantime and secured the white population downtown and the airfield. They told us they would hold the field for three days and nights, which they did. Our missionaries had to sleep on the ground at the airstrip while waiting to be airlifted to Kamina. They were supplied with water and blankets by the local Christians who risked their lives to help them.[6]

Dr. John Miller reported:

> I was a new flyer and followed John Davis. We regularly carried one hundred pounds overweight. Once we had seventeen people in the two planes; some were babies. We had one map between us. One time my battery went dead and, when Davis disappeared in a smoke pile, it was very scary.[7]

For the first time since 1892 the APCM had no personnel in the Kasai. Of the 102 APCM missionaries in the Congo on June 30, only Rev. Alex McCutchen remained in Léopoldville.

Return of the Missionaries

Not for long was the Kasai without APCM representation. One week later the two little planes returned from Salisbury with seven men: John Davis (pilot), John Miller, M.D., Henry Nelson, M.D., Hugh Farrior, M.D., Rev. Earl King Jr., Rev. Bill Washburn, and James A. Halverstadt (business manager). They visited each station and were warmly welcomed. They found property intact except in Luluabourg, where one residence had been looted, and in Luebo, where minor pilfering had taken place. Some of the men decided to remain, while others returned to Salisbury to report that the situation had calmed down and that the missionaries would be welcome to return.

On August 12, one month to the day from the evacuation, nineteen men returned, and by the first of the year forty-five APCM missionaries, including a number of women, were at their posts. The Congo to which they returned was a different place from the one they had left a few weeks before. The nation, the church, and the mission had experienced change so great that its ramifications have yet to be completely understood or resolved.

The Congolese, many of whom were Christians trained in the mission's schools, struggled to manage a chaotic situation. The Belgians were gone and with them the technical and administrative skills needed to keep the wheels of government moving smoothly. The economy was at a standstill, public utilities were not working, and roads were quickly deteriorating. Worst of all, the soldiers and police were out of control. Armed gangs roamed the countryside; alcohol and drugs made them dangerous.

The Presbyterian Church of the Kasai, like the nation itself, was in the throes of acquiring an identity independent of foreign (APCM) control. Most of the 1950s had been spent in working out church/mission relationships, and in November 1959 the Presbyterian Church of the Kasai came into being. This ceremonial granting of autonomy by the mission to the church occurred in a remarkable gathering of church leaders from both sides of the bitter Luba/Lulua struggle.

The role of the church vis-à-vis the mission continued to be a time-consuming and sometimes difficult matter of negotiation involving the Presbyterian Church of the Kasai, the APCM, and the Board of World Missions in the United States. Much energy was expended on decisions about division of responsibility, accountability of funds, operation of institutions, and use of property.

Mulelist/Simba Rebellion (1964–1965)

In many ways the Mulelist/Simba rebellion posed a more serious threat for the APCM than did the period immediately following independence in 1960. From headquarters in Stanleyville to the northeast, a rebel army advanced toward the Kasai. Its terrorist tactics were directed at the European as well as the Congolese population; anyone associated with American "imperialists" were targets for mistreatment. The Methodist station of Wembo Myama north of the Sankuru River was captured; the Methodist pilot was killed and five men held hostage.

The APCM narrowly escaped harm. In August 1964 the rebel army crossed the Sankuru River at Lusambo and proceeded down the road toward Luluabourg (Kananga), some eighty miles away. The mission's planes made daily reconnaissance flights to monitor the advance. Virginia Pruitt's account of events is graphic:

> The rebels were found to be across the river in force with their rolling stock. Nothing but open road now lay between them and Luluabourg. . . . Just then came the good news . . . that the National Army was moving out to meet and halt the rebels. The battle took place about forty miles from Luluabourg. The National Army truck column and the rebel truck column met head-on in a narrow, sandy road. Soldiers jumped from the lead jeep firing at the lead truck of the enemy, killing the commander and witch doctor in the first onslaught. The rebels were demoralized and panicked from that moment. Catholic priests at a nearby Mission told us later they went out the next day and buried 125 rebel dead, most of them youth in their teens. The bullet-riddled and blood-stained lead truck of the rebels [stolen from the Methodists] was brought into one of our stations for repairs and return to its owners.[8]

One final unpleasant crisis occurred in 1967 when foreign mercenaries, engaged to deal with the Muelist/Simba rebellion and retained by Mobutu, revolted, evidently because of problems over pay. When the media depicted this revolt as a plot of "whites" to take over the Congo, the outpouring of antiwhite invective reached a new high. White foreigners, including some APCM missionaries, were placed under house arrest; homes were searched for guns and for radio transmitters. The similarity of the words "mercenary" and "missionary" may have contributed to confusion in the minds of the local authorities.

Mobutu's Military Dictatorship

General Mobutu's bloodless coup d'état in November 1965 seemed a welcome relief. His firm control of government represented reform and discipline. The slogan of his new regime, *Retroussons les manches!*—"Let's roll up our sleeves and get to work!"—held promise for the future.[9]

Incidents of Violence

Missionary correspondence gives many examples of violence affecting Congolese friends and coworkers during these tumultuous days. Although the APCM suffered no casualties, four missionaries narrowly escaped death.

Rev. Kemp Hobson suffered deep cuts on his wrist and elbow when attacked by a machete-wielding devotee of one of the new religious sects. This unusual attack on a white man occurred in 1958 near the remote outstation Mboi, and can, in retrospect, be seen to reflect the growing spirit of revolution.

Rev. David McLean, who was acting as interpreter for an Australian medical team in Bakwanga (Muji Mayi) in 1960, received damaging blows about the face. Christians intervened and saved him from more serious injury and possible death. The Australian government decorated McLean for his courage.

The most serious incident affected APCM medical personnel in 1962 at the Lubondai Hospital. W. Grant McIntosh, M.D., and Jean Baptiste Jung, D.D.S., were cruelly manhandled by angry soldiers who falsely accused them of having given information by radio to their enemies. The two men were bound hand and foot and thrown into the back of a truck for the long ride from Lubondai to Luluabourg (Kananga), where the military high command rescued them from a howling mob. Because of nerve damage caused by the tight binding of his hands, Dr. Jung was unable to practice dentistry for six months. Nolie McDonald, the medical technologist at Lubondai, was roughed up but not seriously injured in this incident.[10] Virginia Pruitt reported as follows:

> All missionaries knew the daily fear of unexpected and unwarranted bullying at the hands of drunk and demanding soldiers, or of harassment at the numerous military roadblocks. Real dangers existed, too, from roving youth gangs and later from armed robbers. . . . We came to have a tremendous, grateful sense of being spared, not only individually at given times and places, but in the sum total of our work as well. While many of our sister missions over the Congo had met disaster, the APCM has been able to carry on continuously and was relatively intact.[11]

APCM Medicine, 1960–1965

The medical situation in the Congo changed radically after independence. The comprehensive health system organized by the Belgian colonial government broke down completely, as some 700 to 800 Belgian physicians departed. Hospitals and clinics in all the districts were unstaffed and unstocked. Some were looted and destroyed, while others continued as dispensaries with a Congolese nurse in charge. The network for medical supplies was disrupted, while the needs of the people increased. Virtually the only hospitals in operation were those run by Protestant and Catholic missions.

Within one week of the evacuation three APCM physicians were back at their posts: John Miller in Lubondai, Hugh Farrior in Bibanga, and Henry Nelson in Luebo. Lukusa, the head nurse at the Bibanga Hospital, tells of having many wounded brought into the hospital after an incident involving Lulua, Luba, and UN troops. Among the wounded were twelve persons who needed major surgery. In desperation he prayed to God and, in what seemed a miraculous answer, the plane with the doctors arrived while he was praying.

In Salisbury, women with children and those whose furloughs were due followed the mission recommendation and left for the United States; some not to return. The Smiths (Tinsley, M.D., and Catherine, R.N.) were en route to the United States for furlough when their plane made a stop in Léopoldville. They were persuaded to deplane in order to help the three physicians who were struggling to meet the desperate medical needs in this capital city of over one million persons. In the fall they returned to Mutoto.

By September the rest of the missionaries who had evacuated to Rhodesia, including women, returned to the Kasai. Schools reopened, evangelistic missionaries made their rounds, and the medical staff resumed their work. By mid-1961 the return of wives and children further strengthened the mission's program.

Between 1960 and 1965 three of the six APCM hospitals—in Bulape, Bibanga, and Lubondai—were continuously maintained and supplied with medical personnel. Hospitals in Luebo, Mutoto, and Moma reverted to clinics. Two of the outstation clinics, in Kasha and Kakinda, were destroyed in the ethnic fighting; Mboi clinic remained open.

The APCM medical work during the five years after independence is described here under three headings: (1) APCM hospitals, (2) response to the plight of refugees, and (3) renewal of the IMCK teaching program and subsequent move in 1964 to Tshikaji near Luluabourg (Kananga).

The APCM Hospitals

Bulape

Bulape, in the relatively stable area occupied by the Kuba people, was considered a safe place after independence for female mission medical personnel. Gladys Smithwick, M.D., Ruth Worth, M.T., and Elizabeth Miller, R.N., were the first to return. They found a new class of nurse's aides waiting for them. These students had applied when there was no instructor in sight and seemingly no chance of having one. "So with a very small staff," wrote Elizabeth Miller, "we [reopened the] training school for nurse's aides. Our students studied hard and did well and all passed the State exams."[12]

Dr. Henry Nelson and his wife, Katie, R.N., moved to Bulape when Luebo became unsafe. In 1961 Dr. Mark Poole returned for four months. Dr. Poole reported:

These were extremely eventful months . . . Some 113 major operations were accomplished and many minor procedures. The hospital and dispensaries were intensely busy; the training school for medical assistants was "going full blast."[13]

Dr. Poole made fifty trips by air to the air dispensaries, taking out food and supplies and bringing urgent cases back to the hospital. UN-donated food and medical supplies were flown in from Luluabourg (Kananga). While in Luluabourg Dr. Poole and Rev. William Washburn were arrested and jailed for a time, but released unharmed.

Others who served in Bulape during this period (1960–65) include John (M.D.) and Aurie (M.T.) Miller, Birch (M.D.) and Margaret (R.N.) Rambo, and Nancy Ross, R.N. (Mrs. Charles).

The long tradition of good relations between the Kuba and the missionaries continued, although ethnic conflict and political instability created periods of tension. A source of tension was the reversion to ancient customs and practices. The Kuba, a conservative people, sought to revive the practice of the poison cup, the traditional test for inno-cence that the Belgian colonial government had outlawed. Missionaries attempted to intervene, but several hundred persons were reported to have died as a result of administration of the poison cup.[14]

On several occasions African Christians intervened and stood by the missionaries in times of crisis. Elizabeth Miller reported:

> Early one afternoon not long after our return to Bulape, several soldiers arrived to search the missionary homes for radios. The Bulape village folk appeared and trailed right along with [the soldiers] literally surrounding them to see that nothing else was taken. When the search was completed, the solders decided they would take Charles Ross with them to Mweka for questioning. There was barely room for Charles [in the car], but our *Pasteur* Mishenge squeezed in beside him and stayed close to him all through that long afternoon. . . . The village people began arriving to speak with Charles and bring food. . . . Finally the military, some-what intimidated, let him and the *Pasteur* go.[15]

In another instance a mob attempted to kill two students suspected of being Lulua. Aurie Miller wrote:

> The villagers in a mob came to get the two boys when they were eating supper one Sunday evening. We were across the street and saw it happening. Johnny [John Miller] and Howard Cameron followed—one near one student, the other with the second one—much to the protest of the crowd. [The mob's] plan was to massacre

the two and they started tearing their clothes off with teasing jabs of spears . . . [Somehow the two, with the help of Christians, escaped to the Miller's attic.] That night the mob surrounded our house and it was two medical men who stood with Johnny on the porch resisting them by refusing to bring the students out. They could have stormed—but for the grace of God. The crisis ended when a truck-load of soldiers came to take both students back to Lulualand.[16]

Bibanga

Bibanga was initially considered unsafe for women missionaries because of its location in the territory of the Luba peoples. The Luba, as previously noted, were attempting to secede from the Congo and establish a Luba nation to be known as the South Kasai. Floods of refugees who were forced out of West Kasai by ethnic fighting returned to their traditional homeland. Until the matter was finally resolved in 1962 the Luba territory was the scene of fighting, famine, and enormous suffering.

Bibanga, east of the Lubilashi (Sankuru) River on the crest of a high hill, was somewhat removed from the center of strife, but patients came in great numbers. Among the refugees were some highly qualified nurses from APCM hospitals in West Kasai; these joined the Bibanga hospital staff. The Congolese staff did much of the routine work at the hospital and were able to carry on in the absence of expatriates.

Dr. Hugh Farrior was the first medical person to return to Bibanga, where he served until 1965; at times he was the only missionary on the station. Dr. John Miller covered Bibanga during Farrior's 1961–62 furlough.

Dr. Farrior commented that the first year in Bibanga was a stressful time. Four different governments successively took control of the area. The numbers of patients were overwhelming, the hospital facilities had deteriorated badly, and it was hard to get supplies. On one occasion the UN brought in an order by helicopter. However, the last three years were almost idyllic: the political situation had stabi-lized; a good staff, competent maintenance personnel, and the reinstatement of the training program made it a rewarding experience medically; and relations with the Zairian church were excellent. Dr. Farrior was even asked to serve as delegate to the General Assembly meeting of the CPZ (Presbyterian Church of Zaire).

Ten Luba IMCK nursing students, whose graduation had been interrupted by the violent aftermath of independence, had taken refuge in Bibanga. Dr. Bill Rule, accompanied by Lucille McElroy, R.N., went to Bibanga several times in the spring of 1961 to prepare these students for their jury examinations. Nine of the ten passed and were awarded their *infirmier diplomé* certificates; one received an *aide-infirmier* certificate. One of the graduates, Benoit Nzengu, went to the United States for a year of high school in Texas; he then became the first black to be admitted to Davidson College. He subsequently studied medicine in Liege, Belgium, and in 1976 became the first Congolese doctor to join the IMCK staff.[17]

Luebo

Luebo was particularly hurt by ethnic strife and was never again preeminent in church leadership. As Virginia Pruitt put it, "The glory of Luebo, once the heart and center of the APCM, belongs to a bygone day."[18]

Luebo Hospital, at the time of independence, had two physicians (Henry Nelson and Gladys Smithwick), one dentist (J. B. Jung), and three nurses (Jean Shive, Katie Nelson, and Margaret McMurry). After the evacuation to Southern Rhodesia, only the Nelsons and Dr. Jung returned. As conflict between the Lulua and Luba peoples intensified, local church leaders advised the missionaries to leave, which they did. The Nelsons moved to Bulape, and Dr. Jung to Lubondai.

In time, the missionaries gradually returned to Luebo. The printing press reopened, and the school for preachers reestablished. The hospital became an active clinic with a few inpatient beds and a large maternity unit. Congolese nurses, supported by regular visits from the doctor in Bulape, operated the facility.

Mutoto

Mutoto, which was located in Lulua country, continued in operation as long as Dr. and Mrs. Tinsley Smith were present. Dr. Smith's account illustrates the seriousness of the Lulua/Luba conflict:

Part of our hospital staff were Luba and part were Lulua. When the tribal wars started up we were caught right in the middle. I had a long talk with our staff telling them that we did not intend to interfere with their lives in the village but that when they were on duty in the hospital they were Christians first and Lulua and Luba second. Patients were to be treated without any notice being taken as to their tribal affiliations. I must say that we never saw at any time when they did not hold to this rule.

There came a day when, from all we could learn, an attack on our Luba would take place the next day. Catherine and I, with Mr. Franklin Watt, were asked by the Station to go to Luluabourg and see if they could send any soldiers as protection. When we got to Luluabourg . . . we told them our story but they said they had so many requests for aid that it was impossible to even start sending soldiers. They advised us to go home and sit tight. . . . We drove back to Mutoto through the forest in a driving rain. For several miles we passed Lulua in the road on their way to Mutoto. They were dressed for battle. Their [bodies were] painted with white luhemba clay, palm fronds were around their heads and waists and they carried old flintlock muskets, swords, spears, etc. As we came up to them, they faded into the forest.

When we got home we found that all the Luba families had come onto the station for protection, and the missionaries had put them into a vacant missionary home that had two floors. When we went over to see them they covered every inch of floor space.

The station decided that some of us would remain up during the night to let the Luba know that we were watching out for them. Mr. Watt and Mr. Stuart took the first shift till 2 o'clock and then Catherine and I took over. We walked around the compound several times showing our flashlight and then got in our car and drove over through the neighboring villages. There was no one in evidence as we drove slowly through the villages, but we knew they were watching us just the same. The night passed with no evidence of the Luluas. We never knew whether our being up kept them from making their attack or not. Shortly after that we evacuated the Luba families.

A local Lulua chief came to the Leprosy village and told the Luba there that since they were already dead—with the disease—they could stay on and not be in any danger. However, this did not hold up and we had to evacuate our Luba families there too.[19]

After it was bypassed by the railroad, Mutoto became isolated and suffered a decrease in population. In a relatively short time it ceased to exist as a mission station. In the fall of 1961 the Smiths retired after thirty-two years of missionary service, and no other PCUS medical personnel were assigned to Mutoto. The hospital continued as a clinic and maternity unit, with a nurse in charge. The Mutoto staff strove to maintain the high standards of cleanliness and order set by the Smiths.

Lubondai

Lubondai at the time of independence was the largest APCM mission station and the site of IMCK, with its nursing and dental schools. The expatriate staff was made up of two physicians (William Rule and John Miller), two dentists (Sandy Marks and Bernard Jackson), three nurses (Lucille McElroy, Alice Longenecker, and Katherine Marks), and two technologists (Aurie Miller, laboratory, and Nolie McDonald, X ray). Indigenous personnel, well trained and dependable, had significant responsibility for clinical teaching and bedside nursing.

When independence came, the Lubondai Hospital was without a mission presence for only about one week. John Miller and Sandy Marks were the first to return; others soon followed.

Dr. Rule wrote:

The [male nurses] at the hospital did an outstanding job of maintaining the organization and dispensing medical care during the [time] they were carrying on alone. They had complete access to everything. I am sure there was some unnecessary waste and probably things were taken here and there, but essentially the hospital and all its equipment are intact. We have a good stock of drugs on hand. . . . The wards are crowded and we stay as busy as we can be. Last week I had 64 prenatal patients at the clinic—twice as many as I have ever had![20]

From 1960 to 1967, although IMCK was not reopened at this location, the hospital in Lubondai functioned as one of the few hospitals in a very large area. It was kept fully staffed by missionaries, patients flooded in, and the facilities were stretched to meet the demand.

Operation Doctor/Operation Refugee

The Congo Protestant Council (CPC) was organized in 1911 to unify and support the work of Protestant missions in the Congo. In 1960, forty missions from at least ten countries in Europe, America, and South Africa were members of the CPC. Since 1956 Dr. Bill Rule had served as the medical secretary. Statistics compiled by the CPC provide a picture of the Protestant medical work as it was in 1958 before independence.[21]

Medical Work of Protestant Missions, 1958		
Hospital beds		6,823
Outpatient cases		1,227,140
Hospital cases		145,274
Major surgical cases		11,113
Deliveries		31,094
	Missionaries	**Congolese**
Physicians	78	0
Dentists	4	0
Nurses	216	69
Nurse's aides	0	513
Midwives	119	0
Technologists	8	0
Pharmacists	1	0

In August 1960, in response to the massive suffering in the area, a group of CPC doctors organized the Congo Protestant Relief Agency (CPRA) with two main branches: Operation Doctor and Operation Refugee. Operation Doctor was designed to offer support to missionary doctors and to recruit Christian physicians for short-term medical service; Operation Refugee was to provide for the needs of refugees. The Luba refugees in the Kasai were of primary concern.

Dr. Rule left the Congo in February 1960 on an emergency medical furlough and was convalescing in the United States at the time of independence. He was asked to accept the position of executive secretary of CPRA and arrived back in the Congo in October 1960 for six strenuous months of organization and administration of this highly successful emergency agency. He visited the missionary physicians in all provinces, talked to Congolese officials, and worked closely with Church World Service, the UN relief agencies, the World Health Organization, and the International Red Cross.[22]

Operation Doctor
Operation Doctor, in the six years of its existence, recruited a total of 67 doctors. They came from around the world and served on short assignments in hospitals and clinics all over the Congo. Among those who responded were Mark Poole, M.D., for four months of concentrated work at Bulape Hospital, and Paul Carlson, M.D., who was killed in 1964 in Stanleyville during the Simba/Mulelist rebellion. The response to the need for medical supplies was also impressive. Approximately a million tons of medicine and hospital equipment was distributed to all parts of the country.[23]

Operation Refugee
Operation Refugee concentrated its efforts in and around Bakwanga (Muji Mayi), where some 250,000 Luba, after being uprooted from their homes and villages, were suffering famine. Distribution of food and supplies that had poured in from around the world became a major problem. Inadequate means for delivery was further complicated by local jealousies, distrust, and suspicion. The government gratefully accepted the CPRA's offer to take over the distribution.

The hero of Operation Refugee was Archie Graber, a Mennonite missionary, who, with only two young Mennonite volunteers and three trucks at his disposal, managed to carry food to villages as far as 100 miles from Bakwanga. Three APCM men responded to Graber's call for help. Over a three-week period, they labored day and night, often in very dangerous conditions, to bring relief to the hungry and dying.[24]

After the threat of starvation subsided, the CPRA under Mennonite leadership brought in building materials and seeds for planting. Some 60,000 baby chicks were flown in from Mennonite farmers in Pennsylvania.

Perhaps the most lasting benefit from the CPRA was the arrival of aviators of the Missionary Aviation Fellowship (MAF). MAF was organized by a group of Christian pilots after World War II. These pilots had a vision of using their skills for missions and churches in

Refugees. Courtesy of Presbyterian Church (USA), Department of History (Montreat, North Carolina).

third-world countries in a flying service conducted with high professional quality and according to strict safety standards. Already operating in South America, the South Pacific, and some African countries, MAF sent its executive officer, Grady Parrott, to talk to Dr. Rule about the needs in the Congo. MAF arrived early in 1961 and has maintained a permanent presence in the Congo to this day. In a country where roads are either nonexistent or impassable, MAF has contributed immeasurably to the work of the church.[25]

Institut Médical Chrétien du Kasai (IMCK)

After a three-year hiatus, IMCK reopened in October 1963 in Lubondai with ten students representing many different tribes. However, it soon became apparent that Lubondai was not a suitable location for the mission's primary medical training center. Two factors seem to have governed the decision in 1964 to leave Lubondai: Lubondai's inaccessible location and ethnic tension.

The area around Lubondai experienced intense ethnic conflict, and relations between the nearby village and the mission became strained. The mission property had originally, as has been said, been donated by the chief of this village and the villagers had a feeling of proprietorship. They deeply resented the predominant presence of Luba as students at IMCK and in positions of responsibility in the hospital. It became necessary to evacuate the Luba and their families to Bibanga. Dr. Rule wrote:

> I was waited upon by a delegation of three church leaders from the local village speaking to me in the name of the Bakwa Tshipanga [a subgroup of Lulua]. . . . It seemed that only one or two of their number had ever been admitted to the school, and we had flunked them out. So there were no Bakwa Tshipanga graduates of IMCK— a school which had existed for six or eight years right in their midst! They had come to tell me they wanted the majority of the students in the school to be young people from their clan. They told me they didn't want to be unreasonable about it and we might take in a few from other tribes, but from here on the majority of graduates of IMCK should be Bakwa Tshipanga.

> Our exchange was gentle and without rancor. I pointed out to them that the students were chosen by competitive examinations and, to date, the local boys and girls had not been well enough prepared in their basic studies to successfully compete with students from other areas. I suggested that their concern should be with upgrading their local primary and secondary schools. I gently explained that the means of entry would not be changed, and that we envisioned the school serving the whole nation and we would receive students from all regions. They did not back away from their position nor I from mine, and we thanked each other and concluded the meeting. . . . Since the ugly head of tribal coercion had been raised, it seemed to me the die was cast. We must move.[26]

Luluabourg (Kananga), the capital of the Kasai, had grown into a city of over 200,000 persons. Located on the railroad, it was the center of government and business activities. Officials in Luluabourg welcomed the establishment of a training center for Congolese medical personnel.

Dr. Rule described the transfer of IMCK to Tshikaji, eight miles from the center of Luluabourg, as the result of three miracles.[27] The first occurred in the spring of 1964 when the provincial government granted

IMCK, free of charge, full title to an abandoned school on the outskirts of the city. This "School for the Sons of Chiefs" had been established by the Belgians in order to give training in leadership skills to these future leaders. The school occupied fifty acres and consisted of some eighteen buildings—administration, classrooms, dormitories, and ten faculty homes. Unfortunately, the buildings were occupied by Congolese soldiers and their families, an armed and unstable lot. Government officials did not offer to clear the squatters from the school.

The second miracle was the arrival of a check from the First Presbyterian Church of Winston Salem, North Carolina, for $27,392 with no strings attached. Dr. Rule and Garland Goodrum, the indefatigable industrial missionary assigned to assist in the renovation of the campus, headed for Southern Rhodesia to purchase furnishings and equipment. Everything, from a diesel generator to 1,200 panes of glass, from kitchen utensils to stoves and a water pump, from cots and desks to metal shelves for the library, was placed into a sealed freight car and shipped to Kananga.

The third miracle was the halting in August of the advance of the Simba rebel army just forty miles short of Luluabourg (as recounted earlier). The escalating tension, which colored the weeks of preparation for the school's opening, was happily resolved when local troops and Simba rebels came face to face around a sharp turn on a narrow road. The troops opened fire and, wonder of wonders, the Simba propaganda of their immunity to bullets proved false. The Simba retreat began the eventual defeat of the Simba/Mulelist movement.

Dr. Rule did not list it as a miracle but the clearing of the campus of its squatters was no small accomplishment. These armed soldiers were undisciplined and unpredictable, especially when lubricated with alcohol or drugs. A series of gentle diplomatic maneuvers finally won the day. The first step was the decision of the Rule family (two adults and four children) to take their two-week vacation in July at the school. The place was in a sad state of repair: buildings were filthy and vandalized, head-high grass covered the campus, and the beautiful trees were being cut and burned into charcoal. Dr. Rule wrote:

> The house was in such filthy condition that I hired two or three water carriers from the nearby village and we scrubbed the place with abundant soap and water medicated with Lysol. Then we set up our cots and mosquito nets, draped the empty window frames,

and barricaded the doors for the night. Since there were no kitchen facilities we put our folding table and chairs on the front porch and cooked over an open fire in the front yard. With only kerosene lanterns for night lights, we sat around the fire during the evening, visiting and singing songs until bedtime.

I set to organizing a "work line" of laborers, and we began to clear off the landscape, cutting down the high grass and marking off straight pathways plus wider roads to allow access for cars and trucks. This afforded convenience for the soldiers as well, so that they tolerated our presence with a sort of detached amusement . . . With much cutting and scrubbing our two weeks was soon spent and, feeling that we had gently gotten our point across, we returned to Lubondai.[28]

In late August the Rules moved back to the Tshikaji campus. As the date for the school to open drew near, Dr. Rule pressed the colonel commanding the troops in Luluabourg to move the soldiers and their families from the school buildings. At first the colonel argued that he had no other lodging in which to billet his men, but eventually, on September 10, he sent word that he had found facilities for relocation but had no rolling stock to transport them. Dr. Rule commented:

We jumped at the opportunity, telling him we would move the Tshikaji squatters for him! Garland Goodrum came with a second truck from Luluabourg and late in the day we began loading soldiers and their families and earthly possessions [in an atmosphere of celebration and gaiety]. . . . It took a long time for the people to pack their belongings and corral scattered children, chickens, and goats, and squeeze as many as possible on a truck. Night caught us and arrangements proceeded even slower in the dark. Garland and I made our first trip and returned for a second. Then a third was necessary. We worked until well after midnight, completely worn out from helping to hoist heavy loads and then unload at the point of destination. . . . The good Lord was with us and we made the transfer of personnel without incident.[29]

Two weeks later, students arrived and IMCK opened with twenty-six students in two classes; the first woman to attend IMCK was among those admitted. The faculty consisted of Dr. Rule (medical subjects), Lucille McElroy (nursing arts), and Ruth Worth (laboratory instructor). Effie Rule (Mrs. William) prepared meals, and Garland Goodrum worked "like a trojan" to complete repairs.

A gala dedication celebration on December 12, 1964, marked the formal opening of the school. This event was attended by government and church leaders. PCUS Moderator Felix Gear came from the United States, and Winston Salem's First Presbyterian Church sent two representatives.

Summary

The 1960–65 period in the history of the Congo was a time of chaos and seminal change as the Congolese and the missionaries dealt with the realities of independence. Joy, hope, and anticipation mingled with frustration, danger, and disappointment.

By 1965 the medical work of the APCM had stabilized. Three mission hospitals at Lubondai, Bulape, and Bibanga were again in operation, and the IMCK was off to a good start on the spacious campus at Tshikaji. Ethnic conflict became somewhat less violent and the plight of the refugees improved as crops were planted and harvested. Virginia Pruitt wrote:

> The mood was generally optimistic. The storms had abated; the ship of state seemed to be sailing now on an even keel. . . . Some old-timers longed for the "good old days" of Belgian stability and efficiency and welfare benefits, but by the large there was a heady pride in the new Congo and a determination to make it work in the Congolese way, by Congolese effort. This did not gainsay the obvious need still for outside aid both in funds and know-how. . . . Specialists of many sorts [including missionaries] were welcome but only insofar as they recognized that the Congolese were running the show, giving the orders, making the decisions.[30]

Notes

1. Virginia Gray Pruitt, "New Nation, New Church: Congo 1960–1970," typescript, 1972, 100.
2. Ibid., 9.

3. Ibid.

4. Ibid., 14.

5. Ibid., 50.

6. Mark Poole, M.D., interview, Dec. 1984.

7. John Miller, M.D., interview, June 1990.

8. Pruitt, "New Nation, New Church," 49.

9. Ibid., 23.

10. Ibid., 50.

11. Ibid., 31.

12. Elizabeth Miller, R.N., interview, March 1984.

13. Poole, interview, Dec. 1984.

14. William Rule, M.D., "Milestones in Mission" (Knoxville, Tenn.: typescript, 1991), 233–34.

15. Elizabeth Miller, interview.

16. Aurie Miller, M.T., correspondence, Feb. 1992.

17. Rule, "Milestones in Mission," 293, 298–99.

18. Pruitt, "New Nation, New Church," 36.

19. J. Tinsley Smith, M.D., interview and letters, 1984.

20. Rule, "Milestones in Mission," 306.

21. Ibid., 215.

22. Ibid., 355.

23. Ibid., 284.

24. Pruitt, "New Nation, New Church," 31.

25. Rule, "Milestones in Mission," 277–78.

26. Ibid., 336.

27. Ibid., 338–43.

28. Ibid., 340.

29. Ibid., 342–43.

30. Pruitt, "New Nation, New Church," 19.

Chapter Nine

Zaire
(1965–1983)

The bloodless coup d'état in November 1965 by Gen. Mobutu Sese Seko was greeted at first with cautious optimism. His promise of reform and discipline seemed to offer an appealing alternative to the chaos that had followed independence in 1960. Unfortunately, under Mobutu's repressive dictatorship, Zaire has become one of the poorest of the underdeveloped countries of Africa. Support of Mobutu by Western powers (mainly Belgium and the United States) contributed to the longevity of his regime. Without attempting a comprehensive description of conditions in Zaire, some of the major features, especially those that affect the PCUS medical program, can be noted.[1]

Mobutu did bring a wildly unruly military under disciplined control; he then deployed troops to control disorder and civil disturbance. Unfortunately, he also developed an oppressive secret police system whose record of intimidation and incarceration without trial was documented by international human rights organizations. A single political party, the *Movement Populaire de la Révolution* (MPR), organized in 1967, supported Mobutu's strong central control; all Zairians at birth became members of the MPR. No opposition group was allowed to develop and no public personality allowed to emerge.

A country with bountiful resources (copper, diamonds, uranium, rare metals, lumber) and a tremendous potential for hydroelectric and agricultural development suffered severe economic crisis. Budget deficits, inflation exceeding 60 percent, mismanagement, and corruption paralyzed industry and business. Basic economic infrastructures (transportation, communication, and power) were not maintained. Support for schools, health systems, and social services dwindled.

Once able to feed itself, the country now imported food. The nation-alization in 1975 of schools and of over 2,000 foreign-owned economic enterprises proved disastrous.

Rural Zairians, some 85 percent of the total population, eked out an existence at or below subsistence level; four-fifths of urban Zairians were unemployed. By 1982 the annual per capita income of $160 was one of the lowest in Africa, and real wages had declined to less than 10 percent of the preindependence level.[2] Life expectancy stood at forty-one years; half the children died before the age of five. Malnutrition was common. Diseases, such as sleeping sickness, which had once been brought under control, again became prevalent.

Mobutu and his close associates accumulated immense wealth. Mobutu himself became one of the richest men in the world, with a personal fortune estimated to exceed U.S. three billion dollars. In Dr. Rule's words:

> The capital crime of this high-handed tyrant is that he has systemat-ically and continuously drawn his personal wealth from the potential riches of a developing country, sucking the means of liveli-hood from a poverty-stricken people. . . . This conduct encouraged a system of corruption in Zaire that can hardly be equaled anywhere else in the world.[3]

Mobutu sought to encourage an ideology of Zairian authenticity sometimes referred to as Mobutuism. For example, people were told to shed their European or Christian names. Mobutu, who was raised a Catholic, changed his name from Joseph Desire Mobutu to Mobutu Sese Seko. A dress code mandated a short-sleeved tropical jacket for men; European-style business suits, coats, and ties were banned.

French was retained as the official language because Zaire has some 450 different languages. However, geographical names with European connotations were changed. The Democratic Republic of the Congo became the Republic of Zaire on October 27, 1971. Names commonly encountered in this book were changed as follows:

Congo River to Zaire River
Léopoldville to Kinshasa
Luluabourg to Kananga

Bakwanga to Mbuji Mayi
Elizabethville to Lubumbashi
Stanleyville to Kisangani

Zaire and the PCUS

The PCUS struggled to define its role in the new situation. The American Presbyterian Congo Mission (APCM) gladly granted the principle of autonomy for the Congo (Zairian) Church but encountered confusion and conflict in the details of its implementation. Points of particular strain were those that concerned the uses of money, property and machinery, and the placement of missionary personnel. In 1966, the seventy-five-year-old APCM ceased to exist. Thereafter, relations were maintained on a church-to-church basis between the Presbyterian Church of Zaire (CPZ) and the PCUS.[4]

In the early 1970s the Zairian government restricted official recognition to only four Christian churches: the Catholic Church, the Greek Orthodox Church, the Kimbanguist Church (an indigenous church made up of followers of Simon Kimbangu), and l'Église du Christ au Zaire (ECZ) or Church of Christ in Zaire (all Protestant denominations.)[5] The more than sixty Protestant "communities" that made up the ECZ were allowed to maintain their own identity while achieving coordination and cooperation with other communities.

The Presbyterian church within the ECZ was called the Presbyterian Community of Zaire (CPZ) (Communauté Presbytèrienne de Zaire). A second community, the Presbyterian Community of Kinshasa (CPK) (Communauté Presbytèrienne de Kinshasa), was formed in 1973 in the capital city to serve the large numbers of Presbyterians who had migrated to that urban setting. The CPZ and the CPK each had its own General Assembly and related to the other as fraternal churches. The PCUS's relation with both churches and with the ECZ could also be described as a fraternal relationship.

When the Zairian church first achieved autonomy, it repudiated the work of the mission except for the medical work. White faces, European culture, and identification with colonial efforts to improve social conditions heightened antagonisms that, after the departure of most of the Belgians, focused on the missionary. Unrealistic expectations and inexperience, especially in financial accountability, complicated the relationship. In time, as the Zairian church matured, attitudes softened, but the evangelistic and educational missionaries continued to experience difficulty in defining their role. Patience became the essential missionary watchword.

During the 1970s, two developments shook the Christian community. The first occurred when the government nationalized all church schools and prohibited the teaching of religion.[6] This move proved unworkable, and the schools were later returned to the churches. Unfortunately, the churches were not equipped to maintain an effective school system on their own. The few educational missionaries who remained were given teaching assignments but had neither the authority nor the responsibility to uphold standards. This tragic deterioration of the mission schools came at a time when good education was desperately needed in Zaire; without education the future was bleak.

The second problem was a financial scandal in which CPZ church leaders were found to be diverting the government subsidy for church medical work for other purposes. Several years passed before this matter was finally resolved. Ralph E. Shannon, M.D., summarized the situation as follows:

> During our term of service we have observed and participated in a number of important struggles in the life of the [Zairian] Church we are associated with. We have lived through a long period where the leadership of the church was anti-missionary except for what they could get out of the missionary being there. At the same time the population remained pretty much pro-missionary. [And] we have lived through a period of time when the Presbyterian Community of Zaire was considered [with good reason] to be one of the three most corrupting influences in the Kasai. We have lived through a period of great struggle resulting in a change of leadership and a time of renewal in the church. That period is still going on.[7]

PCUS Medical Program, 1965–1983

Before independence, medical work was one activity among many the PCUS carried on in the Congo, accounting for 25 percent of the church's effort. After independence, medical work became the principal activity of PCUS in Zaire accounting for as much as 70 percent of the church's effort.[8]

As previously noted, the fairly comprehensive health care system developed by the Belgians broke down completely when Belgian personnel fled the country at the time of independence. As a result, the PCUS medical professionals, along with other Catholic and Protestant mission personnel, found themselves virtually the only functioning medical resource for an area the size of France with a population of around 6 million. This responsibility was indeed daunting in view of limited resources, uncertain sources of supply, and deteriorating transportation system.

With the dissolution of the APCM, the medical work was divided into two programs:

1. The IMCK was set up as an independent institution, with an ecumenical board and its own legal representative; members of the CPZ (Presbyterian Church of Zaire) served on the board but did not have control.

2. The former APCM's hospitals and clinics were turned over to the CPZ. PCUS medical personnel continued to be assigned to the hospitals at Bulape and Bibanga. The other hospitals became clinics and received limited PCUS support.

This division of the medical work into two programs, the IMCK and that administered by the CPZ, was in line with recommendations made by a Long-Range Planning Committee of the APCM in 1962, that the mission "try to continue, insofar as possible, the medical work as organized and distributed across the mission territory, but to anticipate concentration of the medical work on its teaching program."[9] Because of its independent status, IMCK was able to maintain acceptable standards of medical practice and pursue its goal of training Zairians.

Considerable opposition to the teaching center existed among Congolese church members. The necessary concentration of medical personnel at the expense of the more rural facilities meant the depletion of medical services in remote areas. "Voluble resistance was voiced by populations accustomed to resident doctors and readily accessible hospital ministries. . . . The question of how the missionary doctors and nurses ought to be using their time . . . [became] one the most troublesome issues within the church."[10]

Two important medical conferences, or "summit meetings," held in 1965 and in 1980, established principles that shaped the development of the medical work. At the 1965 meeting, PCUS missionaries and representatives from the United States met with national church leaders to consider the overwhelming health needs confronting the limited number of missionary personnel and their equally limited funds. A statement, adopted by both the PCUS and the Zairian church, supported the development of IMCK's program of medical education. The opening section of this document bears reproducing here:

I. Both the church and the mission having come to the considered decision that the primary function of our medical endeavor should be the training of Congolese medical personnel, and with the realization that this will inevitably require a certain concentration of our medical work, feel it advisable to express some of the reasons which have led us to this conclusion.

A. We are increasingly convinced that the efforts of foreign medical missionaries can never adequately meet the crying needs of this land. Our highest expectation is the reproduction of our capacities, our skills, and our convictions in the people we train. It is to them that we look to make a significant impact upon the health needs of their own people.

B. We believe a vital prerequisite to the best medical care is a strong Christian faith. The church and the mission are in a unique position to provide such training.

C. We believe that the creation and operation of an outstanding medical and teaching service will witness to the Christian compassion of the church, both in the Christian and the non-Christian community.

D. In order to produce the quality of medical personnel needed in Congo it will not only be necessary to have good academic facilities, but also clinical facilities for the practical application of teaching that far exceed any which have existed on the APCM heretofore.

E. We believe that this is the strategic time to move forward to a higher standard of service and that it will call for new funds and new personnel born out of new interest in the home church. In our relationship with the Congo government this is also a strategic time, one in which we can be more mutually helpful than ever before.

II. As we have studied our commitment to a certain concentration of our medical work we have come increasingly to realize that this must be in an urban situation.

A. In considering the permanent location of the IMCK the decision of both church and mission has been that it should be placed at Luluabourg [Kananga], capital and largest city in the Province of the Kasai.[11]

Fifteen years later in 1980, the second conference, (held at Lake Munkamba) reviewed the progress made in implementing the 1965 goals and mapped strategy for the future. It was attended by representatives of the Zairian church, the PCUS in the United States, the World Council of Churches, and the Medical Benevolence Foundation (MBF), as well as PCUS missionaries and, most important, Zairian medical professionals. The peer relationship with Zairian doctors was a new and exciting development that gave tangible proof of the wisdom of the decision to emphasize medical teaching. In 1960 (at independence) Zaire did not have a single qualified Zairian physician; IMCK's first Zairian doctor joined the staff in 1976. By 1979 Zairian doctors were on the staff at Bulape Hospital and a Zairian doctor served as director of the Bibanga Hospital.

Out of this conference came the recommendation that would shape the future PCUS medical work in Zaire. The role of IMCK and its teaching mission would not be diminished, but primary health care services would be expanded.[12]

The support for medical work in Zaire from the Medical Benevolence Foundation during the turbulent postindependence period deserves special mention. The MBF, made up largely of PCUS medical professionals in the United States, provided prompt attention to emergency and other needs, raised money, furnished supplies, encouraged volunteers to serve on a short-term basis, and publicized the work throughout the church. The enthusiastic, personal interest of this medically knowledgeable organization was a source of encouragement to the medical personnel in the field.

The story of the PCUS medical work in Zaire from 1965 to 1983 is told here in two parts, first, the IMCK and, second, the CPZ medical program.

INSTITUT MÉDICAL CHRÉTIEN DU KASAI (IMCK)
Tshikaji/Kananga

The development of IMCK at Tshikaji from 1964 to 1983 (the period covered in this narrative) was a significant accomplishment against incredible difficulties. Beginning with the school for nurses (*infirmiers*), IMCK evolved into a medical complex with certified specialists; a teaching program for resident physicians, nurses, and laboratory technicians; an internationally recognized public health department; and, best of all, a staff that included qualified Zairian coworkers. The dream of training Christian Zairian medical leadership became a reality against remarkable odds.

As noted, IMCK celebrated its establishment on the Tshikaji campus on December 12, 1964. The school was organized as an independent legal entity and had an ecumenical board made up of four members each from the PCUS, the CPZ (Presbyterian Church of Zaire), and the Mennonite Church; one Methodist representative; one government representative; and the medical director. This independent status was crucial to the development of the institution.

First Ten Years (1964–1974)

The Tshikaji location proved to have both good and bad features. The isolation, some eight miles from downtown Kananga on spacious tree-shaded grounds, provided an excellent atmosphere for concentrated classwork and study, but student nurses needed clinical training in a hospital setting. For ten years, until the Good Shepherd Hospital opened in 1975, this training was provided at the Lubondai (until 1967), Bulape, and Bibanga hospitals. The training in the "bush hospital" setting gave the students excellent experience in basic practical medicine, but the constant rotation to the hospitals created what Dr. Rule described as a confusing state of "fruit basket turnover."[13] The need for an adjoining hospital was obvious.

The eight miles into Kananga also effectively separated IMCK from the bulk of the patients who so desperately needed the medical expertise of its staff. This problem was met in three ways: an IMCK-operated bus service between Kananga and Tshikaji provided transportation for patients and staff; an airstrip at Tshikaji made it possible for IMCK staff to respond to calls from outlying clinics and hospitals; and IMCK soon established outpatient clinics in Kananga and in the nearby village of Konko. Crowds overwhelmed these outpatient facilities—as many as 1,000 patients were being treated daily in the two locations.

The Kananga facility became a permanent department of IMCK and a major health center in the city. Some IMCK staff found housing in Kananga and commuted to Tshikaji for teaching responsibilities. Eventually IMCK was able to acquire the former Pax (Peace) Hotel which, after renovation, became the Pax Clinic. Dental and eye clinics were integral parts of this outpatient facility.

Kananga, the capital of West Kasai, rapidly grew from around 65,000 people in 1960 to 500,000 in 1983. The neat colonial city of tree-lined boulevards, bungalows, and prosperous shops became a teeming third-world city in which roads deteriorated, electricity and water were uncertain, and bureaucratic regulations complicated every transaction. The Methodists, as well as the Presbyterians, moved their business offices to Kananga. The Presbyterians moved their printing press from Luebo and developed their theological seminary in the Ndesha suburb.

Congenial relations between the PCUS and the Catholics helped to extend medical coverage in Kananga. The improvement in relations between Protestants and Catholics since the advent of Pope John XXIII was truly remarkable. Although the medical work had been less affected, open hostility, and sometimes active persecution, had at times in the past characterized the relationship.[14]

Before the completion of the Good Shepherd Hospital, IMCK physicians took surgical and obstetrical cases to the large Kananga city hospital, which, until independence, had been staffed by Belgian physicians and nurses. For example, when Hugh Farrior returned to Zaire (1968–71) after completing advanced training in obstetrics and gynecology, he was assigned to IMCK instead of returning to Bibanga. In addition to teaching at Tshikaji, he had a very busy obstetrical practice in Kananga; many of his patients were from the international community.

Two Belgian Catholic sisters had managed to maintain control of the operating and delivery room, but Dr. Rule's description of the institution is revealing:

This facility had served the entire city for a number of years and was in much need of repair. Screening had rusted from all windows, allowing flies and other insects to invade the wards. There had been no painting or real cleaning for ages. The supply of medications was dangerously low, since the staff helped itself to sell on the black market. Little or no surgery was done because there were no qualified staff surgeons. Under such circumstances we at Tshikaji offered our expertise for a limited degree. Occasionally we brought our own patients in for surgery, but the big problem was their post-op care. Nurses, hired by the government, had precious few medicines or other materials and what they did have was available only to patients who would tip them. This kind of medical ethics was offensive to us but we had no authority whatsoever over the government-hired nurses. If they ignored our orders we were powerless to correct the situation. Therefore I came to the hospital with the stipulation that I would bring my own bedside nurse to work with me.[15]

Construction of the Good Shepherd Hospital

The need for a teaching hospital in conjunction with IMCK's school for nurses became increasingly acute. The program, split between Tshikaji and the bush hospitals, did not lend itself to the development of the first-class facility so passionately envisioned. But the building of a modern hospital in central Africa at that time was a formidable undertaking. Materials, workmen skilled in construction, and supervisory personnel were scarce or lacking. Step by step, between 1971 and 1974 the essential elements came together for the building of what became the Good Shepherd Hospital.

The Women of the Church furnished the critical initial funds by making IMCK the object of their 1969 Birthday Offering. The opportunity to provide a modern medical facility in the heart of Africa where none existed appealed to PCUS women, and they responded enthusiastically. The $400,000 they raised (their second-largest offering to date) provided the bulk of the sum needed to begin construction. The American Leprosy Mission underwrote, for approximately $150,000, the construction of one of the eight units. The rest came from volunteer agency sources, including Presbyterian Program of Progress funds ($34,370), the Kemp Fund ($17,000), and individual gifts ($17,007). The largest individual gift ($5,000) came from Margaret Liston, the retired

PCUS missionary nurse who had helped found IMCK.[16]

Adequate land had to be acquired. Adjoining the Tshikaji campus and facing the main road from Kananga was a fifty-five-acre plain ideally suited for the purpose. Getting legal title to this land from the some twenty families who were living there and from several chieftains who claimed tribal ownership proved to be expensive and complicated, but this, too, was finally accomplished.

Plans were drafted by Christian & Blake Architects of Birmingham, Alabama, with offices in Kinshasa. Bill Blake, a dedicated Presbyterian, traveled to Tshikaji and carefully surveyed the property before preparing the plans. The plans proved eminently suitable for the tropical setting and, with a series of airy one-story units linked by covered verandas, were somewhat reminiscent of a U.S. Army field hospital. The entire 200-bed layout called for ten of these units, which could be constructed in stages as money was available.

Construction of eight of the projected ten units began in 1971 for a 140-bed hospital. These eight units were spread over ten acres of ground and provided 50,000 square feet of space.[17] Dr. John Miller, assisted by PCUS industrial missionaries Paul Donaldson and Raymond Elkes, was in charge of the building program. The African Inland Mennonite Mission furnished a number of workers who carried out the actual construction.

The Mennonite group was headed by Sam Ediger, a building contractor from Kansas with more than thirty years' experience. Ediger and his wife, Betty, stayed for the three years it took to build the hospital. Other Mennonites who came to help included Solomon and Lavina Ediger, a cousin and partner of Sam's (for six months); Ollie and Tillie Schmidt, who had carpentry and cabinet-making skills (for nine months); Marvin and Esther Neufeldt, who had expertise in metal work (for six months); also Len and Flo Wiens, Galen Widmer, David Ediger, and Ivan Schmidt. These Mennonites brought special skills, practical experience, common sense, and good humor to a difficult assignment. Sam Ediger wrote of his experience:

> We were told that it would take a long time to build the Hospital as we would run out of cement and other building materials and we'd do a lot of waiting. We never quite ran out but we almost did. One time . . . Ray Elkes came to me and said they [the cement company] had written

and informed us that we wouldn't have cement for at least 3 weeks. And he said we better get on our knees and pray! And we sure did just that! It wasn't 3 days later when he came waving a piece of paper saying, "Look what I have!" Cement was on the tracks to be unloaded. Another time we were out of cement and we went to Kananga and cleaned out all the cement bins of broken sacks of cement, but we never ran out! The Lord did provide. Thank you, Lord.[18]

Between fifty and one hundred Zairians worked with the Mennonites. An important contribution was the training the work gave to these unskilled men. Sam Ediger continued:

The workers are hard working and very eager to learn. . . . We are not only building a hospital to care for the sick and to train doctors and nurses but are also giving the opportunity for learning and earning. The men appreciate their jobs. . . . Without the language about all there is left to do is to show one, two, or three times how something should be done. Then as the task is mastered, it is a good feeling to place one's hand on a shoulder and say, *Bimpe* (good). Each day brings new and exciting experiences! We have helped to hand out tracts, deliver babies, build caskets for men who have lost a loved one, and taken sick people to the hospital.

Thanks to the skills of these Mennonite volunteers plus their lavish use of the word *Bimpe*, the Good Shepherd Hospital construction was of substantially better quality than that usually found in the PCUS hospitals in Africa.

Electricity and water remained formidable problems for the hospital complex. Diesel generators (for electricity) and a tower and pumps (for water) proved woefully inadequate. The plan to solve the problem by building a dam and hydroelectric facility in a nearby river evolved over a number of years and became a reality in 1986 (after the period of this narrative). The dramatic story of this accomplishment should someday be recorded. The eventual triumph was due to the dedicated leadership of Frank Vandergrift, former industrial missionary at Bibanga and retired professor of industrial engineering from Auburn University. He was assisted by a series of volunteers, support from the Medical Benevolence Foundation, and funding from U.S.AID and the Evangelical Central Agency for Development Aid (EZE) of Germany.

The Good Shepherd Hospital, of the Institut Médical Chrétian du Kasai (IMCK) at Tshikaji, was dedicated in 1974. The hospital is in the foreground; school, dormitories, and faculty housing are at the top of the picture. Photograph courtesy of Sam Ediger.

One death and the disappearance between Kinshasa and Tshikaji of a German multi-ton turbine are part of that story.

The grand outdoor dedication of Good Shepherd Hospital took place on January 20, 1975, in an atmosphere of uncertainty because of the decree issued by President Mobutu a few weeks before that forbade the display of religious symbolism in public places. The presence of armed soldiers (the governor's guard) added to the tension. Pastor Mbiye, chairman of the IMCK board, courageously raised the Christian flag and proclaimed IMCK a religious institution. Happily, the dedication proceeded without incident. Local officials included the governor, heads of churches, and the American ambassador. Among the overseas visitors were Dr. and Mrs. William Rule, now retired, and Miss Evelyn Green, executive director of the PCUS Women of the Church.

The IMCK at Tshikaji

The IMCK program after the completion of the Good Shepherd Hospital was different in many ways from the PCUS medical effort in Zaire up to that time. The most obvious difference was the concentration in one institution of highly trained medical personnel; several specialties

Drs. Walter Hull, Birch Rambo, and John K. Miller (center three) at the dedication of the Good Shepherd Hospital. Hospital board members at the left and right. Photograph courtesy of John K. Miller.

were represented. A core group of PCUS physicians provided stable leadership during the formative first decade of the institution.

The ecumenical character of support for the IMCK program was a source of strength. Both the Mennonite Central Committee and the Methodists, as participating members of the IMCK board, assigned medical personnel to IMCK.

The use of large numbers of short-term and volunteer assistants enhanced the scope and quality of the program. These short-term workers brought special expertise, covered for staff on leave, and filled many needs. In addition to those funded by the PCUS were U.S. Peace Corps volunteers, volunteers from various organizations, and students on vacation. Providing guest accommodations became a major responsibility for some IMCK missionary wives.

Ongoing financial support for the IMCK came from a variety of sources. By 1982 approximately two-thirds of the operating budget came from patients' fees, including medical insurance from employed persons. The Medical Benevolence Foundation, the Christoffel Blinden Mission, and other charitable organizations provided substantial support in buildings, equipment, drugs, and short-term workers. In later years the U.S. and German aid funds purchased equipment and supplies and helped renovate the Pax Clinic.[19]

The association with professional peers among the Zairians was one of the rewards of service at IMCK. Qualified Zairians, as they became available, were included on the staff, in the administration of the hospital, and on the governing board. In 1976 Benoit Nzengu, M.D.,

Dr. Benoit Nzengu, an IMCK graduate who studied medicine in Belgium and returned to IMCK as the first Zairian physician on its staff, with Dr. Bill Rule . Photograph courtesy of John K. Miller.

the first Zairian doctor, joined the IMCK staff for three years. By 1983 Zairians occupied the positions of hospital administrator, medical director of the hospital, medical director of the Pax Clinic, director of the School of Nursing, and superintendent of nurses in the hospital.

Relations between IMCK and the Zairian church (CPZ) were not always harmonious. The missionaries at IMCK also did not, at times, feel fully supported by the Mission Board in the United States. The board's postcolonial frame of reference and commitment to the fraternal church-to-church relationship seemed to preclude strong support of IMCK, which, while seeking to produce strong Zairian leadership, operated under firm missionary control. Also during this period, the attention of the board seemed focused on reunification of the PCUS and the United Presbyterian Church (UPC). IMCK physician Ralph Shannon has described some of the problems:

> When everything in the church and the country seemed to be falling apart, the IMCK, with much struggling, was able to function a little better than most. It thus became the whipping boy and the scapegoat for the Church leaders and it seemed the Mission Board as well. Instead of being praised for the good work it is doing in training, public health, curative medicine and ophthalmology, it still must spend time defending its existence and what it is accomplishing. This has been discouraging for those carrying the responsibility for the functioning of the IMCK.

> There was a time when those in the leadership positions of the [Zairian] church felt that the medical work was there for them. They tried to institute a church tax of 10 percent of all gross receipts of the hospitals. The hospitals were there to serve them and their families and

to make money for the church. For a good number of people this philosophy still lingers underneath. This explains the desire of the church that each [missionary] doctor be sent to run a separate hospital. There was a severe clash of priorities over a good number of years. Almost to the person the missionary medical personnel felt the importance of training and made this their primary goal. The IMCK is a child of this philosophy. It has been able to exist only because it has a separate *Personalite Civile*. Today the value of this decision is obvious. If this institute had not been there, none of the church hospitals and a number of their dispensaries would not be able to maintain the level of patient care they do. The top officials in the church today are thankful for the leadership the IMCK has shown in medical education.[20]

The story of IMCK following its consolidation at Tshikaji is told here under three headings: the Good Shepherd Hospital, public health, and teaching.

Good Shepherd Hospital (Hopital Bon Berge)

The Good Shepherd Hospital, including the outpatient complex in Kananga, was a "facility with equipment appropriate to the nation but vastly superior to any other hospital in central Zaire."[21] Pathology, clinical laboratory, and radiology made it possible to maintain a relatively high, though technically unsophisticated, level of medicine. The hospital offered internal medicine, obstetrics/gynecology, ophthalmology, orthopedics, pathology, pediatrics, and surgery. Government, industrial, and mission hospitals (Catholic and Protestant) used the services of the specialists at the Good Shepherd Hospital. IMCK soon became a referral center.

Surgery Department

The surgery department was headed by V. Birch Rambo, a board-certified graduate of the University of Pennsylvania (M.D., 1952) described by an associate as a "surgeon without peer."[22] Two major and two minor operating rooms stayed fully busy. The Mennonite surgeon, John Zook, served in Kananga from 1969 to 1973 and at Tshikaji from 1974 to 1977. Dr. Henry Nelson, who had previously participated in IMCK largely through the clinical training programs in the bush hospitals, worked at the Good Shepherd from 1978 to 1982.

OB/GYN Department

Walter B. Hull, a board-certified graduate of Baylor University (M.D., 1963), headed the OB/GYN department. He found that cervical cancer was the most common form of cancer among women in Zaire; such cases accounted for 40 percent of his patients, as compared with 5 percent in the United States. The 110 milligrams of radium that Dr. Hull hand-carried from the United States was the first available in Zaire for the treatment of cervical cancer. Dr. Hull introduced the use of Pap smears and the laparoscope, promoted family planning, and carried out studies on the incidence and causes for infertility.[23]

Pediatric Department

The pediatric department was headed by John K. Miller, M.D. The practice of pediatrics in Zaire is complicated by the high incidence of sickle-cell anemia. Thirty percent of the people of Zaire are afflicted with the sickle-cell trait and 2.2 percent of infants have the disease; most of these babies die before adolescence. In addition to an active pediatric service at both Tshikaji and the Pax Clinic in Kananga, Dr. Miller initiated and directed an outstanding public health program, which is described later.

Ophthalmology Department

The ophthalmology department was headed by Ralph E. Shannon, a graduate of Baylor University (M.D., 1963), the only American ophthalmologist in Zaire and one of two board-certified ophthalmologists in the country. Dr. Shannon located the ophthalmology department in Kananga at the Pax Clinic, where much of his work was ambulatory. He spent considerable time visiting distant hospitals and holding short training courses for physicians and nurse practitioners. Dr. Shannon lamented the inadequate maintenance of equipment and the disintegration of the eye service when he was on furlough ("It was like starting over again").[24] Valuable assistance was provided by opthalmologists from the

Dr. Ralph E. Shannon was one of two board-certified ophthalmologists in Zaire. Photograph courtesy of John K. Miller.

United States who, through MBF, volunteered their services for weeks or months at a time. Eventually, Dr. Kasonga, one of the Zairian interns, decided to specialize in ophthalmology and was able to provide stability to the department.

Internal Medicine Department

The internal medicine department, staffed by a series of short-term workers from the United States, suffered from lack of continuity in leadership. Eddie M. Williams III, Duke University (M.D., 1974), was the first qualified internist to join the staff; he served from 1979 to 1983. His special training in pulmonary medicine was reflected in his concentration on tuberculosis diagnosis and treatment programs. HIV infections (AIDS) did not surface as a major health problem in this part of Zaire until the late 1980s.

Pathology Department

The establishment of the pathology department by Faye Sinclair, M.D., elevated the level of practice both in the hospital and in the training programs. Other medical installations from all over Zaire sent specimens to the laboratories. Dr. Sinclair, a board-certified pathologist, chose not to seek appointment under the PCUS but maintained her practice in Montana while serving several months each year at the IMCK at her own expense.

Orthopedics Department

The orthopedics department was integrated into an ecumenical and international rehabilitation program carried out by government

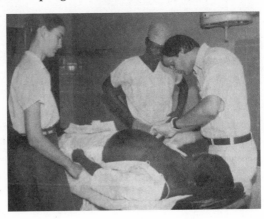

Dr. Eddie Williams examines a patient. Photograph courtesy of Eddie Williams.

and mission (Catholic and Protestant) installations. IMCK provided the surgical component through visiting American and European orthopedic specialists. For example, two Dutch orthopedic surgeons performed twenty-seven operations during one visit. The Jukayi Rehabilitation Center in Kananga, begun by a Catholic sister, was a pleasant complex operated by Catholics. This center contained dormitory space, a brace shop, physiotherapy equipment, and the services of two Dutch physiotherapists supplied on a rotating basis by *Terre des Hommes* of Holland. These men provided postoperative care to the patients recovering from surgery at IMCK. They also did follow-up work in the villages and sought new cases among crippled children, many of whom were kept hidden out of sight. The name *Jukayi*, meaning "Stand Up," reflected an important change in attitude toward people with disabilities: a child who could stand somehow became a person again.[25]

Ambulatory/Outpatient Department
The ambulatory/outpatient department was based in the Pax Clinic in Kananga. The ophthalmology and the community health departments also conducted most of their activities at this facility. The patient load often threatened to overwhelm the clinic. The eight-mile commute to Tshikaji remained a serious problem for patients and for staff. Whereas transportation in a developing society could reasonably have been expected to improve, in the regressive situation under Mobutu's rule, the roads continued to deteriorate and became incredibly bad.

Nursing Department
The nursing department of the hospital was ably staffed by IMCK graduate and student nurses; many of the graduates had years of nursing experience. Annette Kriner, R.N., who served at IMCK from 1974 to 1978, set up and organized the nursing service in the new facilities to provide clinical training for the Nursing School. She was dedicated to the goal of training a Zairian to take charge as soon as practical; missionary nurses thereafter served in supportive roles in the hospital or provided specialties not otherwise available. Ann Rutherford, R.N., for example, was certified in inhalation therapy. Clinical training of the nursing students was a major concern. A number of short-term nurses, volunteers, and wives with nurse's training enriched the program in many ways.

Graduates of the IMCK Nursing School. IMCK brochure.

Administration

A series of businessmen helped with the administration of IMCK: Albert M. Harris, Antoine Harlé, Donald M. Johnstone, and William Simmons. Simmons (1980–83), a successful American businessman, developed on-the-job training in management and accounting practices, which greatly improved the efficiency and accountability of the administrative personnel. He also encouraged the appointment in 1983 of a Zairian, Shamba Manenga (Pierre), as IMCK administrator.

Shamba Manenga received his education in the United States through PCUS scholarships. He was the first black to attend Austin College, Sherman, Texas (B.A., 1964). He then went to Howard University, Washington, D.C. (M.A., Sociology, 1966). He returned to Zaire and worked in education until he joined the staff at IMCK. The PCUS sent him in 1982 to Coret (a school for administration and management in Nairobi, Kenya) and to St. Anthony's Hospital, London, for six months of practical training in hospital management (1982–83). Shamba Manenga was skilled in dealing with hospital personnel and in handling the sometimes

Shamba Manenga (Pierre) became the IMCK administrator in 1983. Photograph courtesy of John K. Miller.

difficult relations with government and church officials.

A number of people contributed significantly to the running of the hospital. Among these were Nancy Hull (Mrs. Walter), who served as treasurer and business manager for a period; Elsbeth Shannon (Mrs. Ralph), a native of Switzerland, whose skills in the French language were a help to the administration; and Margaret (Peggy) Rambo, R.N. (Mrs. Birch), Western Reserve University (M.S.N., 1951), who organized the hospital supplies. Peggy Rambo's system of storage, delivery, and recordkeeping provided a model for the correct handling of medical supplies. Each year the IMCK received some 100 barrels of White Cross material from the women of the PCUS.

IMCK, unlike most hospitals in Zaire, furnished food to the patients from a central kitchen. The operation of this kitchen was no small feat.

The need for permanent skilled maintenance personnel remained a critical problem at IMCK. Many short-term people filled in from time to time but were not able to provide consistent support in this area. Hard work by short-term volunteers, including teams of young Americans on vacation, was helpful and appreciated but did little to solve the basic problems. "We need *two*, not one, good maintenance persons," was a common sentiment.[26]

Public Health

Department of Community Health
The IMCK public health work had its start in Bulape during the period before the construction of the Good Shepherd Hospital and became an important element of the IMCK program in Tshikaji/Kananga. Two physicians with specialty training provided leadership in this field: John K. Miller, who had acquired a master's in public health from Harvard while on furlough in 1965, became head of the Department of Community Health at IMCK. Richard C. Brown served in Bulape (his work is described later in connection with Bulape Hospital).

Drs. Miller and Brown were the first physicians with public health specialty degrees to be assigned by the PCUS to their medical mission work worldwide. While public health was an important element of the mission's medical work from the beginning, it was considered an adjunct responsibility to the curative aspect of medical practice. Also,

Dr. John K. Miller with patient. Photograph courtesy of John K. Miller.

the tropical medicine course required of all medical missionaries by the Belgian government (before independence) was designed primarily to equip physicians to treat tropical diseases; in later years the course was modified to offer a degree in public health.

Public health, as a professional specialty in the United States, did not develop a high profile until after World War II. In church circles, public health did not come into its own until after a number of international church conferences in the 1970s. The emphasis gradually shifted from curative to preventive medicine as public health physicians became available. Experience over time proved the necessity for both curative and preventive health in a balanced program.

The IMCK Community Health Department developed a number of programs that were organized as pilot projects to teach IMCK students and to demonstrate to government and other health providers practical approaches to some of the serious health problems of the area. Three of these experimental programs were recognized in international public health circles: (1) the nutritional rehabilitation program for the treatment of malnourished children, (2) the "Under Fives" mobile teams, and (3) the participation in SANRU (a nationwide primary care program).

Malnourished children

While in Bulape between 1967 and 1969, Dr. Miller won recognition for an innovative nutrition program for the treatment of malnourished children. Among these were children with kwashiorkor, a form of malnutrition that is caused by severe protein deficiency and usually occurs in children who stop drinking mother's milk when displaced by a younger sibling.

A child with kwashiorkor gets a bath. Photograph courtesy of John K. Miller.

The basic concept of the program was to teach the mothers how to feed the children properly using locally available foods. Mother and child were admitted to a nutrition rehabilitation village apart from the hospital where, under supervision for a four- to six-week period, the mother used village-style cook fires and pots to prepare and feed the child a prescribed diet made up primarily of peanuts, corn, and beans with eggs, fruits, and vegetables as available. Once the momentum was established, the mothers taught newcomers the routine. As malnourished children began to flourish, the lesson was taught in a way that no mother failed to understand. A similar nutrition rehabilitation village was established near the new Good Shepherd Hospital and was administered by the IMCK Department of Community Health. Dr. Miller comments:

The principles are simple, and the program must be simple to succeed. We found it was fatal to give a child a transfusion, as all the credit for the cure went to the transfusion. Likewise with that useless excrescence of our society—vitamin pills. We had to try to keep everything so that the day the mother took her child home she could easily continue to do the same thing instead of attributing recovery to the witchcraft of the hospital milieu.

There were simple health lectures, but no slides, movies, puppet shows, etc. We had already learned that the women couldn't make heads or tails of such things. In the unit there were always sick and swollen newcomers, thin children beginning to progress, and fatter ones going home. Only an idiot could fail to grasp the fact that corn-beans beat manioc. Because of serious anemia [3–4 gm hemoglobin] we had to make one compromise and give each child a teaspoonful of iron solution once a day. . . . It was a constant battle to keep our valiant missionary colleagues from dosing the kids with [donated] skim milk.

We found there were reverberations. When Mother went home she fed her other children as she had done in the hospital. Some mothers began to tell of what had happened with such enthusiasm that they became feeding evangelists. . . . The gospel they teach is that "Manioc [the traditional African diet] Makes Babies Sick and Corn-Beans Makes Them Well."[27]

"Under Fives" mobile clinics

While in Bulape Dr. Miller also pioneered in setting up the "Under Fives" clinics. This innovative concept introduced a significant new level of child care. In the Kananga area these clinics were known as the "Muamba Nkuvula's Clinics," *Muamba Nkuvula* being Dr. Miller's Zairian name; as a child growing up in Mutoto, he was given the name of a Lulua chief.[28]

The "Under Fives" mobile team went on a regular schedule to designated areas, frequently meeting under a tree. A team, consisting of a nurse, student nurses, a nutrition teacher, and chauffeur, might go to as many as forty places in a month. These mobile clinics were set up to follow children during their preschool years by monitoring nutrition and growth, providing immunizations, giving malaria prophylaxis, and treating minor illnesses. Children requiring more sophisticated care would be taken to the hospital. Breast-feeding was

*Public health vehicle. Photograph
courtesy of John K. Miller.*

strongly promoted over bottle-feeding. In 1981 IMCK reported that
more than 6,000 new children were registered, and that the health
teams had visited 53,802 children at 399 locations. Nutrition education and family planning were major emphases. Catholic mission
personnel and U.S. Peace Corps volunteers (working with the Zaire
Health Department) assisted in this program.[29]

Diarrhea is a common and frequently fatal condition among
young children. Dr. Miller was a pioneer in promoting oral rehydration for the treatment of diarrhea. His experience contributed to and
supported the findings of other researchers. Oral rehydration has
now become accepted worldwide as the proper treatment for diarrhea. Dr. Miller enjoys telling how, long after he had introduced the
procedure, enthusiastic young staff from Atlanta's Centers for
Disease Control (CDC) arrived at IMCK to instruct him in the efficacy
of oral rehydration!

SANRU

Before independence the Zairians enjoyed a health system that had
been organized by the Belgian colonial government to provide medical
facilities and personnel to every district of the country. As noted, the
sudden breakdown of this system resulted in a tragic drop in health
throughout the country. In the early 1980s the SANRU[30] program, a
nationwide program of primary health care, was organized and subsidized by U.S.AID in cooperation with the Department of Health of the

Zairian government and the Protestant churches of Zaire. Dr. Miller served as a consultant in planning and setting up the program.

IMCK, along with the Bulape and Bibanga hospitals, was designated a Regional Reference Hospital for SANRU. IMCK was also put in charge of a "health zone" consisting of 150,000 people. Responsibilities included supervision of twenty-three city and rural health posts, training of health workers on various levels, updating of skills through refresher courses, and provision of a constant supply of basic medicines. The success of the program depended on the ability to stimulate local people to accept responsibility for their own health. Graduates of the IMCK Nursing School worked with Dr. Miller to carry out the SANRU program. U.S. Peace Corps volunteers assigned to the Department of Health also contributed to this work.

Teaching

The medical teaching mission remained the primary focus of IMCK/Good Shepherd Hospital. All the missionaries who worked with the young Zairians involved have acclaimed the importance of the teaching program and the reward in its fulfillment.

The teaching mission had four components: the nursing school, the laboratory school, physician training, and continuing education. Dr. Hull became the director of medical education, with broad oversight of all aspects of the training program.

Nursing School

The nursing school, IMCK's pioneer experiment in formal medical education, continued its four-year diploma course, training young men and women in nursing, midwifery, and public health. By 1982 the school, which was approved and partially supported by the government, had 105 students and was rated as one of the top three nursing schools in Zaire.[31]

Directors of the nursing school include Katie Nelson, R.N., Ph.D. (1973–74; 1978–79), the Mennonite missionary Jeanne Zook, R.N. (1974–77), and Annette Kriner, R.N. (1978). The faculty was made up largely of IMCK graduates. In 1979 Katie Nelson took great pleasure in turning the directorship over to Mpoi Lumpungu, an IMCK nursing school graduate.

The development of nursing education in Zaire is exemplified by Mpoi Lumpungu, who first graduated from the training program for

*IMCK student nurses at a
"bush hospital." Photograph
courtesy of John K. Miller.*

nurse's aides at Bibanga, which he entered after finishing five years of
primary school. He then attended the IMCK School of Nursing and
graduated with high school and nursing diplomas. After several years
he entered a three-year graduate program at the *Institut Supérieur
Technique Médical* in Kinshasa, where he studied teaching and administration. As director of the IMCK School of Nursing, he was described by
Dr. Hull as "Christian, honest, and a compulsive perfectionist"[32] and by
Katie Nelson as "doing a superb job in administration and teaching."[33]

IMCK graduates often headed departments in other hospitals,
became teachers in nursing and midwifery schools, or entered the
public health delivery system. Some, like Mpoi Lumpungu,
continued their education. Another outstanding graduate was Dr.
Mulaja Mukendi, who, after graduating from IMCK, became a
nursing instructor and then went on to medical school in Kinshasa.
He interned in Kinshasa and returned to IMCK as the medical
director of the Pax Clinic in Kananga.

Laboratory School

The laboratory school, despite repeated efforts, was not established until 1974, when Good Shepherd Hospital was finished.
Leaders in the founding of the school include Anne Greenlee
(1975–77), a member of the U.S. Peace Corps; Anita Jantzen, (1978–80),
a Mennonite missionary; and Nancy Norman, (1980–83+). Nancy
Norman, a graduate of the University of Virginia (M.T., 1948), had
had over twenty-five years of teaching experience.

The laboratory school, one of only two in the country, offered a
four-year course for high school graduates.[34] Forty-seven students
(men and women) enrolled for the 1982–83 year. Because graduates

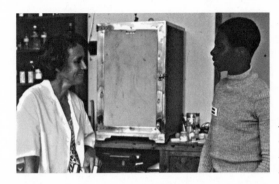

Aurie M. Miller, M.T., with laboratory student, IMCK. Photograph courtesy of John K. Miller.

would not have access to high-tech equipment, the school taught manual techniques wherever possible. Clinical training for the laboratory students was supplied by qualified medical technicians in the hospital. In 1964 Ruth Worth moved to Tshikaji where she set up a clinical laboratory that served the entire IMCK medical program. PCUS medical technologists included Aurie Miller (Mrs. John), Elizabeth Templeton, Peggy Connell, and Linda Kimball. Over the years, five Peace Corps medical technicians were assigned to work at the Good Shepherd Hospital. Graduates were in great demand as Zairian hospitals sought to upgrade their services with laboratory facilities. The acquisition of supplies and the maintenance of standards remained difficult problems for the graduates.

Physician Training
Physician training on the intern/resident level developed more slowly. There were few qualified applicants because of the problems encountered in developing a university system and medical school in Zaire. In 1982 the National University Medical School in Kinshasa assigned four graduates a year to IMCK for one-year internships.

More satisfactory results were accomplished through a system in which a young physician worked for a period with one or more of the missionary physicians. Ngoyi Kadima, M.D., a graduate of the medical school in Kinshasa, studied surgery under Dr. Birch Rambo. Dr. Ngoyi later became the medical director of the Good Shepherd Hospital.

Continuing Education
Continuing education for physicians, nurses, and laboratory technicians became one of the most appreciated services offered by IMCK.

An annual medical education seminar (in French) was organized for all physicians in the two provinces of East and West Kasai. This seminar provided information for updating and improving medical care in an area where no other such program was available.

The nursing and laboratory schools also offered annual refresher courses. Nurses from government as well as from other medical facilities attended these classes, which emphasized primary care and preventive medicine.

During school vacations, Nancy Norman, the director of the laboratory school, visited graduates working in other hospitals. She was able to help them organize and update their procedures.

Finally, the Christian Medical Society (in the United States) organized a biannual Continuing Education Course (held in Kenya) to help missionary doctors meet the educational requirements for maintaining their U.S. medical licenses. Volunteers from the United States, recruited by the Medical Benevolence Foundation, made it possible for the missionary doctor to attend these classes by taking over the missionaries' duties during the two weeks they were away. In later years Zairian staff were invited to participate in the course.

THE CPZ MEDICAL PROGRAM

The postindependence decision to concentrate the PCUS medical resources (personnel and financial) in the IMCK training center radically changed PCUS medical work in the Kasai and resulted, as has been noted, in two medical programs: the IMCK and the CPZ medical program. Although the PCUS and the CPZ collaborated in both programs and there was some overlap in personnel, the administration and goals of the two programs were quite different. The IMCK had its own independent board (with CPZ representation) and concentrated on teaching; the CPZ medical program was under the supervision of the CPZ General Assembly and tried to provide medical services in rural areas.

The CPZ medical program began in the former APCM medical facilities and evolved to include rural clinics, the central pharmacy, the dental office in Kananga, and the Christian Health Center in Mbuji Mayi.

Former APCM Hospitals

At the time of independence all six of the APCM mission hospitals and the three clinics in the so-called outstations were staffed and fully operational under missionary supervision. The following years of social and ethnic unrest severely disrupted the work. With the dissolution of the APCM in 1966, the hospitals, along with other mission property, were turned over to the CPZ.

The Bulape and Bibanga hospitals, and the Lubondai Hospital until 1967, continued their historic roles as active and effective bush hospitals. Until the Good Shepherd Hospital opened in 1975, they provided clinical training for the IMCK students. IMCK graduates greatly enhanced the level of care in these hospitals and played an active role in the teaching of the nursing students. Missionary staffing, especially at Bulape, was continuous and strong.

The other mission hospitals operated on a much-reduced scale, as clinics with Zairian nurses in charge. The PCUS continued to provide a subsidy and White Cross supplies. After Zairian physicians became available in the late 1970s, the CPZ developed plans to reactivate these former hospitals. Lack of maintenance of the plants presented a serious problem.

Bulape Hospital

Bulape Hospital's 120-bed facility remained full and its outreach program (which included three air dispensaries, leprosy and tuberculosis villages, and various maternal and child care programs) developed community health initiatives that raised the health in the surrounding area. The school for nurse's aides was discontinued in 1964 after Bulape Hospital began providing clinical training for the newly established IMCK nursing school. After 1975, it reverted to a typical bush hospital along the preindependence model and the school for nurse's aides was again put into operation. Drs. Richard Brown, Bill Rule, and Kenneth McGill served between 1975 and 1983. Zairian physicians (Tshiswaka Kayembe and Tshibangu Mangala) joined the staff in 1979.

Public health in Bulape was greatly enhanced by the work of Drs. John Miller and Richard Brown. Dr. Miller's nutrition program for undernourished children and the "Under Fives" clinics have been described (see IMCK, Public Health). Dr. Brown, a diplomate of the American Board of Preventive Medicine, earned his M.D. from the

University of Virginia (1963) and his M.P.H. from Harvard (1966). He developed effective community health programs in villages within a fifty-mile radius of Bulape.[35] A number of Peace Corps volunteers were assigned to the Bulape area in the 1970s and took part in these programs.

With his wife, Judith, who had a Ph.D. in anthropology, Dr. Brown carried out intensive demographic surveys of the Bulape area. The published reports of their research in demography, family planning, nutrition, and iodine deficiency made a significant contribution to international public health.[36] The Browns wrote some twenty-five medical articles and books (including material in the Tshiluba language) for dealing with tuberculosis, goiter, and infant nutrition. Dr. Richard Brown wrote, "Research was a very important part of [our] work at Bulape and the most enjoyable. . . . Especially rewarding was to publish the data and to make contact with scientific colleagues in Europe."[37]

Dr. Brown is also remembered for designing what became known as the "Mercedes Community Toilet," a pit latrine that, when viewed from above by plane, resembled the Mercedes symbol and provided privacy to three occupants at a time.

In 1977 Dr. Bill Rule was asked to come out of retirement to take over the management of the Bulape Hospital. Because no other missionary physician was available and because of the misappropriation of hospital funds by CPZ officials, the hospital was in danger of being degraded to a simple dispensary.[38] Dr. Rule agreed and spent three very productive years (1977–80) at Bulape.

Dr. Rule, in his "Milestones in Mission," vividly described the management problems faced by the medical missionaries in Zaire. Under the heading "Reasons Why a Refined and Self-Respecting Doctor Would Be Unwilling to Associate Himself with the Work at Bulape Hospital," he listed the problems resulting from the habitual lack of water; a plumbing system continually out of order; the infestation of lice, bedbugs and cockroaches; and the free run of goats, dogs, and chickens in the compound and corridors. Petty thievery was encountered at every turn: "Two favorite objects to pilfer were curtains snatched from windows (prized for women's head scarfs or men's shirts) and screens (made into sieves to sift the flour they pounded out of manioc roots)." He added:

> I am led to comment [on] the capacity of a young church in a developing country to handle its own business and keep its household in

order. I am speaking of "improvidence"—the inability to look ahead and plan for the future. You may recall my observation that the attitude of affluence is entirely different from that of poverty. The "haves" are occupied with keeping what they have, or watching it grow. They look to the future and preserve against a "rainy day." On the other hand, the "have-nots" take little thought of the future. . . . Their constant "living on the edge" inclines them to use today whatever comes to hand, and they are alarmingly improvident about tomorrow. . . . This attitude spills over into hospital administration, chiefly concerning medicines and supplies. My attitude was to husband them with all my might. But let it be known that a new shipment of drugs had arrived and my African cohorts wanted to give them in generous dosage to every patient that darkened the door! The same went with linen and dry goods supplies.[39]

In addition to conducting an active practice and managing a busy plant, Dr. Rule had two experiences that seem to stand out during this period of service. The first was the request from the CPZ to reopen the school for nurse's aides, a two-year course after grammar school. For Dr. Rule, whose missionary career had been dedicated to raising the level of nurse's training, this request was ironic, and he admits to being "rather aghast" when he heard it. However, the request was not unreasonable; the needs of the church hospitals and dispensaries were not being met by the few better-trained nurses, who were being wooed away to higher-paying jobs. Workers trained at a lower level as "auxiliary nurses," as they were now called, could help fill the gap.[40]

Dr. Rule was able to persuade Lucille McElroy, R.N., the second-generation missionary with twenty-seven years of teaching experience at Lubondai and IMCK, to return from the United States, where she had been retired for seven years. She arrived in February 1979 and helped the ten young men and ten young women of the first class complete the prescribed work by June. Shortly thereafter she developed thrombophlebitis of the femoral vein, went into profound shock, and died. Dr. Rule wrote:

The Christian community responded, this time for one whose natural family was far away in the States, but whose missionary family and African family were near at hand, expressing their love and grief in many ways. Her body was conducted to the church by

all her boy and girl students serving as pall-bearers, and a Christian
memorial service was held, after which the earthly remains were
laid to rest in the small Bulape cemetery for missionary families. . . .
Only God, in his goodness and grace, knows the answers to
perplexing questions raised by our poor minds at such times as
these.[41]

The second memorable experience for Dr. Rule was the arrival in
1979 of two young Zairian doctors (Tshiswaka Kayembe and
Tshibangu Mangala), just out of medical school in Kinshasa, to work
at the Bulape Hospital. Dr. Rule wrote:

> One of the fondest dreams a missionary doctor can have is to see the
> day when African physicians join him and move in to take over the
> leadership in medical ministry. But if someone had told me I would
> see this come to pass during my tenure on the field, I would have
> shrugged with much skepticism. . . . Now my cup was truly running
> over. I had TWO African doctors as colleagues, and I had never
> expected to have even one.[42]

Kenneth H. McGill, M.D., followed Dr. Rule at Bulape in 1980 (to
1987). Dr. McGill, a graduate of Vanderbilt University (M.D., 1952)
and a board-certified surgeon, found his special calling in the "bush"
hospitals operated by the CPZ. He was a skilled surgeon and teacher;
four Zairian physicians (Drs. Katambwe, Tshiswaka, Tshibangu, and
Muambi) looked on him as their mentor.

Dr. McGill carried out a number of building projects for the
nursing school and the hospital at Bulape. Funds were raised

*John Gutzke, the genius of the
solar panels, and Kenneth H.
McGill, M.D., examine a young
patient at Bulape. Photograph
courtesy of Nancy McGill.*

Bulape Hospital. Apparatus for collecting rain water in foreground; solar panels on the roof provide electricity. Photograph courtesy of Paul S. Crane.

primarily by MBF and by the Clover Mission (a group from McGill's home town of Clover, South Carolina, who organized to provide him support). Dr. McGill was open to innovative ideas. With the help of John Gutzke, a highly qualified (though unconventional) electrical engineer, he experimented with the installation of solar panels for electricity; he solved the problem of making intravenous fluids by developing a simple filter system for rain water; and, in order to ensure an adequate water supply in the hospital—the villagers looked on water as a community resource and did not hesitate to use the hospital cisterns—he encouraged a program of cistern building in the surrounding villages.

Dr. McGill's comments reflect the pressures of medical practice in the "bush":

> Mission medicine is the best the country has but is some 35 years behind. Even IMCK is far from being what it should be. Many types of diagnostic equipment are not available; maintenance of them would be virtually impossible . . .

> In addition to practicing medicine and teaching there is administration and maintenance. None of this is simple in Zaire. Support help [nurses, maintenance people, and administrative personnel] has not been adequate—I have to see why the grass isn't cut; why goats have wandered into the wards. There is real difficulty in getting supplies: for example, an electrocardiograph ordered three years ago has not yet arrived; a gastroscope needs repair . . .

Medically it is exciting work with something new and unusual each day. Pathology is more advanced than usually seen in the United States. Primary liver cancer is the most common kind of cancer; we see three to four cases each month. Malaria is still a major problem. Tropical diseases include sleeping sickness, leprosy, and tuberculosis. Preventive medicine has made progress but has a long way to go. Problems have to do with supervision and finding dependable people . . .

Training of Zairians has been the primary aim of the work. The presence in recent years of trained Zairian doctors is a great advance. The presence of short-term workers from the United States is not too helpful; they are time consuming. The language barrier is a problem . . .

Frustrations include dealing with lack of honesty, too many guests, administrative problems, and dealing with church bureaucracy [both CPZ and PCUS].[43]

Comments by Nancy McGill also are illuminating:

I work in the administration of the hospital: hold the purse, keep books, place orders, keep up with supplies, translate orders to English, handle White Cross, help write the Annual Report. Most difficult is the role of policing hospital supplies, an unpleasant but necessary job. Sometimes the staff seem like children and act like it is just a game . . .

The hospital operates under the Medical Committee of the CPZ. On-site responsibility is carried by a hospital committee which meets every Monday. This committee is made up of the three doctors [one missionary and two Zairian], head nurse, chaplain, director of the nursing school, and secretary. The public health work in Bulape is strong but needs supervision. Most rewarding has been to work with the Zairian doctors and see them develop both professionally and in Christian leadership . . .

John Gutzke has found his niche in Bulape. His Tshiluba name means "Helping Hand," and he has made a splendid contribution with the solar power system. He is working to provide this source of electricity to other CPZ medical facilities where no electricity is available.[44]

Bibanga Hospital

Bibanga Hospital, in the province of East Kasai, was the other former mission hospital to continue in full service after the mission's institutions were turned over to the CPZ. It offered medical, surgical, pediatric, OB/GYN, and outpatient services. Its public health program emphasized nutrition education and the early detection of leprosy and tuberculosis. It supervised four air-dispensaries in remote villages, monitored "Under Fives" clinics in thirty-three outlying villages, supported the leprosy and tuberculosis villages, and, eventually, reopened the school for the training of nurse's aides. Bibanga had a hydroelectric installation that remained operative most of the time and was a tremendous boon to the work of the hospital. PCUS missionary personnel continued to be assigned to Bibanga Hospital as available. During the 1970s a number of Peace Corps young people assisted in the community health program; one worked for a while in the laboratory.

Ralph Shannon, M.D., who went to Zaire after one year of internship expecting to serve for three years under an experienced doctor, found himself put in charge of the Bibanga Hospital from 1965 to 1968. He wrote:

> I was sent to Bibanga where I ended up working as the only doctor for three years. I was inadequately trained to assume the responsibilities of running a hospital, ordering the supplies, taking care of the medical problems, and doing the surgery that needed to be done. . . . During those three years the hospital was often left without a doctor: when I went to Switzerland to get married, when we went to Bulape for the birth of our first child, and when we were evacuated to Kananga in case we had to be flown out of the country during the unrest of those years.[45]

In Bibanga Dr. Shannon developed an interest in ophthalmology. Not only was he unable to handle the eye problems he encountered, but there was no other doctor adequately trained to do so. As a result Dr. Shannon decided to make ophthalmology his field of expertise and took residency training at the University of Pennsylvania before returning to the IMCK.

Kenneth H. McGill, M.D., began his missionary career at Bibanga and served from 1968 to 1978 with a two-year break during which he took residency training in plastic surgery and orthopedics. During his years at Bibanga, the hospital increased its capacity from 120 beds to 176 beds (there were usually 190 to 200 patients, many sleeping on the floor on mats) with the addition of three new wards built by the American Leprosy Mission. These wards provided care for leprosy patients unsegregated from general medical cases, a new concept at that time. Walter B. Hull, M.D., served for three years (1970–73) during Dr. McGill's absence. Dr. Hull told of his Bibanga experience:

> The first assignment to Bibanga turned out to be the best and the most difficult three years in my life. I worked with Ken McGill for a short time but was there alone for two years. It was a growing experience professionally, culturally, and spiritually. In this remote location I was forced to participate in the church and the community. I learned the rural as well as urban languages. There were many "hard knocks," and it was often emotionally draining. However, I look back on it as a very valuable experience. . . . I believe that in an urban setting, such as Kinshasa, it would be difficult to develop a similar feeling of community with church and people as was possible in Bibanga.[46]

During his last two years at Bibanga, Dr. McGill had as his assistant a young Zairian just out of medical school. When Dr. McGill

Katambue Nkoma, M.D., became the first national to head a PCUS hospital in Zaire when he took charge of the Bibanga Hospital in 1978. Photograph courtesy of Dot Temple.

left on furlough in 1978, Katambue Nkoma, M.D., was put in charge of Bibanga Hospital. His effective performance led McGill to move to Bulape rather than return to Bibanga. Dr. Katambue has the distinction of being the first Zairian to take over the full administration of one of the church hospitals. Under his leadership the work grew and prospered.[47] Virginia King, R.N., returned to Bibanga in 1983 to help with correspondence, orders, supplies, and the teaching of the nurse's aides.

Lubondai Hospital

Lubondai Hospital, as has been noted, continued operation under missionary direction for seven years after independence. The three main PCUS physicians during this time were John Miller (1960–61), William Rule (until IMCK moved to the Tshikaji location in 1964), and Henry S. Nelson (1964–67). Additional assistance came from a number of short-term doctors (William G. McIntosh, a Scotsman from the Brethren Mission; Neal Ratzlaff and Paul Hodel of the Mennonite Central Committee; and Ralph E. Shannon). J. B. Jung practiced dentistry but did not attempt to reopen the dental school. Nurses were Anna K. Dickson, Elizabeth Miller, Katie Nelson, and Barbara Hodel; Nolie McDonald and Elizabeth Templeton handled the X-ray and medical technician work.

Henry Nelson described his three years at Lubondai as extremely productive. Lubondai Hospital was the only hospital in a 150-mile radius where there had been ten to twelve hospitals. It had 100 beds and two operating rooms. Many patients were flown in by bush plane. A hotel was set up for ambulatory patients and another area was set aside where families could live by village-type camping. It was an interesting time surgically, and clinical teaching for IMCK students continued in the hospital. Dr. Nelson taught a formal class in pharmacology.

Katie Nelson spent much of her time in a nearby Lulua village where she gathered material for her Ph.D. dissertation, "Child Rearing Patterns in a Lulua Village of South Central Congo" (George Peabody College, Nashville, Tennessee, 1968). Her study is a real contribution to the understanding of the indigenous tribes and their customs. She did this work, with the blessing of the mission, under a fellowship from the National Institutes of Health (NIH).

Katie Nelson administered anesthesia on occasion and taught nutrition to the IMCK nursing students. She found these high school graduates working at a more advanced level than students she had taught before.[48]

After 1967 (when the Nelsons completed their term), Lubondai Hospital became a clinic under the CPZ. Maternal and infant care became a primary focus of activity.

Rural Clinics

From its inception the CPZ took an active and commendable interest in promoting better health care in rural communities at a time when there was virtually no other source of such care for most of the population. Government medical services outside the larger cities were at a virtual standstill.

By 1980 the supply of Zairian doctors substantially exceeded the number of foreign doctors in the country. However, about one-half of the 1,500 Zairian doctors stayed in Kinshasa and another third went to major cities, leaving very few for the great majority of the population who lived in rural areas.[49] Dr. Rule described the situation:

> The cry of the Christian people across the land has been repeated over and over again that the church must help us get medical help near at hand in our own rural villages. When the baby has fever in the night, when there is a laceration which requires a few stitches, when there is a cinder in the eye, the need is immediate and not after you have walked twenty or fifty miles to a hospital. From this need the idea of rural dispensaries with a resident *aide-infirmier* was born. It caught on with great enthusiasm, and churches in all the presbyteries formed their medical councils and accumulated funds for buying into the project.[50]

The CPZ rural clinics were generally located near a primary school or a strong church congregation. Many were in remote, quite primitive areas. Once approved by the CPZ and by the local or provincial health department, the clinics had access to drugs and supplies from the Central Pharmacy. The clinics quickly proliferated and provided simple remedies where none had been available.

Among the CPZ clinics were those located at the former APCM hospitals at Lubondai, Luebo, Mutoto, and Moma and the former "outstation clinics" at Mboi, Kasha, and Kakinda. PCUS nurses helped in these clinics when their husbands were assigned to these locations. For example, Virginia King (Mrs. Earl) worked in Mboi from 1962 to 1965 and in Luebo from 1965 to 1970. Blanche W. Carper (Mrs. Day) was in Moma from 1963 to 1971.

Blanche Carper reported that at the time of independence, Moma Hospital was just getting started in a newly built, forty-bed unit. When Dr. and Mrs. Dickerson (Melford, M.D., and Frances, R.N.) left on regular furlough and did not return, the hospital reverted to its clinic status. The Carpers were the only missionaries in Moma for most of their stay. "The doctor from Lubondai came at regular intervals or could be summoned by radio. We were supported by our Zairian friends and everything seemed always to work out all right."[51]

The program of rural clinics was not without problems. No overall design was in place, nor was the function of the clinics clearly defined. They popped up haphazardly and, without adequate supervision or direction, had the potential for an unacceptable and even hazardous level of medical practice.[52] In some cases, the sale of drugs became a source of income and, in the absence of adequate accounting controls, provided an opportunity for corruption.

Eventually the problems were addressed by the appointment of Dr. Tshibangu Mangala (see Bulape) as director of the Rural Health Program. He oversaw the proper functioning of the clinics, ably assisted by Badibanga Mukole, an IMCK graduate.[53] The SANRU program (see IMCK) was designed to provide better supervision and training opportunities for persons working in the clinics.

Central Pharmacy

Suppling the medical facilities of the CPZ soon loomed as a serious problem. Placing an order, filling out import documents, and arranging transportation were difficult, and thievery was a major problem. Dr. Rule's description gives some idea of the situation:

> Following the example of its renowned leader [Mobutu], Zaire has been recognized for a number of years as a nation of abysmal corruption. It is a land in which a booming black market is always operating. One of the hottest items is medicines. Almost any medicine will do since the African buyers have little or no knowledge of their pharmaceutical properties. The pilfering of drugs begins at the port of entry and continues even to their administration to the sick in pharmacies, clinics and hospitals. Our skimpy drug supply, never adequate to meet the needs, continually ran the gauntlet, and . . . was never all which had been ordered and anticipated for the care of patients . . .

> From time to time drug orders were placed with pharmaceutical houses in Europe. One was sent to a company in England in early 1977. In June of 1978 the first two of thirteen cases composing this order arrived at Bulape. No others came until January 1979, almost two years after the order was made! Suddenly six more cases

arrived, but they had been broken into and precious supplies had been taken. Out of 50,000 capsules of tetracycline shipped, 23,000 were stolen. None of the 20,000 tablets of Isoniazid for tuberculosis made it. Five of the cases never showed up. We estimated we lost $3,500 worth of drugs with that order.[54]

The creation of a centralized method for the systematic handling of hospital drugs and supplies was proposed by the Zairian church and implemented by Dr. Henry Nelson during his tour of 1978 to 1982. The Central Pharmacy was located in the center of Kananga and had adequate space for storage, recordkeeping, and distribution.

Using the United Nation's list of drugs for developing countries, Dr. Nelson placed an order for some fifty drugs. The Medical Benevolence Foundation funded this basic order and set up a rotating fund for keeping drug orders stocked. Sample drugs donated by physicians in the United States and White Cross supplies also could be processed through this central office.

Various stratagems were devised to ensure the safety of the orders. Orders often accompanied travelers as checked baggage; unaccompanied orders were met at the port of entry and personally escorted to the Central Pharmacy.

By 1983 some seventy clinics and six hospitals, including the IMCK, depended on the Central Pharmacy for their supplies. Funding for salaries and for drugs was supplied by the CPZ and the recipient pharmacies.[55]

In 1981 the PCUS appointed William R. and Sarah C. Altland, both of whom were graduate pharmacists, to take charge and further develop this important service. This consolidation in purchasing and importing drugs and supplies was a great financial saving and a boon to the medical work.

Kananga Dental Clinic

After independence no attempt was made to start up the dental training program. Drs. Marks and Jung practiced some dentistry in Lubondai and, after IMCK moved to Tshikaji, a dental office was opened in Kananga. Three PCUS dentists, John L. Hillsman (Emory University, D.D.S., 1961) Jack A. Shannon (University of Illinois, Chicago, D.D.S., 1968), and Robert O. Zanone (University of Tennessee, D.D.S., 1953), conducted an active dental practice in this clinic until 1976. Thereafter (Isaac) Kabamba Secombe, a graduate of the IMCK dental program, carried on the practice. One-third of the income of the CPZ is said to have been generated by this clinic.[56]

After returning to the United States in 1961, Dr. Marks, the founder of the IMCK dental program, became a professor at the University of North Carolina School of Dentistry. He kept in close touch with the dental clinic in Kananga, helping to provide needed equipment and supplies. He visited the clinic in 1967 and again in 1980, when he took part in the Lake Munkamba Conference. He made it possible for Kabamba Secombe to get additional training at the University of Kentucky. After Dr. Marks retired from the University of North Carolina (and beyond the time frame of this account), he returned to Kananga (1987–89) to reactivate a teaching program for graduate dentists.

Mbuji Mayi Christian Health Center

The CPZ, the official Zairian Presbyterian Church or "community," was made up of two synods corresponding to the two provinces of East and West Kasai. The majority of former APCM mission facilities were located in West Kasai, whose capital was Kananga. Since Bibanga, the primary mission site in East Kasai, was in a rural area removed from population centers, church officials of the East Kasai were very eager for a PCUS-sponsored hospital to be established in Mbuji Mayi, the capital city. The PCUS, hard-pressed to support IMCK adequately, did not have the resources to respond to this request, but did agree to support the founding of a Christian Health Center in Mbuji Mayi. This decision was in line with the recommendation of the 1980 Lake Munkamba conference for emphasis on community and public health initiatives.

Mbuji Mayi, whose lights twinkling in the valley below could be seen at night from Bibanga, was known as the diamond capital of Zaire. It had been developed by the Belgians into a well-planned, tightly controlled city. During the ethnic struggles at the time of independence, Bakwanga, as it was then called, experienced severe fighting and was overrun by refugees. By 1980 Mbuji Mayi was a large urban center with a population of around 600,000; Belgians had been induced to return to operate the mines. Because of the diamond industry, security was strict and pervasive, and antiforeign outbursts were not unknown.

Mbuji Mayi Christian Health Center (1982). Photograph courtesy of Dot Temple.

The Mbuji Mayi Christian Health Center opened in 1980 and was the special project of Orange Presbytery in North Carolina, which enthusiastically raised funds, collected supplies, and sent members to observe and to help with the construction. Dr. Richard Brown of Bulape drew up plans for the building and designed a comprehensive program that combined health, nutrition, community development, and agricultural services as part of its broad approach to public health. In time, a Zairian physician was employed to conduct an outpatient clinic.

PCUS missionaries, working under the premise that they were "not here to stay,"[57] helped set up the center. Among them were Annette Kriner, R.N., an experienced organizer; Marcia Berta Murray, business manager; and two agricultural specialists, Frank Dimmock (1979–80) and Donald Welch (1980–83). Zairians were thoroughly involved in both the planning and the execution of the plans for the center. Ilunga Kalenga, an IMCK graduate with experience in a hospital in the United States, was trained to become director. Eventually, the center was operated entirely by Zairians. A number of PCUS "volunteers in mission" worked at Mbuji Mayi, as did a group of Peace Corps volunteers.

Innoculations! Mbuji Mayi Christian Health Center. Photograph courtesy of Dot Temple.

CPK HEALTH CLINICS
Kinshasa

In 1980 the PCUS, in cooperation with the Presbyterian Community of Kinshasa (CPK), for the first time undertook to do medical work in the capital city of Kinshasa. Protestants, Catholics, and representatives of the *Cooperation Belge* worked with medical officers of the Zairian government to devise an urban public health program designed to cope with the appalling health needs of Kinshasa, which by this time, had a population of well over two million. The program sought to implement the World Health Organization's ambitious Alma Alta Declaration of "Health for All by the Year 2000."

The city was divided into twenty-two health zones, with 100,000 people to a zone. Each zone was to have ten primary health care centers, one maternity center and one referral hospital. The CPK agreed to work in two zones, the Masina and Kingabwa zones, and by 1983 had completed one center with two more in the planning stage.

To head this project, the PCUS assigned Annette Kriner, R.N., whose talent for training Zairians to accept responsibility, as demonstrated at both IMCK and Mbuji Mayi, made her an excellent choice. Working with her was JoAnn B. Ellington, R.N., who had worked in a number of medical facilities since being assigned with her husband to Kinshasa in 1964. The estimated cost per health center was $30,000 to $40,000; operating expenses for one year totaled $10,000 ($4,000 for salaries and $6,000 for the operating budget).

This program provided a Christian outreach that was an expression of the church's desire to serve those in greatest need. The ecumenical and international character of the project was exciting. By 1983 in the Masina zone, for example, there were four health centers: one Catholic, two Salvation Army, and one Presbyterian. Two more centers, a Catholic and a Presbyterian, were scheduled to open soon. The

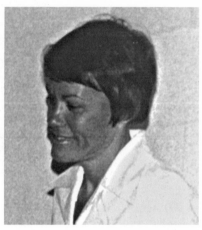

Annette Kriner, R.N., served at Bulape, IMCK, Mbuji Mayi, and Kinshasa. Photograph courtesy of Dot Temple.

Salvation Army operated a maternity center, and there was hope that the Belgian government would fund a referral hospital.

Annette Kriner's statement of the philosophy underlying the program in Kinshasa could be said to encapsulate the PCUS commitment in medicine in Zaire in 1983:

> The goal is to help the Zairians learn how to do the work and manage the program. Our working philosophy is to teach those who seem willing to learn and, though they may not yet be highly qualified, to coach them into positions of responsibility. A big challenge is to seek ways whereby the medical work can achieve autonomy

Public health clinic in the capital, Kinshasa. Photograph courtesy of Paul S. Crane.

once the capital investments have been made, thereby breaking the chains of dependency that have characterized the past.[58]

Summary

The PCUS maintained a medical program as part of its Christian witness in Congo/Zaire for seventy-six years (1906–83). Twenty-five (full-term/regular service) physicians, six dentists, fifty-five nurses, and seven medical technicians plus a host of short-term and volunteer workers worked in a difficult and challenging environment to bring Western scientific medicine to a very large area of central Africa. This systematic investment of well-trained, highly motivated medical personnel demonstrated what could be done, with limited resources, to improve the lives of people in an undeveloped and primitive culture.

For fifty-four years (1906–60) the PCUS worked under the Belgian colonial regime. This regime maintained law and order and a fairly good infrastructure of roads, utilities, and communication; in time, it provided a comprehensive health system for the country. The PCUS institutions were incorporated into this system and contributed to providing a reasonable level of medical care for the people. With the establishment of the IMCK in 1954, the PCUS emphasized teaching in order to train a medical profession made up of nationals.

As the new government struggled to establish itself following independence in 1960, the PCUS medical people found themselves almost alone in providing medical care in the Kasai region, an area the size of France. Unable to meet the awesome needs, they chose to give IMCK and the teaching programs a high priority, with the exhilarating result of having Zairian peers begin to take leadership in the profession. Preventive medicine and community health became important aspects of the work. The Central Pharmacy provided a system for acquiring and distributing drugs, medical supplies, and equipment.

In 1983, when the PCUS ceased to exist, serious problems remained and Zaire continued to be a difficult place in which to live and work, but the future held hope. Unfortunately, the continued political instability, degradation of the standard of living, mounting tensions between tribes, and pervasive corruption combined to undermine any substantial progress either in the country as a whole or in the level of medical care. The year 1983 was bright in comparison with what has followed.

Notes

1. *Encyclopedia Americana*, International Edition, vol. 29 (Danbury, Conn.: Grolier Inc., 1991), 741A-741L.
2. Sanford J. Unger, *Africa: The People and Politics of an Emerging Continent* (New York: Simon & Shuster, 1985), 501, 361.
3. William Rule, M.D., "Milestones in Mission" (Knoxville, Tenn.: typescript, 1991), 350.
4. Virginia Pruitt, "New Nation New Church: Congo 1960–1970"(typescript, 1972), 73, 79.
5. David B. Barrett, *World Christian Encyclopedia* (New York: Oxford University Press, 1981), 759.
6. Ibid., 761.
7. Ralph E. Shannon, M.D., correspondence, April 1985.
8. John Miller, M.D., interview, April 1985.
9. Pruitt, "New Nation, New Church," 59.
10. Ibid., 60.
11. Rule, "Milestones in Mission," 332–34.
12. Lake Munkamba Medical Consultation, 1980.
13. Rule, "Milestones in Mission," 350.
14. John Miller, M.D., interview, April 1985.
15. Rule, "Milestones in Mission," 358.
16. *Introducing IMCK* (Nashville, Tenn.: Board of World Missions brochure, 1970), 36.
17. Sam Ediger, letter, Dec. 1992.
18. Ibid.
19. V. Birch Rambo, M.D., "Report for U.S.AID.," July 1982.
20. Ralph Shannon, M.D., correspondence, April 1985.
21. Birch Rambo, interview, April 1985.
22. Elizabeth Miller, R.N., interview, March 1984.
23. Walter B. Hull, M.D., interview, 1985.
24. Shannon, interview, April 1985.
25. Margaret Rambo, R.N., interview, April 1985.
26. Ibid.
27. John Miller, "Nutrition Program—Bulape Hospital; Kwashiorkor Unit," paper, 1969.
28. John Miller, interview, July 1985.
29. Birch Rambo, "Report for U.S.AID."

30. Ibid., and John Miller, interview.
31. Birch Rambo, interview, Feb. 1984.
32. Hull, interview.
33. Katie Nelson, R.N., Ph.D., interview, Jan. 1984.
34. Birch Rambo, "report."
35. Rule, "Milestones in Mission," 489.
36. John Miller, M.D., "Presbyterian Medical Work in Zaire," report prepared for the 1980 Munkamba Consultation.
37. Richard Brown, M.D., correspondence, Jan. 1990.
38. Rule, "Milestones in Mission," 748, 505
39. Ibid., 499–500.
40. Ibid., 492.
41. Ibid., 512.
42. Ibid., 493–94.
43. Kenneth H. McGill, M.D., interview, July 1985.
44. Nancy T. McGill, interview, July 1985.
45. Shannon, correspondence, Nov. 1985.
46. Hull, interview.
47. William Rule, M.D., "One Hundred Years of Presbyterian Medical Mission in Congo/Zaire," typescript, 1990.
48. Henry and Katie Nelson, interview, 1984.
49. John Miller, "Presbyterian Medical Work in Zaire."
50. Rule, "One Hundred Years of Presbyterian Medical Work."
51. Blanche Carper, R.N., telephone conversation, 1994.
52. John Miller, "Presbyterian Medical Work in Zaire."
53. Rule, "One Hundred Years of Presbyterian Medical Work."
54. Rule, "Milestones in Mission," 506.
55. Henry Nelson, interview, Aug. 1984.
56. Sandy C. Marks, D.D.S., interview, Nov. 1984.
57. Annette Kriner, R.N., interview, July 1985.
58. Ibid.

PART IV
Mexico

United States
of America

Gulf of Mexico

Matamoros •

Morelia •

Mexico City ★

Belize

Pacific Ocean

Alcapulco   Ometepec

Guatemala

——— *Chapter Ten* ———

Mexico
(1921–1972)

Mexico was the fourth country in which the PCUS established a
medical component to its mission's program. The Mexican
medical enterprise was unusual in at least three ways.

First, Llewellyn J. Coppedge, M.D., pioneered the medical work in
Mexico in 1921, as he did the medical work in Congo/Zaire in 1906
(see Congo/Zaire, Luebo). Thus the medical work in both countries
benefited from the energy, dedication, and vision of one man.

Second, the medical program in Mexico was initiated almost fifty
years after the PCUS began its mission to Mexico in 1873 and took
place at the time when the PCUS, under an agreement with other
denominations, moved its area of operation from the northeastern
border with the United States to the southwestern part of Mexico.
Enthusiasm for the new venture was increased by plans for establishing a hospital.

Third, PCUS mission involvement in Mexico, including the
medical work, ended in 1972 at the time of the centennial celebration
of the Presbyterian Church of Mexico, when, in recognition of the
independence of the national church, Presbyterian mission bodies
withdrew from Mexico. The two hospitals that had been established
by PCUS continued under Mexican supervision.

Historical Background

A brief summary of Mexican history sets the stage on which the
PCUS operated its mission.[1] Spain ruled Mexico for three hundred years
after the landing of Don Francisco Hernandez de Cordova in the
Yucatan in 1517, at which time he claimed the land for the crown of
Spain and the people for the Roman Catholic Church. Under Spanish

348

colonial rule society was divided into four distinct classes: a privileged aristocracy, consisting of European-born Spaniards and higher clergy; the creoles, or Mexican-born Spaniards; the mestizo, who were mixed European and Indian; and the Indians, who were virtual slaves. In addition, a number of slaves from Africa were imported. Political, social, religious, and economic power was concentrated in the aristocracy.

Three major revolutions over a 100-year period finally brought freedom to the masses. The first of these revolutions (1810–21) brought independence from Spain and established Mexico as a federal republic. The creoles and the church were the chief beneficiaries of this revolution; both acquired power and wealth at the expense of the mestizos and Indians.

The second revolution (1854–57) was led by Don Benito Juarez, a full-blooded Indian. He promoted the writing of the constitution and reform laws that promised emancipation for the masses, equality under the law, religious toleration, and agrarian reform. Church property was nationalized. Juarez was followed by a thirty-five-year dictatorship (1876–1911) under Porfirio Diaz, which slowed progress; again the mestizos and Indians failed to benefit appreciably. Most of the land was acquired by a few large landowners and 95 percent of the people were without land. However, the reform laws remained on the books and it continued to be lawful to read the Bible and teach the Protestant faith.

The third revolution, sometimes referred to as the Madero Revolution after its leader, began in 1910 with the overthrow of Diaz. In the decade of violence and dramatic political upheaval that followed, Mexico had ten presidents. The election in 1920 of President Obregon brought a measure of stability and economic growth that has continued to this day. A new constitution in 1917 brought about land reform, encouraged industrialization, separated church and state, and instigated compulsory public education with the abolition of all church-related schools.

Relations between the United States and Mexico have often been troubled. War with the United States in 1846–48 resulted in the acquisition by the United States of all or parts of what are now ten states (Texas, Arizona, New Mexico, California, Nevada, Utah, Wyoming, Kansas, and Colorado). Mexico was paid $15 million. During the Madero Revolution, the United States became only peripherally involved: in 1914, U.S. Marines seized Veracruz in order to control the shipment of arms; and in 1916, after Francisco (Pancho) Villa had raided the small hamlet of Columbus, New Mexico, U.S. nationals, including missionaries, were evacuated from the country for a period.

The government of Mexico since 1920 has made steady progress toward revolutionary economic and social change based on the principles of the 1917 constitution. While striving to arrive at a thoroughly modern society, it is sympathetic to the needs and desires of its working-class people. Between 1920 and 1940 the emphasis was on land reform, education (free, obligatory, and secular), and labor (a minimum wage and the right to organize and strike). After World War II the fundamental task was to "modernize the economy by developing a dynamic capitalism within constraints imposed by the Revolutionary goal of social justice."[2] An extensive bureaucracy reflected the deep involvement of government in social programs. A rich cultural renewal manifested itself in art, architecture, and literature. Problems of urbanization, unemployment, poverty, overpopulation, exploitation by foreign agencies, and corruption continued to plague society, but progress was exciting and real. For the PCUS missionary, Mexico was an interesting, though not always a comfortable, place to be.

The PCUS in Mexico

Protestant missionaries began work in Mexico soon after the 1854–57 revolution when a new constitution promised religious toleration. The PCUS began its mission in 1873 with the appointment of Rev. Anthony T. Graybill, who first worked out of Brownsville, Texas, and then moved across to Matamoros and the border provinces. The PCUS mission in Mexico prior to the revolution of 1910 was small—composed of about two dozen persons, the majority of whom were women (only six men). The work was evangelistic and educational. Schools were founded and work among the youth, primarily mestizo and Indian, was strong. Evangelistic missionaries traveled into remote areas by wagon, horse, and mule.

Many Protestant missions were working in Mexico, with the result that the efforts in some areas overlapped while other areas were inadequately covered. In 1914, during the period of evacuation from Mexico because of the Madero Revolution, a conference of eight Protestant mission bodies was held in Cincinnati, Ohio, at which a comity agreement, known as the Cincinnati Plan, was enacted.[3] Under this plan each denomination carried on its work in assigned areas. The plan also provided for a union theological seminary, a union press, and a union newspaper. The PCUS was assigned an area in southwestern Mexico consisting of the states of Michoacan and Guerrero and parts of the states of Mexico and Morelos. The Methodists were assigned the north-eastern provinces previously worked by the PCUS.

The Cincinnati Plan was not without problems. The Mexican churches felt that the plan had been implemented without their being properly represented. Some churches, resentful of the arbitrary separation from their founding churches in America, refused to join the denomination of the newly assigned mission. The Presbyterian Church of Mexico, for example, continued to grow in the north.

In 1921, with a great deal of enthusiasm, the PCUS prepared to move to its new territory. In the period of renewed interest and commitment in the "home church" after World War I, thirteen missionaries were recruited for this new venture, which, with eleven former missionaries, made a total of twenty-four PCUS missionaries. The appointment of a doctor and nurse introduced an exciting new dimension to the mission's program.

The PCUS territory, with 2,125,000 people in an area the size of North Carolina (52,000 square miles) was one of the most heavily populated parts of Mexico. The region was geographically attractive and very different from the semiarid mountains and coastal plains in the north. Range upon range of high mountains rose from 500 miles of Pacific coast. Rivers, plentiful rainfall, and rich farmland in narrow (and a few large) valleys provided heavy tracts of timber and rich agricultural products (peaches, apples, limes, lemons, bananas, pomegranates, mangos, coffee, corn, wheat, oats, sweet potatoes, and garden vegetables). Mining was a major industry. The climate, in towns and cities ranging in altitude from 4,500 to 8,000 feet above sea level, was pleasant and healthful.

The population in the PCUS territory was predominantly Indian, in contrast to the north where most were mestizos. In addition to Spanish, the language consisted of many Indian dialects. Illiteracy, poverty, ignorance, and superstition were prevalent. Political turmoil, the result of the revolutions and (in some cases) outright banditry, afflicted the area; some parts of the state of Guerrero were considered unsafe. Persecution of Protestants by Catholics had been heavy; of the more than eighty Protestant martyrs in Mexico, a large number came from this area.

Important dates mark the progression in relationship between the PCUS and the Presbyterian Church of Mexico from a mission program to a fully independent and autonomous church.[4]

1872. The United Presbyterians began work in Mexico; the PCUS arrived one year later in 1873. The Presbyterian Church of Mexico dates its birth from 1872.

1884. The Presbytery of Tamaulipas was organized in northern Mexico.

1901. The National Synod of the Presbyterian Church of Mexico was formed.

1947. The "Diamond Jubilee," seventy-five years since the founding of Presbyterian work in Mexico, was celebrated by the organization of the General Assembly of the Presbyterian Church of Mexico. The General Assembly was made up of three synods and nine presbyteries and reflected the work of three U.S. denominations: the PCUS, the United Presbyterians, and the Reformed Church of America.

1948. At its first meeting, the General Assembly of the Presbyterian Church of Mexico terminated the Cincinnati Plan as obsolete. It also created what eventually became known as the Committee on Cooperative Work to deal with relationships (financial and personnel) between the national church and the cooperating missions.

1972. At the "Centennial Celebration," the National Presbyterian Church of Mexico assumed full responsibility for the direction and support of its institutions and work. The PCUS agreed to withdraw missionary personnel and subsidy funds from the Presbyterian Church of Mexico. This action was interpreted "not as a severance of relationship but as an expression of fraternal confidence in the maturity and self-reliance of [the Presbyterian Church of Mexico], and as a symbol of our assurance of the work of the Holy Spirit in the life of that church."[5] A few missionaries, at the request of the Presbyterian Church of Mexico, continued in special lines of service.

The PCUS Medical Program in Mexico, 1921–1972

Although the PCUS medical program in Mexico was not established until 1921, it should be noted that in 1881 J. Walton Graybill, M.D., joined his brother, Anthony Graybill, the pioneer PCUS missionary to Mexico. Walton Graybill was one of the first three physicians appointed by the PCUS to mission medical work (see Richard Baxter Fishburne to China, and George William Butler to Brazil). Like Dr. Fishburne, Walton Graybill served for only two years (1881–83) and withdrew because of ill health. Dr. Graybill is remembered, however, for heroic service during a yellow fever epidemic in the Matamoros area in 1882, when he made 100 visits into affected homes within one twenty-four-hour period.[6]

Llewellyn J. Coppedge, M.D., went to the Congo as a bachelor in 1906 and married while on furlough in 1912. For Coralie Lobdell Coppedge, the Congo was a disaster. Within a year of her arrival she was evacuated by stretcher to the United States where their first child was born. She returned to the Congo after two years but, by furlough time in 1918, it was apparent that continued service there would not be possible. Dr. Coppedge joined the U.S. Army, then fully engaged in World War I, and was stationed with the Sixteenth Cavalry Regiment at Fort Brown, Texas, on the border of Mexico near Brownsville. His duties included the care of Mexican workers and their families, and he became aware of the paucity of medical services available in Mexico. Wishing to continue in missionary service, the Coppedges gladly responded to the opportunity to initiate the medical component to the PCUS mission program in its new location in southwestern Mexico. Pattye Southerland, R.N., a newly graduated nurse, joined him in this endeavor.

The PCUS established two hospitals in Mexico: the Sanatorio La Luz in Morelia, Michoacan (opened 1923), and the Sanatorio de la Amistad (Friendship Hospital) in Ometepec, Guerrero (1958). The two hospitals were quite different. Sanatorio La Luz, located in the capital of the state, became a 130-bed, multispecialty, teaching hospital with a resident staff and nursing school. Sanatorio de la Amistad, in an isolated mountain region, remained a small (45-bed) primary facility with a training program for nurse's aides. Both hospitals were headed by capable Mexican physicians when PCUS personnel were withdrawn in 1972.

354 A LEGACY REMEMBERED

A defining characteristic of the medical work in Mexico was the difficulty in securing medical licenses; graduates of foreign medical schools were prohibited from practicing medicine in Mexico. Dr. Coppedge, after considerable negotiation, was granted a license, but a second physician, Earl Zolicoffer Browne, returned to the United States in 1926 after just one year because he was not granted a license. Three other physicians (J. Hervey Ross, James R. Boyce, and W. Rion Dixon) attended (and graduated from) medical schools in Mexico in order to qualify for their medical licenses. This difficulty in licensure reflected the always sensitive and sometimes hostile relationship between the United States and Mexico. American nurses working under doctors with Mexican licenses did not need Mexican licenses.[7]

A second characteristic was the initial hostility of the Catholic Church experienced by both hospitals. In both cases this animosity moderated over time and changed to appreciation for the medical services offered to the community.

The evangelistic outreach in both hospitals was strongly supported and developed. Both hospitals maintained strong chaplaincy staffs with outreach into the communities. A number of women missionaries who were trained nurses combined evangelism in rural areas with treatment of the sick.[8] Among these were Iona Smith (1929–48), before joining the staff of the Sanatorio La Luz; Mildred Beaty (1940–44, 1948–54); and Phyllis R. Douglas (Mrs. Dale).

SANATORIA LA LUZ
Morelia

Morelia, the capital of the state of Michoacan, is a colonial city dating back to the days of Spanish rule; it contains a cathedral, aqueducts, and many buildings constructed in the sixteenth century. The city was named for Jose Maria Morelos, a Mexican-born Catholic priest, who was executed in 1811 for his revolutionary leadership against Spain and the Catholic Church. The city is located in a valley surrounded by high mountains. Its elevation of 6,400 feet, combined with the subtropical latitude, provides a climate said to be "as near perfection as can be found anywhere in the world."[9] The University of Michoacan (San Nicholas), the second-oldest university on the North American continent, was founded in 1540. In 1920

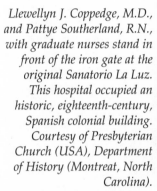

Llewellyn J. Coppedge, M.D., and Pattye Southerland, R.N., with graduate nurses stand in front of the iron gate at the original Sanatorio La Luz. This hospital occupied an historic, eighteenth-century, Spanish colonial building. Courtesy of Presbyterian Church (USA), Department of History (Montreat, North Carolina).

Morelia had a population of around 40,000; in 1984 it was 300,000.

The history of the Sanatorio La Luz (Hospital of the Light) in Morelia between 1923 and 1972 falls into three distinct periods that parallel the stages of development of most mission hospitals: the initial stage, a period of expansion, and the transfer to national management and operation.[10]

Initial stage, 1923–1945

The initial stage of some twenty-two years was under the leadership of Dr. Llewellyn Coppedge, who described his practice as a "one doctor affair." Serving with him were Pattye Southerland, R.N., (until her death in 1944) and Quinnie Johnston, R.N., a Canadian (for two years).

It would be hard to imagine a greater contrast than that between the practice in Morelia and the practice in the primitive interior of Congo/Zaire where Dr. Coppedge worked from 1906 to 1918. In both countries, however, local officials were initially hostile. Dr. Coppedge's ability to dissipate this hostility doubtless rests in his personal characteristics, for his associates described him as a "lovable" man with a good sense of humor who was polite and kind, able to relate to poor and rich people alike, had wide interests ("talking encyclopedia"), was an avid reader, loved flowers, and had many friends.[11]

Dr. Coppedge wrote of his early years in Morelia:

> It is noteworthy that when I went to Mexico to open a hospital, a pastoral letter from the Archbishop was read in all twenty-nine Roman Catholic churches of the city warning the faithful of the Protestant Hospital shortly to be opened in an effort to seduce *true* Christians from the faith of their fathers to embrace a strange, false and foreign doctrine. As the years went by, I served, in my professional capacity, thousands of Catholic laymen, more priests than I can count on my fingers, also some nuns and children at the Catholic orphanage. I have had presents from priests including two handsome canes, books, razors, etc. Once [when] I was ill, a priest whom I did not know called to say that masses were being said for my recovery. . . . The doctors of the city shared generally the hostility of the Roman Church. Eventually, after ten or twelve years, I was invited to join the local medical society. I was also a member of the Rotary Club and a frequent after-dinner speaker.[12]

The PCUS was able to purchase two homes in the historic section of Morelia. The $15,000 purchase price was provided by Sunday school offerings from PCUS churches in the United States.[13] Dating from 1775, both buildings were built of thick stone around attractive courtyards. One became the hospital, the other, the Coppedge home. Dr. Coppedge, who had worked for twelve years in a mud and thatch clinic in the Congo, wrote, "We have a beautiful building for a hospital."[14]

The Sanatorio La Luz opened its doors on May 23, 1923, with twelve beds, an operating room, pharmacy, simple laboratory, doctor's office, and examining room. The practice was varied; it included surgery, internal medicine, obstetrics, dentistry, and ophthalmology. In 1942 an adjoining courtyard was incorporated into the hospital, bringing the total beds from around twenty to sixty.[15]

The first order of business for Dr. Coppedge was to acquire a Mexican medical license, which he was finally able to do. The failure, two years later (1925), of Rev. Earl Z. Browne, M.D., to secure a

Mexican license dashed the dream of building up a strong hospital with two missionary physicians. Fortunately, some professional help was locally available: in 1925 Dr. Karl Iverson, a German resident of Morelia, joined the staff for a period; and in 1933, Dr. Samuel Reyna, a skillful surgeon and distinguished Mexican Christian, began his forty-year collaboration with the Sanatorio La Luz. Dr. Reyna acted as director when Dr. Coppedge was away on furlough.[16]

The three-year School of Nursing, begun in 1929, graduated its first two students in 1931. These students had primary school education and were of Indian or mestizo background.

With the passage of time the Sanatorio La Luz came to occupy an influential and respected place in the community of Morelia.

Period of Expansion, 1945–1967

J. Hervey Ross, M.D., provided the leadership over the next twenty-two years that saw the development of Sanatorio La Luz from Dr. Coppedge's "one-doctor affair" to a modern, multispecialty, teaching hospital with a strong Mexican staff. Two nurses, Iona Smith and Mary K. McBee, serving for some twenty years each during this time, gave continuity and strength to the nursing program. Mildred Beaty, Octavia Sizer, Doris J. Brown, and Ann S. Dixon, served for

The new Sanatorio La Luz was dedicated in 1953. Photograph courtesy of Pauline R. Ross.

shorter periods. Charlotte E. Hudgins, M.T., directed the laboratories from 1961 to 1967 and taught laboratory techniques to the nursing students.

Dr. Ross, the son of Rev. and Mrs. Hervey L. Ross, was born in 1914 in Brownsville, Texas, while his parents, pioneer PCUS missionaries to Mexico, were refugees from their work in northern Mexico during Pancho Villa's incursion into the United States. After graduating from Davidson College (B.S., 1936, Phi Beta Kappa) he returned to Mexico in 1937 for medical school in order to satisfy Mexican, law which, as has been noted, since 1935 had required graduation from a Mexican medical school in order to practice in Mexico. He married Pauline (Polly) Ribelin in 1940; they moved to Morelia on January 1, 1945, and began work with Dr. Coppedge. Dr. Ross became director of the Sanatorio La Luz in 1948 when Dr. Coppedge suffered the heart attack that forced his early retirement.

Expansion of the Sanatorio La Luz occurred in the post–World War II burst of renewed interest in and support of PCUS mission work. The Program of Progress fund provided $80,000 to help finance the construction of a modern building located about one mile from the increasingly inadequate original site. A city block was purchased in a newly developed section of Morelia, and the new Sanatorio La Luz was constructed and dedicated in September 1953. The one-story, 100-bed facility was modern in every respect with private and semiprivate rooms, wards, two operating rooms, laboratories, X-ray facilities, and eight doctors' offices with examining rooms. The outside of the building "conformed to traditional Mexican architectural patterns in many pleasing features, so that it seemed at home in the ancient city of Morelia."[17]

Construction of a nurses' home on property adjoining the new hospital was completed in 1955; in 1957 a second floor was added. This building provided housing for sixty student nurses. The beautiful old wrought-iron gate was moved from the old hospital and installed between the hospital and the nurses' quarters.

In 1952 the School of Nursing, renamed the "Dr. L. J. Coppedge School of Nursing," became affiliated with the National University of Mexico in Mexico City. Iona Smith, R.N., continued as director of the nursing school. The entrance requirement was raised from primary to secondary school, and graduates were officially certified as registered nurses; their diplomas carried the crest of the university.[18] The student body increased so that by 1964 it numbered up to 100, with about 30 in

The historic gate was moved to the new facility. Photograph courtesy of Pauline R. Ross.

a class. Graduates of this school, which made up 10 percent of the registered nurses in Mexico, were in demand all over the country.

Ten years later, in 1963, Santorio La Luz was again enlarged by the addition of a second floor. A $50,000 grant from the Board of World Missions and $37,000 from the Birthday Offering of the Women of the Church (PCUS) helped fund the construction and equipment. The second floor contained dental clinics, pediatric and obstetric wards, a medical library, and classroom space for the nursing school; hospital beds were increased to 125.

The development of the Mexican staff was a distinguishing feature of this expansion period. In 1947 the staff was enlarged to include Melchor Diaz, M.D., pediatrician, and Nicanor Gomez, M.D., oncologist; both had received specialized training in the United States. When the new building was completed in 1963, it became possible to further enlarge the staff. In 1958 the Sanatorio La Luz received certification from the Medical School of the University of Michoacan for an accredited internship program; from five to eight interns/residents a year took part in this program.[19]

The Sanatorio La Luz had an "open staff" policy. Physicians fell into one of three categories: 1) missionary doctors, who worked full time and had no private practice; 2) salaried Mexican staff, who worked half time at and for the hospital but whose main source of income came from their private practice; 3) nonstaff doctors, who were given hospital privileges but carried on a private practice with private patients. By 1960 Dr. Ross reported, "More and more of the work is devolving upon the splendid young Christian Mexican doctors who comprise the staff . . . so that the Mission hospital is gradually becoming more and more a Mexican hospital in fact as well as in name, as under God's guidance it should be."[20]

A list of the Mexican doctors at the Sanatorio La Luz shows the diversity and breadth of the staff; several were Roman Catholic.

Dr. Samuel Reyna, surgery, (1933–69)
Dr. Melchor Diaz, pediatrics; director from 1967 to 1982
Dr. Nicanor Gomez, surgery and oncology
Dr. Nacor Reyes, obstetrics/gynecology
Dr. Eliezer Moreno, cardiology
Dr. Hector Alvarez, surgery and general medicine
Dr. Mario Carrillo, surgery
Dr. Luis Mora, internal medicine
Dr. Jesus Pineda, thoracic surgery and TB specialty (trained in France
    after graduating from medical school at the University of Mexico)
Dr. Luis Serrato, cardiology
Dr. Alfonso Del Valle, internal medicine
Dr. Samuel Padilla, surgery and internal medicine; director since 1982
Dr. Alberto Rodriguez, dentistry[21]

Melchor Diaz, M.D., a boyhood friend and classmate of Dr. Ross in medical school, was a multitalented leader in the community— elder of the Presbyterian Church of Mexico, congressman in the National Congress of Mexico, rector for the University of Michoacan and director of its medical school, mayor of Morelia, treasurer of the State of Michoacan, outstanding pediatrician and surgeon, and director of Sanatorio La Luz from 1967 until his death in 1982.

Because of the full and capable staff at Sanatorio La Luz, there was little need for visiting physicians from the United States. However, three young doctors (Jim Mitchner and "Guv" Pennington from Vanderbilt and Hank Watt from Johns Hopkins), spent the summer after their graduation from medical school in Morelia. And Dr. Beverly Douglas, a renowned plastic surgeon from Vanderbilt, spent a month teaching skin-grafting techniques and other plastic procedures.

In addition to his full-time practice, Dr. Ross was often called to help Americans in Mexico with physical and legal difficulties. He visited the prisons to help those who had run afoul of the law. The U.S. embassy in Mexico City often sought his council on sensitive cross-cultural matters; for instance, he was asked to help compile

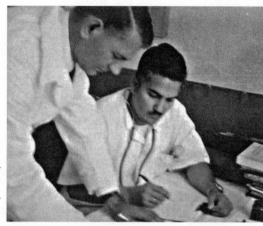

Drs. J. Hervey Ross and Melchor Diaz. In 1967, Diaz succeeded Ross as director of the Sanatorio La Luz. Photograph courtesy of Pauline R. Ross.

death certificates for Americans who died in Mexico. Movie stars, who on occasion were in Morelia to make movies, were among his friends. Errol Flynn, after injuring his back in a fall, spent considerable time with Ross and is reported to have said, "If it were possible, I would swap my life for yours in a minute." Mel Ferrar and Audrey Hepburn, even after being warned of the deplorable conditions they would encounter, insisted on accompanying Dr. Ross to visit an American prisoner languishing in the penitentiary.[22]

The post–World War II period saw remarkable progress in the level of health care in Mexico through its Social Security and Health Departments. The Sanatorio La Luz contributed to this progress through its multispecialty service of good quality and its educational program for nurses and interns.

Dr. Ross resigned from the Mexican Mission while on furlough in 1966 in order to accept the position of medical secretary (overseeing medical missions) for the PCUS Board of World Missions in Nashville, Tennessee. Dr. Melchor Diaz then became the director of the Sanatorio La Luz.

Mexican Leadership, 1967–1972

Between 1967 and 1972 the Sanatorio La Luz remained an institution of the PCUS but leadership and responsibility moved from the missionaries to Mexican nationals. In 1972 when PCUS withdrew its mission from Mexico, the institution was prepared to continue operation under Mexican control.

However, this period in the history of Sanatorio La Luz began with a crisis. Several of the interns and members of the medical staff became involved in a conflict between the students of the University of Michoacan and the governor. Dr. Samuel Reyna, staff surgeon since 1933, was made interim director of the hospital and provided the leadership that made it possible for the hospital to remain open and fully functional during a difficult time. The PCUS 1967 annual report described the situation as follows:

> *Medical Work, Morelia*—External political pressures made an impact on the medical area of service late in 1966. Following student violence at the University of Michoacan, the La Luz Hospital in Morelia faced an economic crisis in 1967. As a result, questions arose: Should we give up the work and turn over the hospital to the General Assembly or the Mexican government? Or should we continue this ministry of healing with the awareness of ever-increasing expenses? . . .
>
> The time of testing at Morelia has helped both missionaries and nationals reset their spiritual compasses. In August the Mission voted to adopt a new strategy in medical work. Mobile units, maternity clinics, and day clinics are to be emphasized. Concern to integrate the ministry of health and healing into the National Church is increasing. In this way it is hoped there will be a better balance between Message and Ministry.[23]

Fortunately, the economic situation at the hospital was resolved when Mr. Edson Johnson, the mission's treasurer, took over the business administration and reorganized the finances on a sound basis. Dr. Diaz resumed the directorship and Dr. Samuel Moreno Padilla became "subdirector." Clara Leal, a graduate of the Dr. L. J. Coppedge School of Nursing, became the director of the nursing school.

In 1968 a board of trustees *Compañia Michoacana de Sanatorios, Acción Civil* was established. This body was composed of representatives from the General Assembly of the National Church of Mexico, the Presbytery of the South, the Women's Union of the Presbytery of the South, and the Board of World Missions (PCUS).[24]

In 1966, Rev. W. Rion Dixon was appointed to Morelia in order to enroll in the Medical School of the University of Michoacan. Rion Dixon had had a very successful career in business when, in 1960, he decided, in response to what he described as a "mountain top" religious experience, to become a medical missionary. He applied to his missionary career the enthusiasm, energy, and creativity that had made him successful in business. He attended Columbia Theological Seminary (M.Div., 1965) while taking premed courses at Agnes Scott College (one year) and Emory University (one year), studied Spanish for one year in Costa Rica, and entered medical school at the University of Michoacan, where he was elected president of his class in his third year.[25] While attending medical school he also applied his business skills to the business office of the Sanatorio La Luz. After graduating (M.D., 1969) Dixon served one year of internship and one year of general practice at the Sanatorio La Luz. He transferred to Haiti when the PCUS withdrew from Mexico.[26]

Ann S. Dixon, R.N., worked at Santorio La Luz while her husband attended medical school. For part of the time she was superintendent of nurses in the hospital, supervising a staff of twenty-two graduate and eighty-eight student nurses. She also taught dietetics to the student nurses and supervised the diet kitchens. She enjoyed working in a well-established teaching hospital. "Watching young students mature into some of the best nurses in all of Mexico made one feel proud to be a part of the ministry."[27]

In 1972 the PCUS officially ended fifty years of service at the Sanatorio La Luz. Thereafter, contact was largely through personal relationships. Iona Smith, who retired in 1971, maintained her residence in Morelia and often took part in exercises at the School of Nursing. Dr. Ross and others visited on numerous occasions. In 1981 PCUS contributed funds for the construction of a third floor for the hospital.

SANATORIO DE LA AMISTAD
Ometepec

In the state of Guerrero an isolated maze of mountains known as a "rich and dangerous land" rises from the Pacific Ocean southeast of Acapulco.[28] PCUS missionaries rarely penetrated the area

364 A LEGACY REMEMBERED

until, in the expansive post–World War II era, two young couples, James and Marguerite Boyce and John and Madge Wood, were sent to pioneer a permanent mission station in the town of Ometepec (25,000 population). Both men were ministers and pilots; Boyce was a recent (1949) graduate of the University of Mexico School of Medicine and had his Mexican medical license.

Ometepec was located above the Pacific coast where farmers, merchants, and fishermen lived in a hundred or more ranches, villages, and towns. Tribes of Indians, living much as they did before the arrival of the Spaniards, occupied remote mountain valleys. Descendants of African slaves lived in coastal villages in round thatched huts; many of their customs, including the practice of voodoo, were closely related to Africa.

Donkeys provided transportation over jungle trails that could be navigated by truck and four-wheel-drive vehicles only in the dry season. By the late 1940s a network of "taxi planes" flew into the larger towns and, as described by Marguerite Boyce, "without knowing about trains or automobiles, the people were going from tediously slow travel by donkeys to flying like birds over the mountains."[29] Not until 1964 were rivers bridged and a road was paved into Ometepec. Electricity was installed in 1967 and telephones followed in 1969.[30]

The Missionary Admiral

All accounts of mission work in this part of Guerrero begin with the story of Capt. (Reginald) Carey Brenton, sometimes referred to as the "Missionary Admiral."[31] Born in 1848 in Somerset, England, Brenton joined the British navy at age thirteen and became "Commander" by age twenty-six. In 1891 the Mexican government requested permission for Brenton to become the "Captain and Instructor" of the SS *Zaragosa*, a corvette used as a training ship for Mexican naval cadets. As a courtesy to then President Diaz, Queen Victoria granted Brenton permission to accept this assignment. During the five years Brenton served as brigadier of the National Mexican Armada, the SS *Zaragosa* circumnavigated the globe and spent at least one year on the west coast of Mexico at Acapulco.

Captain Brenton was converted to Christianity at age eighteen and developed a desire to become a missionary. In 1904, after his retirement from the navy, he returned to the Acapulco area as a colporteur for the American Bible Society. With Enrique (his horse) and Catalina (his donkey), he traveled the rough mountain trails selling or giving away Bibles, gospels, and tracts. In March 1921, sick with malaria and dysentery, he arrived in the little town of Ometepec; he died a month later, on April 18. A simple wooden cross marked his grave. Brenton's personal Bible (in Spanish) was preserved by young Ramon Reguera; an inscription from the Bible, "The entrance of thy word giveth light," was to be chiseled over the altar of the first Presbyterian church to be built in Ometepec. Thirty years after Captain Brenton's death, in May 1951, the Boyce and Wood families took up residence in Ometepec.

Beginnings

James Reid Boyce arrived in Mexico in 1940 shortly after graduating from Columbia Theological Seminary in Decatur, Georgia. Boyce entered the country under what was known as the "student plan" which allowed a student to establish permanent residence after completing five years of study.[32] The seven-year course of study at the University of Mexico included a year of internship and one year of social service in a needy area. Boyce spent his year of social service in the small town of Cacalutla on the upper coast of Guerrero, where he made a study of the incidence of malaria. Between semesters he took flying lessons and obtained a pilot's license. Boyce graduated in 1949 and received the coveted Mexican medical license.

The mission asked Dr. Boyce to survey the state of Guerrero for the best site for a hospital. After being advised by the head of Guerrero's public health department (an uncle of a medical school classmate) that the area surrounding the town of Ometepec was in greatest need, the Boyce family spent several weeks in Ometepec before going to the United States on furlough in 1950. What they found was not promising. The road from the Papagallo River (near Acapulco) to Ometepec was impassible during the six-month rainy season. The location at the base of the San Andreas fault made it vulnerable to severe earthquakes. The climate was tropical and hot with "thousands—yea, millions, of rats, bats, flies and mosquitoes" (also roaches and scorpions). The Catholic Church and the citizens of the town were hostile. But the lack of medical service was appalling and the spiritual needs overwhelming.[33]

The mission decided to assign the Boyce and Wood families to Ometepec for one year, beginning in 1951 when the Boyce furlough was completed; a final decision would then be made regarding a permanent assignment. The year was a hard one, complicated at the beginning when all four of the Boyce children developed polio.

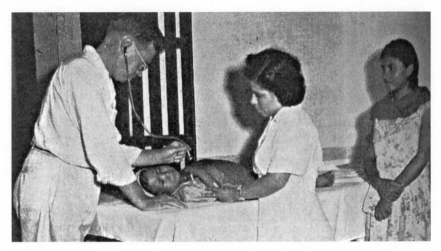

James R. Boyce, M.D., examines a child in the clinic of the Sanatorio de la Amistad at Ometepec. Courtesy of Presbyterian Church (USA), Department of History (Montreat, North Carolina).

However, after much discussion, the mission voted unanimously to place the new medical/evangelistic venture in Ometepec.[34]

It took three years for the mission to purchase property and another four years to complete construction of the hospital. In the meantime, friends were made and hostility was gradually overcome. A busy clinic acquired an X-ray machine and a simple operating room. Outpost work was carried on with the help of *El Mensajero* (*The Messenger*), a two-seater Piper Cub plane.

First Ten Years (1954–1964)

Construction of the Sanatorio de la Amistad began in October 1954 with funds from the Program of Progress and was completed in 1958 despite an earthquake in 1957, which caused considerable damage. The name "Friendship Hospital" was chosen by PCUS youth at their summer conference in Montreat, North Carolina.[35] The hospital had a capacity of twenty-five beds (later expanded to forty-five), operating and delivery rooms, outpatient clinic, dental department, X ray, pharmacy, and laboratory. In 1963 Birthday Offering funds ($25,000) from the PCUS Women of the Church enlarged and improved the facility[36]

Dr. Alfreda Yañez, surgeon, joined the staff in 1962. Other Mexican physicians who served at the Sanatorio de la Amistad

Dr. Alfreda Yañez (in scrubsuit) with an associate on the grounds of the Sanatorio de la Amistad in Ometepec. He became the director in 1972. Photograph courtesy Paul S. Crane.

include Pablo Olvera, M.D., internist, and Ramon Reguera, dentist and the preserver of Captain Benton's Bible. A training program for two interns a year was begun in 1970.

Chavela Espinosa, a graduate of the Sanatorio La Salud Nursing School in Mexico City, helped pioneer the work in Ometepec between 1952 and 1956. When she left to get married, she recruited a classmate, Sara Zaragosa, who continued in service until 1972. These two Mexican nurses had an important role in establishing the hospital. Missionary nurses were Paula West (1957–71) and Edna Garza (1964–69). Graduate nurses from the Sanatorio La Luz also helped staff the nursing department.

Virginia Pipe, M.T., ran the laboratory from 1968 to 1971. Marguerite Boyce helped wherever needed: office, bookkeeping, receptionist, kitchen oversight, and "anything but nursing except in an emergency."[37]

A school for nurse's aides was begun in 1966. A number of these young women were members of the Amusgo tribe, a primitive Indian tribe some eight hours away by horseback. Contact with the Amusgo began after Dr. Boyce was called to see an Indian girl who had split open her abdomen when she fell off a runaway horse with a machete in her hand. The Amusgo student nurses, in order not to be expelled from their tribe because of wearing "modern dress," had to enter into an agreement with the elders of the tribe: they were allowed to wear their student uniforms while on duty but would wear the typical dress of their tribe during the off-duty hours.[38]

Relations between the Sanatorio La Luz in Morelia and the Sanatorio de la Amistad were close. Graduate nurses from Morelia served on the staff and taught in the school. Student nurses went to Ometepec for their year of social service (a government requirement for nurses as well as for physicians). Sanatorio La Luz also accepted nurses and laboratory workers from Ometepec into their training programs.

The practice of medicine in Ometepec was broad. Typhoid, malaria, and parasite infestation were the most prominent diseases; tuberculosis, malnutrition, donkey bites, snake bites, and leprosy also were seen. The PCUS 1963 annual report stated that 51 percent of the inpatients were maternity cases and told of a program for educating village women in prenatal care.[39] Ometepec was feuding country, and machete cuts and gunshot wounds were common "sew-up" jobs. "Getting bullets out of the body is part of our job," commented Dr. Boyce, "but getting Christ into the heart remains the greatest challenge on the mission field."[40] In later years victims of vehicular accidents outnumbered those with gun shots.[41]

In 1966 the area suffered a major flood disaster following a heavy rainy season and a violent tropical hurricane. The Ometepec staff was actively involved in rescue and relief in affected areas. Their knowledge of the area and, in particular, their experience in flying to remote places, proved helpful to relief authorities.[42]

Support from Abroad
The program at the Sanatorio de la Amistad was greatly enhanced by accessibility to the United States, where support from churches and friends could be channeled in practical ways. Among the donations were a truck full of supplies and equipment (from Charlotte, North Carolina), a portable sawmill (given by a donor in Corinth, Mississippi), and a truck to transport the sawmill (from a church in Dallas, Texas). In 1964, at the height of the green stamp era (when stores gave out stamps that could be redeemed for merchandise), PCUS women collected over five million green stamps in order to acquire a replacement for the tired *Messenger*. This *Messenger II* was known as the Green Stamp Plane.[43]

The Sanatorio de la Amistad also benefited from visiting physicians from the United States; most went under sponsorship of the Medical Benevolence Foundation. These specialists provided a level of care that would not otherwise have been available in this remote section of Mexico at that time. A guesthouse was built to provide accommodation for these volunteers.

Hank Watt, M.D., surgeon from Tallahassee, Florida, went many times himself and sent members from his group. In 1970 Watt left behind a special surgical nail for use in bone fractures, which, he jokingly said, was made for a tall American. A few months later, "Don Nacho" (Ignacio Castaneda), the beloved pastor of the Ometepec Church, was in a serious accident in which his leg was fractured in three places. Don Nacho was a tall man and the intramedulary nail exactly fit.[44]

Roger Hehn, M.D., facial surgeon from Jacksonville, Florida, took a team of doctors to repair harelips. The local Lions Club sponsored radio announcements of the project and the response was amazing. One of the doctors is said to have exclaimed, "That's more harelips than I saw during all my years of medical training!" Dr. Hehn, who had an excellent command of Spanish, returned every Easter for more than twenty years.[45]

A group of ophthalmologists from Houston, Texas, did more than fifty eye operations in one week and, upon examination, found that many of the Amusgos Indians suffered from farsightedness. Soon the wearing of glasses, signifying the ability to read, became a status symbol among the Indians.[46]

Dr. Jerre Freeman, an ophthalmologist from Memphis, Tennessee, spent every Thanksgiving week examining eyes and doing cataract surgery. "There are no more radio announcements about the visits, for everyone knows the doctors who can make blind people see will be there the fourth week in November." People were always waiting.[47]

Dr. Robb Hicks, an ophthalmologist from California, made several working visits. He was accompanied by a CMS (Christian Medical Society) group with as many as ten to fifteen people. Another CMS group from West Palm Beach, Florida, went three times.

Tragedy
January 16, 1964, was a day of tragedy for Ometepec, for John and Madge Wood died when their Cessina 180, named *Wings of Truth*,

John and Madge Woods (later killed in a plane accident) are shown here with their five sons. Photograph courtesy of Marguerite Boyce.

crashed into the side of Asuncion del Monte mountain shortly after takeoff from Mexico City. They were survived by five boys, ages five to sixteen. The reaction of the townspeople to this event was witness to the profound change in attitude that had occurred in the twelve years since the Boyce and Wood couples moved to Ometepec. Mrs. Boyce wrote:

> Ometepec has never seen a funeral like that of John and Madge Wood. The coffins were placed under the big tree just outside their living room. The family sat inside the house and hundreds of people sat or stood in the yard on all sides of the tree. . . . We had planned to use the jeep truck to take the coffins to the cemetery, but the local men asked if they could have the privilege of carrying them, as is the custom here. It is about a mile from this side of town to the cemetery, but many many men stepped up . . . to help carry the caskets. By the time we reached the cemetery there were almost a thousand people in the funeral procession. . . . Six local pilots flew overhead and

threw out flowers and confetti as we passed along main street. . . .
The two graves [were placed] immediately to the right of [Capt.
Carey Brenton's grave].[48]

Dr. Boyce continued serving at the Sanatorio de la Amistad until
1971, which marked his twentieth year in Ometepec (fourteen years
since the opening of the hospital) and thirty-first year as a PCUS
missionary in Mexico. The other PCUS missionaries, Paula West, R.N.,
and Virginia Pipe, M.T., also retired in 1971.

Since 1971 the Sanatorio de la Amistad has operated under
Mexican church leadership. A newly appointed board of directors
met for the first time in October 1971. Dr. Alfreda Yañez was made
director, a position he carried out by giving one week each month
from a busy practice in Mexico City. Drs. Pablo Olvera and Ramon
Reguera were resident staff. Mr. Edson Johnson, the former mission
treasurer, became hospital administrator for one year during the transition from mission control to local doctors and board. Physicians
from the United States continued to visit and the Boyces returned at
regular intervals.[49] While some other medical resources developed in

*The Sanatorio de la Amistad was severely damaged in the 1982 earthquake but
suffered no casualties. Photograph courtesy of Paul S. Crane.*

Ometepec, the Sanatorio de la Amistad remained the only twenty-four-hour medical facility within 100 miles.[50]

In 1982, Ometepec was hit by a severe earthquake (9.2 on the Richter scale). The hospital was badly damaged but fortunately no injuries were sustained by staff or by patients. The PCUS raised funds for the restoration and renovation of the buildings.

Conclusion

Dr. and Mrs. Boyce returned to Ometepec in 1983 for the twenty-fifth-year celebration of the Sanatorio de la Amistad. Dr. Boyce commented that at first he "felt like Rip Van Winkle."[51]

> The biggest change is in the attitude of the people of the town. The animosity from the Catholic church has largely disappeared. The hospital is recognized as important to the whole region and is in full operation having been repaired following the earthquake. Leadership has been provided by "Don Nacho," pastor of the Ometepec Presbyterian Church, by Dr. Alfredo Yañez, who continues monthly supervision from Mexico City, and by Dr. Thomas Steinamann, a Swiss physician who visited Ometepec in 1974. Steinamann converted to Christianity and, after going back to Switzerland, returned to marry a student nurse and practice medicine [at the Sanatorio de la Amistad] in Ometepec. He works full time as an internist. Other physicians include Drs. Neli Zacapala and Alfredo Yañez Jr., a heart specialist who practices in both Mexico City and Ometepec.

> There were no Protestants in Ometepec in 1951. Now there are three organized Presbyterian churches: one in the Amusgo village of Xochistlahuaca; one in a coastal village; and one is the Fe y Luz [Faith and Light] Presbyterian Church in Ometepec. Designed by the pastor "Don Nacho" and built by its members of stone and open cement blocks, the Ometepec church is simple in construction and yet beautiful.[52]

At Ometepec the Boyces and the Woods engaged in an almost classical pioneer type of missionary endeavor. They sought to introduce the gospel into a poor, primitive, isolated, hostile region by first meeting the physical needs of the people. The Sanatorio de la

Amistad demonstrated once again the validity of this type of traditional medical mission work. The Boyces endured many trials but also experienced the joy of seeing a dream fulfilled in the development of a strong Christian community in Ometepec.

Notes

1. *Encyclopedia Britannica*, vol. 15, 1969, 323–43, and the *Encyclopedia Americana*, vol. 18, 1991, 806–46.
2. *Encyclopedia Americana*, vol. 18, 1991, 846.
3. PCUS, United Presbyterian, American Reformed Presbyterian, Methodist Episcopal, Southern Methodists, Congregational, Disciples, and the Friends (Quakers).
4. Hervey L. Ross, "Sixty-four Years Making Old Mexico New (1905–1969)," typescript, 1972, chapters I and XIX.
5. Ibid., 111.
6. Alice J. McClelland, *Mission to Mexico* (Nashville, Tenn.: PCUS Board of World Missions, 1960), 18.
7. Marguerite P. Boyce, correspondence, Aug. 1993.
8. McClelland, *Mission to Mexico*, 76.
9. Annual Report (Minutes of the General Assembly, PCUS, 1957), 6.
10. J. Hervey Ross, M.D., interview, Feb. 1984.
11. Eliza C. Thomas, interview, March 1991.
12. L. J. Coppedge, M.D., letter to Dr. Spence, Feb. 5, 1965, with Coppedge papers at the Department of History, PC(USA), Montreat, N.C.
13. Annual Report, 1921, 45.
14. Coppedge, "Medical Work and the Gospel in Morelia," *Missionary Survey*, March 1923, 181.
15. Ibid., 68–71.
16. Ibid., 70–71.
17. McLelland, *Mission to Mexico*, 75–76.
18. Ibid.
19. Ibid.
20. Ibid.
21. J. Hervey Ross, interview.
22. Ibid.
23. Annual Report, 1967, 54–55.
24. Hervey L. Ross, "Sixty-four Years Making Old Mexico New," 75.
25. Annual Report, 1967, 54.
26. W. Rion Dixon, M.D., interview, 1994.

27. Ann Dixon, R.N., letter, 1993.

28. Annual Report, 55.

29. Marguerite P. Boyce, *I Heard the Donkeys Bray* (Franklin, Tenn.: Providence House Publishers, 1992), 10.

30. Ometepec Hospital Survey Team, report, Sept. 29–Oct. 3, 1971.

31. Ruffus C. Morrow, *El Almirante Misionero (The Missionary Admiral)* (Mexico: Piblicaciones El Faro, S.A., 1965).

32. McClelland, *Mission to Mexico*, 64.

33. Marguerite Boyce, correspondence, Aug. 1993.

34. M. Boyce, *I Heard the Donkeys Bray*, 25–29.

35. Ibid., 110.

36. Hervey L. Ross, "Sixty-four Years Making Old Mexico New," 75.

37. M. Boyce, correspondence, Aug. 1993.

38. Hervey L. Ross, "Sixty-four Years Making Old Mexico New," 75.

39. Annual Report, 1963, 137.

40. James Boyce, interview, Sept. 1984.

41. M. Boyce, *I Heard the Donkeys Bray*, 110.

42. Ibid., 153–60.

43. Ibid., 132–34.

44. J. Boyce, interview.

45. M. Boyce, *I Heard the Donkeys Bray*, 147–48.

46. Ibid., 164.

47. Ibid., 17.

48. M. Boyce, missionary correspondence letter, Department of History, PC(USA), Montreat, N.C., Jan. 24, 1964.)

49. Survey Team, report, Oct. 3, 1971.

50. M. Boyce, *I Heard the Donkeys Bray*, 190.

51. J. Boyce, interview.

52. Ibid.

PART V
Brazil, Japan, Taiwan

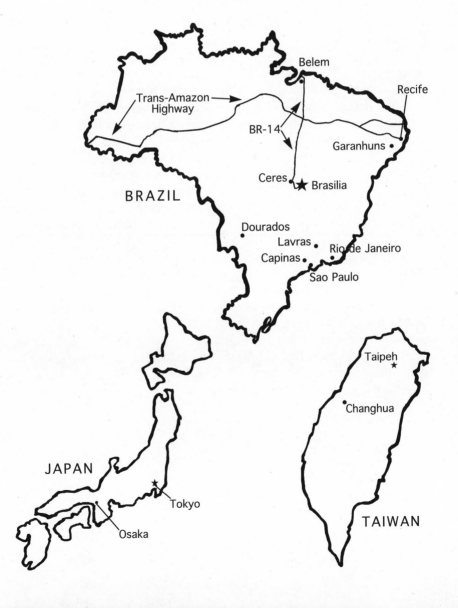

Part V

Worln War II, together with the preceding Depression years, a period when some hospitals were closed and all suffered serious financial constriction, can be described roughly as a halfway break in the history of PCUS overseas medical missions. Except for China, which remained permanently closed, peace ushered in a period of increased support, fresh approaches, and youthful enthusiasm. During the 1940s and 1950s the PCUS undertook new medical initiatives in three countries: Brazil, Japan, and Taiwan. Not until the 1970s did PCUS begin more new medical projects, in Haiti and Bangladesh.

The three goals that came to dominate the latter half of PCUS medical history were (1) the medical education of indigenous peoples, (2) the emphasis on community public health programs, and (3) the expanded role of local peoples in operation and control. In contrast, earlier medical work might be said to be characterized by the establishment of facilities dedicated primarily to the care of sick people (missionaries and local peoples); some institutions in China developed strong training programs for doctors and nurses. The presentation of the Christian message through healing remained the underlying constant from beginning to end.

Chapter Eleven

Brazil
(1883–1983)

The Brazil Mission, established in 1869, was one of the first PCUS overseas missions. It had the largest area and the largest missionary force of any mission field. The PCUS did not, however, initiate medical work in Brazil as it had in other countries. The Brazilian government and the medical profession there put up barriers that made it difficult to obtain medical licensing. Eventually, medical licenses for physicians and nurses were issued but only to graduates of Brazilian institutions.

Yet some medical work was done. This work is reviewed here through (1) the careers of two pioneer "reverend physicians," George Butler and Horace S. Allyn; (2) the founding of the Dr. and Mrs. Goldsby King Memorial Hospital at Dourados; and (3) the clinic work carried on by a number of nurses and by Dr. Alan G. Gordon and his wife, Alma.

It should be noted that nonmedical missionaries responded to the sick and suffering around them as best they could and engaged in works of compassion such as the distribution of food and relief supplies and the teaching of hygiene and nutrition. A number of clinics operated by Brazilian nurses received support; money was budgeted for charity cases in local facilities; and after mission planes came into use in the late 1950s, missionary pilots were often called upon to transport sick patients from remote areas. Martha Little began the Little Children's Fund through which she channeled funds to many children and young people with crippling deformities resulting from birth defects (harelip, clubfoot) or accidents.

Brazil is a former colony of Portugal, and Portuguese remains the official language. In contrast, the Spanish colonies in South America divided into separate countries. Brazil achieved independence from Portugal in 1822. Diverse forms of government since that time have included an early empire with a king, republics, and military dictatorships. Although separation of church and state was legislated in 1889, Catholicism has been the religion of the majority. Because of the enormous size of the country and difficulty in transportation, the PCUS operated through separate missions: the South, the East, the West, and the North Brazil Missions. In the late 1970s these missions became one Brazil Mission of the PCUS.

The strength of Catholicism proved to be a major factor in the work of the PCUS in Brazil. According to David Barrett's authoritative *World Christian Encyclopedia* published in 1982, of the 96.3 percent of the population professing Christianity in 1900, 95 percent were Roman Catholic; by the mid-1980s, the figures had not changed greatly: of the 94 percent of the population professing Christianity, 87.8 percent were Catholic. Barrett further states that the "recognized elements of doctrine in Brazil are derived for the most part from the Council of Trent, namely, insistence on participation in the sacraments and persistent anti-Protestantism."[1] However, James E. Bear, in his *Mission to Brazil*, argues that although there was Roman Catholic opposition to and persecution of Protestants in Brazil from the beginning of the mission, the persecution was usually inspired by the local priest or bishop; the government was tolerant of Protestantism and tried to maintain religious liberty.[2]

THE REVEREND DOCTORS

The Reverend George William Butler, M.D.

Dr. Butler in 1883 was the third missionary physician to be appointed worldwide by the PCUS. Unlike the two who preceded him (Richard Baxter Fishburne in China and J. Walton Graybill in Mexico), both of whom resigned after two years, Dr. Butler served for thirty-six years, until his death in Brazil in 1919.

George Butler was born in Roswell, Georgia, in 1854 and attended the University of Maryland Medical School (M.D., 1882). He was appointed to Brazil in 1882 to teach and to practice medicine. He arrived in Recife in 1883 but briefly returned to the United States in 1884 for treatment of eye problems. While there he married Rena Humphrey of

Rev. George W. Butler, M.D.,
and Mrs. Rena H. Butler. Dr.
Butler was the third physician appointed by the PCUS
worldwide. He went to Brazil
in 1883 and served until his
death in 1919. Courtesy of
Presbyterian Church (USA),
Department of History
(Montreat, North Carolina).

Goldsboro, North Carolina, and was ordained to the ministry by the
Presbytery of Maryland. In 1896 he studied for several months at the
University of Bahia, took the medical examination, and obtained his
license to practice medicine in Brazil. Dr. Butler was assigned to the
North Brazil Mission and served primarily in the state of Pernambuco.[3]

Although trained as a physician, Dr. Butler has been described as
having the heart of an evangelist. Throughout his missionary career
he pursued a preaching ministry and traveled widely throughout the
region. His success brought persecution, as his 1897 report demon-
strates:

The work began in the Garanhuns field with stonings and threats of
death, which at last came true. Twice the worship was closed and
once the workers were compelled to flee for life. Then commenced a
persecution which lasted nearly a year and took the form of stoning
houses, and all conceivable little annoyances, even to the stealing
and breaking up of the material for a church building . . . Following
these petty annoyances came an epidemic of yellow fever, lasting
five months, and although the Lord saved all the believers, still the
daily hearing of the woes of others, and seeing their dead, made us
all feel that we were in the very midst of the plagues of Egypt. Just
as we began to think we had gotten to a resting place, an attempt at
taking my life resulted in the stabbing and immediate killing of my

companion at my side. He was wounded through the right lung, and
before I could open his clothes to find the wound, all his blood was
spilled for Christ's sake and for me.[4]

For Dr. Butler, this incident, in which the friend who interposed
himself was killed by the weapon aimed at the missionary, came to
symbolize Christ's supreme sacrifice for mankind.

In 1898 the Butlers moved to the small town of Canhotinho (near
Garanhuns) where, from his home, Dr. Butler treated an ever-
increasing number of patients. He also regularly visited some
twenty-two "stations" in a 200-mile radius. He wrote:

> Missionary journeys are made each week and they vary in length
> from 18 to 150 miles. . . . The visits to these stations have been accom-
> plished with difficulty and danger, and ordinarily require long rides
> on horseback, one station requiring four days journey to be reached.[5]

A fellow missionary wrote of Dr. Butler:

> Dr. Butler lives at Canhotinho, but his influence is felt in the whole
> [mission] field. In fact, we could not hold this field, humanly
> speaking, without his influence. By his wonderful cures and surgical
> operations he has established a reputation for himself and a name
> for us in every part of the interior. He has the friendship of many of
> the political chiefs, whose word and will is the only law in these
> parts. It is this friendship and protection that makes it possible for
> the native workers to escape the wrath of the priests and the igno-
> rant, fanatical Romanists. Every train brings from afar persons to
> Canhotinho to be treated.[6]

In 1915, thanks to a gift of $5,000, a small hospital was built in
Canhotinho. As noted in that year's annual report, "Time was when
Dr. Butler had to go out and find people to preach to, but now they
come to him to be treated. . . . Many go home with new life and new
hope." In 1919 Dr. Butler, described as "the worst hated and best
loved" man in the whole of north Brazil, died at Canhotinho. With
his death the medical work of the North Brazil Mission came to an
end.[7]

The Reverend Horace S. Allyn, M.D.

Dr. Allyn arrived in Brazil in 1896 and was assigned to the ancient city of Lavras, Minas Gerais, in what was then known as the South Brazil Mission (in 1906 it became the East Brazil Mission). Allyn had graduated from both medical school (the University of Michigan School of Medicine) and theological seminary (Columbia Theological Seminary). In 1906–07, after attending a course at the Rio de Janeiro Medical School, he took the Brazilian medical examinations and qualified with honor for his Brazilian medical license.

Dr. Allyn's assignment was described as evangelistic and medical. He never established a hospital but had an extensive practice, especially among the poor.[8] In 1921 he moved to Varginha, some fifty miles southwest of Lavras, and established the elementary school that eventually was named the Allyn Evangelical School in his honor.[9] The Allyns returned to the United States in 1925 because of health problems.

DR. AND MRS. GOLDSBY KING MEMORIAL HOSPITAL
Dourados

Far to the west of Brazil in the state of Mato Grosso, some 200 miles from the nearest railroad station, is the remote frontier settlement of Dourados. Here, in 1929 four denominations (the Presbyterian Church of Brazil, the Independent Presbyterian Church of Brazil, the Brazilian Methodist Church, and the PCUS) established a joint mission among the Caiua Indians. This 10,000–member tribe occupied a large jungle reservation only a few miles away.

Rev. and Mrs. Albert S. Maxwell were the pioneer PCUS missionaries among the Indians from 1929 until 1939, when they returned to the United States due to ill health. A comprehensive program included a church, school, orphanage, clinic, and agricultural project. After the Maxwells left, Rev. Orlando Andrade and his wife, Dona Loide Bonfim, took charge of the work. Dr. Nelson de Araujo, a graduate of a Brazilian medical school, was in charge of the clinic; Dona Loide supervised the care of tuberculous patients. James E. Bear described this work:

1938—Dr. Nelson de Araujo's little shed that he uses for hospital was filled to capacity. . . . Now don't jump to conclusions that he had a great crowd of patients—there were only two beds. More are needed of course.

1954—Recently a modest wooden house was built to shelter six aged Indians, and a small isolation ward for the ubiquitous tuberculosis cases is under construction.[10]

In 1938 yellow fever broke out among the Indians, and the Rockefeller Foundation sent a team of doctors to fight the disease. They used the mission's buildings while the missionaries moved, temporarily, to Dourados.

In 1942 the PCUS expanded its mission in Dourados to the Portuguese-speaking people who were flooding into the area as part of the "March to the West" movement, in which thousands of Brazilians were being encouraged to settle in undeveloped parts of the nation. Support for this Dourados Mission came in part from the 1941 Birthday Offering of the Women of the Church, which was designated for Pioneer Evangelistic Work in Brazil. Rev. J. Marion Sydenstricker and his wife, Myrtle, responded to this opportunity with enthusiasm: "You couldn't pay us to stay—but we like it!"[11]

Mr. Sydenstricker is generally credited with promoting the construction of a hospital in Dourados. The Misses Annie and Dulie King of Selma, Alabama, in memory of their mission-minded parents, provided the money for the Dr. and Mrs. Goldsby King Memorial Hospital in Dourados, as they had for the hospitals in Zhenjiang, China (1924), and in Mutoto, Congo/Zaire (1924). In 1946 this twenty-five-bed hospital, known locally as the Hospital Evangelico, was described as the showplace of Dourados:

It is a beautiful, one-story building with two wards, four or five private rooms, a clinic, a laboratory, an operating room, sterilizing room and sanitary installations. The kitchen and dining room are still under construction, and are in a separate building joined by a covered walkway.[12]

The delight of the people of Dourados was reflected in their response to a request from the mayor for them to furnish the kitchen utensils and bed clothes for the hospital. Even the local priest told the people that it was their duty and privilege to support the hospital in every way.

The Dr. and Mrs. Goldsby King Memorial Hospital in Dourados was known locally as the Hospital Evangelico. Courtesy of Presbyterian Church (USA), Department of History (Montreat, North Carolina).

In 1956 responsibility for the hospital was assumed by a board of directors made up of representatives from the Brazilian Presbyterian Church, the local Dourados Presbyterian Church, and the PCUS. By 1960 the hospital had achieved financial independence from the PCUS except for the salary of the director. It had expanded to sixty-seven beds and, in addition to operating a busy outpatient department, sent staff to clinics of the Indian Mission and in the homestead area.

Dr. Antonio Duarte served as the director until 1963, when he was elected to the state legislature. Dr. Nelson de Araujo, formerly the physician at the Caiua Indian clinic, became the assistant director. A Brazilian graduate nurse and a technician joined the staff, and eventually a school for practical nurses was begun.

In 1960 Miss Annie King visited the hospital:

The whole city of Dourados rose up to pay her homage. Besides a dinner party, a reception by the women of the town in the club, and a banquet in Miss King's honor, there were more invitations than she could accept during her brief stay. She received gifts and flowers and was made an honorary citizen by the mayor and town council. She confessed that she had never dreamed it possible to feel so perfectly at home in a foreign city.[13]

The PCUS assigned only three medical missionaries to the Goldsby King Memorial Hospital. Margaret P. Wood, R.N., a former PCUS missionary to China, served from 1954 to 1957; Alan G. (M.D.) and Alma D. (R.N.) Gordon, from 1972 to 1979. The Gordons, both children of missionaries to Brazil, were a superbly qualified young couple, fluent in the Portuguese language and armed with Brazilian medical licenses. Alan received his medical education at the University of São Paulo Medical School (M.D., 1965) and went to the United States for five years of graduate study. Alma earned her B.S. in nursing in 1956 at the University of Connecticut and her Brazilian nursing diploma in 1965 from the University of São Paulo School of Nursing.

Dr. Osamu Arakaki, a Japanese Brazilian, was director of the Goldsby King Memorial Hospital when the Gordons arrived. The hospital had departments in surgery, orthopedics, internal medicine, pediatrics, and maternity. The operating room was well equipped and maintained the standards of cleanliness of a modern surgical unit.

Alan Gordon, just out of his surgical residency in the United States, brought fresh ideas and new techniques to the institution. Alma Gordon worked with the school for practical nurses (LPN). Entrance requirements were raised from fourth-grade to eighth-grade level and accreditation was obtained both for the school and for those former graduates who had continued their education.

During their seven years (1972–79) at the Goldsby King Memorial Hospital, the Gordons' career conformed to the traditional medical missionary role in a hospital-based environment. The hospital's reputation was enhanced, and good Brazilian doctors were attracted to its staff. It grew into a 230-bed facility with a staff of ten full-time and twenty part-time doctors, and it became the preeminent hospital for a large and remote area of Brazil. Dr. Gordon expressed disappointment that "while the administrator, head nurse, and other staff persons were Christian, most of the doctors were not. This dilutes the strong Christian witness that might have been made."[14]

The PCUS continued to support the Goldsby King Memorial Hospital through representation on its board and regular financial assistance. In 1975 the Medical Benevolence Foundation campaigned for $27,350 to upgrade the plant and operating rooms.[15] In 1982 MBF raised $20,000 for construction of a new ward.[16]

CLINIC WORK

The Nurses

In 1951 Margaret Poague Wood, R.N. became the first medical person assigned by PCUS to Brazil since 1896, when Horace Allyn, M.D., was appointed. She accepted assignment to Brazil when the Communists terminated her missionary career in China. After two years in language study, she proceeded to Dourados where she worked at the Goldsby King Memorial Hospital. She compared her two posts like this:

> The situation in Brazil was entirely different from that in China. The country was at peace, and the dire need found in other of the mission areas did not exist. The country had a medical system with trained medical professionals. Medical supplies were more readily available but the licensing of foreign-trained medical people was virtually impossible. My assignment was nursing and nursing education at the Goldsby King Memorial Hospital. I was not able to get a nursing license because of the regulations imposed on foreigners by the National Nurses' Association. The nursing was done by practical nurses and nurse's aides. I taught nursing skills on a one-on-one basis.[17]

After serving three years at the Goldsby King Memorial Hospital in Dourados, Margaret Wood transferred to the Language and Orientation School in Campinas, São Paulo, a union institution run by the PCUS, UPUSA, Methodist, and Southern Baptist missions, where her primary service was to missionaries and their families. Between 1958 and 1963, 100 babies were born to missionaries (not all PCUS).[18]

This abundance of missionary offspring reflected an exuberant period of growth of the Brazil Mission. In response to the enormous development in Brazil in the 1950s and 1960s, the PCUS made that country an area of primary mission focus. Contributing to the enthusiasm were the improvement in relations with the Catholic community;

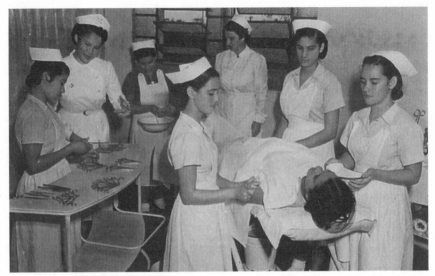

Margaret Wood, R.N., supervises the training of student nurses at the hospital in Dourados. Courtesy of Presbyterian Church (USA), Department of History (Montreat, North Carolina).

the construction of the new capital, Brasilia, in the geographical center of the country; and the building of a new highway, known as the BR-14, running 1,375 miles due north from Brasilia to Belem on the Amazon River. The PCUS undertook a number of new initiatives—in education, agricultural extension, and the production of audiovisual materials; in an air service piloted by missionaries to help cope with the tremendous distances; and in a program to enlist missionary nurses for public health and primary care.

Between 1959 and 1966 the PCUS, in order to implement the public health initiative, appointed ten registered nurses whose assignment was to "medical work." All but three of these nurses were married to missionaries; most were unable to acquire Brazilian licenses. They worked primarily in church-related clinics with Brazilian nurses and doctors.

Mary Elizabeth "Merry" Long, R.N., who, with her husband, transferred to Brazil from Congo/Zaire at the time of independence (1962), was stationed at Ceres, on the BR-14 near Brasilia. Unlike the frontier portion of the highway in the north, Ceres was an old town with a strong church community. Merry Long considered her work in

Africa more interesting and challenging but enjoyed the close contact with families in Brazil. She described the work as follows:

> My work was very basic. I set up clinics for mothers and children on a weekly basis in local churches, or out in the country churches where I went only once a month. Church women assisted me in giving injections, wrapping up medicines, teaching nutrition and how to care for sick children. These women conducted a Bible study and did the charting. Sometimes there would be another nurse who would help me in diagnosing and treating patients. Basically we gave DPT shots and treated for worms and malnutrition, but ended up trying to treat the whole family. Often we would see 200 mothers and children in an afternoon; one year we had 12,000 consultations . . . [I worked] under local doctors who usually gave free consultations to patients I sent them.[19]

BR-14 Highway

The building of the BR-14 highway provided a unique opportunity in a desperately needy situation. Working with the public health and state authorities who were attempting to develop a medical program for the BR-14, the PCUS undertook to provide what were essentially (at first) the only professional medical services along the 500-mile northern section of the highway. Three full-time nurses, Haydee Torres, Edna Quinn, and Janice Olson, were appointed to implement the program. Brazilian physicians from as far away as Campinas and São Luiz (in 1966 there were seven) volunteered their time for short periods.

The northern section of the BR-14 was unpaved, and living conditions among the migratory population were primitive. Poverty, poor housing, inadequate food supplies, and lack of hygiene were almost insurmountable problems. Tuberculosis, malaria (one of the worst areas in Brazil), anemia, malnutrition, and worms were major health problems. Life expectancy in 1966 was thirty-five years and infant mortality around 60 percent.[20]

Funding for the BR-14 medical program came in part from the 1941 and 1963 Birthday Offerings of the PCUS Women of the Church. While most of the Birthday Offerings went to church buildings and schools, three clinics received some funding, and many of the churches developed clinics.[21]

Left, jungle highway in the making. Brazil constructed the north/south B-14 and the east/west Trans/Amazon Highways during the 1970s and 1980s. These roads brought an influx of settlers to remote parts of the country where living conditions were primitive. Photograph courtesy of Jule Spach. Right, the BR-14 logo. Courtesy Presbyterian Church (USA), Department of History (Montreat, North Carolina).

The assignment of Haydee Torres, R.N., in 1961 was greeted with great enthusiasm. A native of Colombia with impressive postgraduate study in the United States, she initiated a medical program to include social service and public health. Working with public health officials in Belem, she established clinics in three towns (Paragominas, Imperatriz, and Estreito), trained a group of girls to serve as aides in obstetrics, and instituted a training course for health workers for the BR-14 medical program.

Although the work was carried on with government encouragement and some support and with the help of other agencies (World Neighbors was one), the financial situation was precarious; in 1966 the PCUS provided $2,850 for operating expenses. John Lane, one of the visiting physicians, commented, "It is our opinion that the workers are doing excellently, but that the Board of World Missions would not be proud of the circumstances in which this work is carried out." And, in view of the appalling need, Edna Quinn, R.N., who arrived in 1963 wrote, "We earnestly desire to be provided with the minimum tools of our trade."[22]

Edna Quinn, R.N., pioneered medical work on the newly constructed BR-14. Photograph courtesy of Edna Quinn.

Edna Quinn, a Duke University graduate (B.S.N., 1960), developed a program with Haydee Torres that supplemented clinic activities (priorities were maternal and child health, preventive medicine, and emergency care), with home visitation, sanitation work (building of wells and privies), distribution of food, gardening projects, health and hygiene classes in the schools, day nurseries, and vaccination and anti-malarial campaigns. Family planning was an integral, and ultimately controversial, part of the program. A fellow missionary described Edna Quinn's work as follows:

> Her first effort after analyzing the situation was a major campaign for cleanliness with soap and water. This in itself reduced dramatically the sickness in the area . . . It was through this cleanliness program that [she] became well known and in time verified that another of the most serious problems related to health care was that of annual pregnancy with a high rate of infant mortality and the death of mothers. It was then that Edna attempted to start a family planning program using classes for women and the application of the contraceptive IUD [intrauterine device]. The response was amazing.[23]

The family planning program became well known and stimulated opposition that received nationwide media attention. Catholic authorities were especially antagonistic. Edna Quinn was in America in 1966 trying to raise funds and equipment when she was accused of genocide; she was advised not to return to Brazil.

Soon after, the PCUS, influenced by this publicity and the charges of genocide, as well as the lack of personnel and the expense of running the program, decided to discontinue the BR-14 medical program. However, as pointed out by Jule C. Spach, former missionary and moderator of the PCUS, the BR-14 medical program, although short-lived, was one of the major contributions made by the PCUS in Brazil. The controversy it ignited became the catalyst that, a few years later, legitimized family planning for the whole nation.[24]

Although a number of missionary wives with nursing degrees continued to work in church-related clinics, after 1966 no nurses were appointed for medical work in Brazil except for Alma D. Gordon.

Good Samaritan Clinic

In 1979, after serving for seven years at the Goldsby King Memorial Hospital in Dourados, the Gordons moved to São Paulo, where the Evangelical Beneficent Association (EBA) had invited Alan Gordon to become director of the Good Samaritan Clinic. The EBA, a fully Brazilian entity, was founded in 1930 and supported by contributions from Brazilian Christians. In addition to the clinic, the EBA ran eight day-care centers, two homes for children, a trade school for adolescents, a hospital, and a home for the elderly. The Christian emphasis in each of these institutions was very strong.

The Good Samaritan Clinic served part of a slum population of about two million poor people in São Paulo. It was started in 1940 by Dr. Pires, a distinguished Brazilian physician and professor at the medical school. When Dr. Pires became ill and was forced to retire, Dr. Gordon was invited to become the director.

The clinic was staffed, in addition to the Gordons, by two part-time Brazilian doctors and one licensed practical nurse (LPN). It was open eight hours a day and served some forty to

Alan G. Gordon, M.D., with a young patient at the Good Samaritan Clinic, São Paulo. Photograph from Presbyterian Church (USA) brochure.

fifty patients each day. The patients were the poorest of the poor and had no resources for health care. They got good-quality care. Dr. Gordon comments:

> The Brazilian government has had a highly effective immunization program. Their "Polio Day" in which every child under five gets inoculated, has been cited by Dr. Sabin as one of the best in the world. Not so good has been their care of the poor with general health problems. Common conditions seen at Good Samaritan Clinic include malnutrition, intestinal parasites, diabetes, obesity, high blood pressure, heart disease, dermatology, and some leprosy.[25]

The clinic offered free medical services to its patients and strived to provide compassionate care to mind and soul as well as to the body. Support for the clinic came primarily from the Evangelical Beneficent Association. The PCUS contributed the support of Dr. and Mrs. Gordon, and some drugs were purchased with PCUS funds.

In addition to providing nursing care, Alma Gordon attempted to meet the educational, social, and spiritual needs of the people. She taught health and nutrition, led Bible studies, or helped people find a job, get dental care, or enroll their children in school or day care.

In addition to operating the clinic, the Gordons worked on a number of projects, some of which were designed to introduce medical students and young doctors to the Christian concept of concern for the whole person. In 1979 the Gordons, at the request of the World Relief Commission (Chicago), spent a number of weeks on the Thai/Cambodian border to help with Cambodian refugees. There they worked in a hospital where some 1,300 seriously ill, injured, and malnourished were cared for.

Conclusion

Although the PCUS did not establish a traditional mission medical program in Brazil, it did have a medical presence. In 1983, at the dissolution of the PCUS, this medical involvement could be seen in three areas: the Dr. and Mrs. Goldsby King Memorial Hospital, the work of missionary nurses in church-related clinics, and the Good Samaritan Clinic in São Paulo.

Notes

1. David B. Barrett, ed., *World Christian Encyclopedia* (New York: Oxford University Press, 1982), 188–89.

2. James Bear, *Mission to Brazil* (Nashville, Tenn.: PCUS Board of World Missions, 1961), 3.

3. Ibid., 40

4. George Butler, M.D., quoted in ibid., 52.

5. Ibid., 60.

6. George E. Henderlite, quoted in ibid., 60.

7. Ibid., 61

8. Ibid., 106.

9. Ibid., 120.

10. Ibid., 145–47.

11. Ibid., 149.

12. Ibid., 150.

13. Annual Report (Minutes of the PCUS General Assembly, 1960), 47.

14. Alan G. Gordon, M.D., interview, Feb. 1984.

15. *Link* (MBF newsletter), winter 1976, 4.

16. Ibid., Winter 1982, 4.

17. Margaret Wood, R.N., interview, May 1990.

18. Ibid.

19. Mary Elizabeth Long, R.N., letter, 1993.

20. Edna Quinn, R.N., "Report to the North Brazil Presbyterian Mission of the Medical Program—BR-14 Highway," typescript, July 1966, 1.

21. Patricia H. Sprinkle, *The Birthday Book: First Fifty Years* (Atlanta, Ga.: PCUS Board of Women's Work, 1972), 109, 121.

22. Quinn, "Report," 2, 3.

23. Jule C. Spach, letter, December 5, 1994.

24. Julie C. Spach, *Every Road Leads Home* (Chapel Hill, N.C.: Professional Press, 1996), 341. An ironic postscript: Edna Quinn was a member of the team of American family-planning experts that later was invited to evaluate programs promoted by the Brazilian Congress.

25. Gordon, interview, Feb. 1984.

———————— *Chapter Twelve* ————————

Japan
(1950–1983)

T he PCUS began its mission to Japan in 1885 and, in a comity
agreement with other Protestant mission bodies, carried on evangelical and educational work in the Kanto region of central Honshu and
on the island of Shikoku until 1941. The mission closed shortly before
Pearl Harbor in the face of an increasingly hostile environment.

PCUS established no medical work in prewar Japan. There were
two main reasons: (1) The Japanese government made it virtually
impossible for an American physician or nurse to secure a license to
practice in Japan. (2) In its zeal for modernization, Japan had turned
to Germany for technical training including medicine; medical
schools and hospitals proliferated. Thus a system of Western medical
practice was in place and, although the system differed in many
respects from that in the United States, the needs were not of the
magnitude found in other mission areas. Indeed, medical missionaries were not welcome in Japan.[1]

After World War II the PCUS faced a difficult problem in
renewing mission work in a defeated Japan occupied and ruled by the
U.S. military government. The PCUS decided, in view of post-war
conditions, to explore the feasibility of establishing medical work as a
way to demonstrate Christian compassion.

In 1949 the Japan Mission asked Frank A. Brown Jr. (Washington
University, St. Louis, M.D., 1942), who was en route from China to the
United States, to stop in Japan for six months to survey the situation.
Brown, the son of China missionaries whose own missionary career in
China ended with the establishment of Communist rule, was
uniquely qualified to carry out this assignment. During two years of
service in the U.S. Army (1944–46), Brown had been assigned to the

U.S. Army of Occupation in Japan. In preparation for this assignment, he attended the military government school in Charlottesville, Virginia, and the Yale University Institute of Far Eastern Studies, where he studied the Japanese language. In October 1945, only a few weeks after U.S. troops had landed, he arrived in Japan with the first military government unit and was eventually assigned as the public health officer for all of northern Japan. For a year he traveled widely, gaining an intimate knowledge of the medical situation and meeting many Japanese doctors, some of whom were Christian.[2]

Dr. Brown, who has been characterized by colleagues as a man of enormous energy, intelligence, and compassion, undertook the PCUS assignment with enthusiasm and began a careful study of the area in which the PCUS operated. He found that, in the postwar devastation, large numbers of people were receiving inadequate medical care; the need was great. He discovered that the U.S. military government offered a small window of opportunity for the licensing of missionary physicians by allowing foreign doctors to take the national medical examination in English; foreign nurses were not given this privilege. Japanese doctors and friends in the U.S. occupation forces urged him to recommend that a mission hospital be established. As a result of his study the PCUS approved the establishment of the first PCUS hospital in Japan.[3] The Browns (Frank, M.D., and Ann, R.N.) were assigned to this hospital after completing a year of furlough in the United States.

The city of Gifu was first considered, but that location was opposed by the medical community and the church. Osaka was chosen after the "Osaka Christian Inviting—Medical and Service—Committee," established by Christian doctors, ministers, and other Christians, along with the Osaka Prefectural Welfare Department formally requested the Japan Mission to establish the hospital in Osaka. The location received final approval in 1953.[4]

YODOGAWA CHRISTIAN HOSPITAL
Osaka

The story of the Yodogawa Christian Hospital (YCH) from its founding in 1955 to 1983 is traced here by addressing (1) the staff and administration, (2) the development of the physical facilities of the institution, (3) the practice of modern medicine, and (4) outreach through a Department of Medical Social Work, the evange- listic department, and involvement in community and overseas missionary work. For the first fifteen years, missionary leadership at YCH was strong and the administration was primarily a mission responsibility. By 1976 YCH was an independent, self-supporting institution, and the PCUS was only minimally involved.

Staff and Administration
Frank Brown, surgeon, was the superintendent until his retire- ment in 1976. Ovid B. Bush (University of Georgia, Augusta, M.D., 1945), an internist whose missionary service to Korea was interrupted by the Korean War (see PMC, Korea), welcomed the opportunity to become part of the founding team for this pioneer PCUS medical effort in Japan. Marion Powell, a Canadian Presbyterian obstetri- cian/gynecologist (University of Toronto, M.D., 1946), served from 1954 to 1960. She brought her special concern for women and children to YCH during its formative years. Nell S. Swenson, R.N., and Elizabeth C. Lundeen, R.N., built up the nursing service. Florence Bush, with experience in bacteriology and parasitology, helped in the laboratory. June Lamb established the Department of Medical Social Work and helped develop the X-ray department. Oscar Marvin, a hospital administrator, joined the staff in 1957. During his three years of service he organized the business structure of the institution and introduced concepts of modern hospital administration.

The founding of the mission hospital stimulated considerable interest among the PCUS missionary community in Japan, and many actively supported it. The Rev. William McIlwaine and Mrs. Pauline McAlpine, experienced prewar missionaries, gave especially valuable assistance as the project began. McIlwaine, with his great reservoir of knowledge about Japan, gave practical advice and spiritual encour- agement; McAlpine wrote a medical text to help the medical missionary staff with Japanese terminology. Others served on boards and medical committees, helped with secretarial needs, and taught English to the staff.[5]

Foreign missionary personnel at YCH, as they left or retired, were replaced by competent Japanese medical professionals. From 1968 to 1976, Dr. Brown was the only PCUS *medical* missionary on the staff. The Rev. Lardner Moore, chaplain with the evangelistic department, and his wife, Mollie, continued as the only PCUS missionaries at YCH until well into the 1990s. They provided an important link with the church in the United States.

The Osaka Christian Inviting Committee, which was instrumental in selecting Osaka as the site for the medical program, continued to support YCH activities. In 1958 a ten-person board of councilors, made up of leaders in many fields, was formed with Mr. Ryozo Okumura as the first chairman. In 1969, upon official designation as a "General Hospital," a board of directors took over from the Japan Mission the responsibility of running the institution. Mr. Okumura, chairman and then chairman emeritus until his death in 1983, and Dr. Takeshiro Kodera provided outstanding leadership to this board. It is interesting to note that in order to operate under Japanese government tax regulations, the Yodogawa Christian Hospital continued to operate under the legal holding body of the PCUS and, after the reunion of Presbyterian churches in 1983, the PC(USA). The Presbyterian Church (USA) still (1993) holds the official seal for all legal matters.[6]

Following Dr. Brown's retirement, the hospital experienced a difficult period when the physician groomed for the job of director decided instead to enter private practice. National insurance rates were unrealistically low, and medical costs were rapidly rising; there

Dr. Seiya Shirakata became director of the Yodogawa Christian Hospital in 1978. Photograph courtesy of the Yodogawa Christian Hospital.

were problems in keeping up the standards required by the government; the facilities began to deteriorate; and, in the face of competition, it became difficult to attract patients and to hire and hold good staff. For several years the hospital operated with deficit financing.[7]

The appointment in 1978 of Seiya Shirakata, M.D., as director brought revolutionary changes. An outstanding neurosurgeon and a Christian, Dr. Shirakata had graduated from the medical department of Kyushu University, studied for sixteen months at St. Barnabas Medical School in New York, and served as assistant professor at Kobe University School of Medicine. With the support of the governing board, he stabilized the financial situation. A man of vision, Dr. Shirakata initiated a dramatic new building program, upgraded technical equipment, encouraged further development of such programs as the hospice program while maintaining and strongly promoting the hospital's commitment to Christian service to the whole person. He also encouraged the staff to be aware of the problems and needs (especially medical needs) of people in Asian countries.[8]

Kasuke Tsujimoto, M.D., a surgeon, and Tetsuo Kashiwagi, M.D., director of the hospice program, both of whom were dedicated Christians, served jointly as vice-superintendents of the hospital for many years. These three men, Drs. Shirakata, Tsujimoto, and Kashiwagi, made extraordinary contributions in leadership to YCH.

Development of Physical Facilities

In 1952 Osaka, Japan's second largest city with about four million people, still bore the scars of the disastrous bombings of the war and was just beginning to develop into what was to become one of Japan's most vibrant industrial centers and busiest port. Factories, as yet not

Yodogawa Christian Hospital in the early 1960s. Photograph courtesy of the Yodogawa Christian Hospital.

rebuilt, were surrounded by some of the worst slums in Japan, in which hundreds of thousands of Japanese lived in shacks. With the help of Christian leaders, the PCUS purchased over four and one-half acres of land in a poor area of Osaka at a very favorable rate. This large plot of land, which increased enormously in value over the years, provided financial security for the institution and made possible its future growth and expansion. The name, Yodogawa, was the traditional name for Osaka and came from the Yodo River, which flows through the city.

The area was occupied by many *burakumin*, an outcast segment of the lowest level of Japanese society. The nondiscriminatory hiring practices at the hospital, as in other PCUS institutions, provided training and jobs for the *burakumin* and other disadvantaged groups as well as for people on all levels of society.[9]

Construction of YCH

1956	Original building contained 75 beds.
1963	Nurses' dormitory increased total beds to 109.
1966	West Wing increased total beds to 135.
1970	East Wing increased total beds to 152.
1974	Nurses' dormitory
1977	X Wing increased total beds to 195.
1980	Brown Memorial Chapel
1982	South Building (begun) increased total beds to 371.

Funds for the construction of the original hospital came from the Program of Progress Fund ($100,000) and the 1955 Birthday Offering ($206,677) of the PCUS Women of the Church. Presbyterian women responded to this opportunity to demonstrate Christian love to former enemies by raising the largest Birthday Offering to date. An annual shipment of White Cross materials reflected their continued concern. As U.S. forces withdrew from Japan, surplus U.S. Army equipment and supplies became available and were a major contribution.

The building of a seventy-five-bed facility with an outpatient service and quarters for twenty-five nurses began in the fall of 1955. At the same time a small clinic was opened on the construction site in a shed. On March 8, 1956, the dedication was celebrated with the unveiling of a plaque which read:

Inscription on plaque at the Yodogawa Christian Hospital. Photograph courtesy of the Yodogawa Christian Hospital.

Yodogawa Christian Hospital, dedicated to the glory of God and the salvation of man through the ministry of healing. Given by the Women of the Church, Presbyterian Church, U.S.

Until 1970 additional construction was funded largely from church sources in the United States. In 1963, the nurses' dormitory was a gift ($35,000) from the First Presbyterian Church, Dallas, Texas. This dormitory created space for additional beds by freeing the third floor of the hospital where the nurses had been housed and, at the same time, improved the comfort and the morale of the nurses. The West Wing, built in 1966 with the help of $20,000 from PCUS development funds, raised the bed capacity to 135. In 1967 the Medical Benevolence Foundation, in addition to its regular funding, provided a grant that enabled the hospital to open a Department of Ophthalmology.

After 1970 construction was funded largely in Japan. Part of the funds came from selling pieces of the land. The East Wing in 1970, a new nurses' dormitory in 1974, and the "X" Wing in 1977 brought the hospital beds to 195. The ambitious construction project begun in 1982 came partly as a result of the city's decision to build a highway through a portion of the property. Reimbursement made it possible to begin replacement of some of the buildings and to add a thoroughly modern seven-story complex. The South Building, completed in 1984, was only the first step in this plan, which would eventually increase the beds to 607.[10]

In February 1980 the Brown Memorial Chapel, funded by a gift from Dr. and Mrs. Ryoichi Naito and others, was dedicated in honor of the founder, Dr. Frank A. Brown. In May of the same year Yodogawa Christian Hospital celebrated its twenty-fifth anniversary.

The physical development of YCH reflected not only its success as a medical institution but also the remarkably improved economic development of Japan during this postwar period. It also reflected the quality of Japanese Christian leadership that continued the witness and service of the Yodogawa Christian Hospital.

Practice of Medicine

The need to define the role of a "Christian" hospital in what was basically a secular society received serious and ongoing attention at YCH. The treatment of the patient as a person became the basic principle on which the hospital operated, and the ever-recurring phrase "making men whole" came to sum up this concept.

Japanese medicine grew out of the German tradition and, from the first, excelled in research and in the development of technical equipment; clinical medicine generally showed little concern for the individual patient. As Dr. Brown wrote:

> Since the war, through military government doctors and visiting teams of American university professors, there has come about a better understanding of the limitations of Japanese medicine. For, while it is true that Japan has been far ahead of other Asiatic countries in this respect, professional standards have been far below those prevalent in most western countries. And then, of course, the war . . . still further depressed these standards . . .
>
> A potent reason for *the introduction of Christian* medical work is the lack of feeling on the part of most doctors for the sick as human beings. At best the patient is considered a technical problem of some interest; more commonly simply as a source of income . . . [for example] a local better-than-average obstetrician takes his regular days off, vacations, and attends distant meetings without any provision for his patients whose babies are due at that time. [This is] not an exceptional case, but is quite typical of the attitude of the medical profession out here—and the people expect no more.[11]

YCH implemented its concern for the whole person in a number of ways. Fundamental was the maintenance of the highest possible professional standards of medical practice, including the pioneering of new initiatives in medicine and the development of a close relationship with Osaka University Medical School for teaching and research. Strong departments of medical social work, evangelism, and hospital chaplaincy further addressed the social and spiritual, as well as the physical needs of the patients.

Although the founding of the mission hospital in Osaka was supported by church and community, it encountered opposition from the local doctors' association. However, in the spring of 1958 the staff was invited to join the Yodogawa Medical Association. The 1958 annual report noted:

> The invitation itself was a sign of greatly improved relationships with the local doctors, and progress since that time has been marked by more referrals of patients to our hospital by doctors in the neighborhood, invitations to medical educational meetings, vast reduction of outspoken criticism of "that Christian hospital," and an increased respect for the modern medical facilities available there.[12]

The prompt response of YCH to two disasters also helped dissipate hostility to the institution. In 1958 a series of flash fires in Osaka destroyed many homes. The hospital provided food, clothing, and blankets to those in need. The next year (September 1959) the horrendous Ise Bay Typhoon devastated a large area near the city of Nagoya. Again the hospital, under the leadership of Dr. Bush, organized a medical rescue team that worked in the area for approximately six months.

Ovid B. Bush, M.D., at the site devastated by the Ise Bay Typhoon. Photograph courtesy of the Yodogawa Christian Hospital.

Dr. Brown, in addition to carrying out his administrative responsibilities, practiced surgery. He spent his furlough years in advanced
training in general surgery, orthopedics, and anesthesiology and in
1972 became a diplomate of the American College of Anesthesiology.
He developed a surgical team of proficient and respected Japanese
surgeons. The sophistication of surgical practice at YCH was demonstrated in 1975 by the separation of Siamese twins by a team led by Dr.
Kasuke Tsujimoto. This surgery was the second successful such separation in Japan and the nineteenth in the world.[13]

Dr. Bush, a fellow of the American College of Physicians, was one
of the few internists (as opposed to surgeons, pediatricians, obstetri-
cians, generalists, etc) to serve in the PCUS medical mission. One
colleague has described Dr. Bush as a "medical visionary" who
constantly tested the boundaries of knowledge.[14] His specialty training
in internal medicine gave him a strong commitment to medical excellence in practice, teaching, and research. Another observer commented,
"Dr. Brown could almost always be found poring over figures and Dr.
Bush could always be found at the bedside of the sick."[15] Together the
two men provided a balance of theory and practice and demonstrated
an ability to work as a team in their leadership at YCH.

Nell S. Swenson, R.N., organized and administered the nursing
department. She was later joined by Elizabeth Lundeen, R.N. Although
no nursing school was established at YCH, clinical training was
provided to two local nursing schools. The nurses also worked with the
Osaka Health Department to establish a training program for practical
nurses; some of this training was carried out at the YCH. Other PCUS
missionaries who assisted for short periods of time included a number
of nurses (Dorothy T. Mooney, Beverly June Hill, and Jane E. McDaniel)
and dietitians (Aurine McIlwaine and Coline G. Cain).

YCH initiated a number of specialized programs, including blood
exchange transfusions for infants, a clinic for premature babies,
research, and the hospice program. The designation of YCH as the
emergency hospital for foreign visitors to the 1970 Osaka World
Exposition gave further evidence of public respect for the institution.

Blood Transfusions for Infants

The blood exchange transfusion program for infants with blood
incompatibilities (such as Rh negative and yellow jaundice) was a
dramatic innovation of Drs. Bush and Powell. In 1957 Dr. Brown

donated the blood that saved the life of the first child to be transfused. This event attracted media attention, including television programs, movies, lectures, and a best-selling book. As a result, infants were brought to YCH from all over Japan. The hospital became well known throughout the country, and doctors came to train in the procedure.[16]

Perinatal Clinic

In 1960, at the urging of the local health department, Dr. Bush, together with Dr. Powell, opened a clinic for premature babies. Later, in 1972, a sophisticated Perinatal Center was established to care for mothers with problem pregnancies, premature babies, and sick infants (including those with blood disorders). This "Level III" Newborn Intensive Care Unit (NICU) was the first in the Osaka area and has continuously provided outstanding service.[17]

Research

Under the leadership of Dr. Bush as director of research, the physicians at YCH were able to establish a close, mutually beneficial relationship with the Osaka University Medical School. This relationship resulted in the exchange of lectures, cooperation on research projects, and the initiation of an intern/residency training program on the postgraduate level.

Among the research projects were (1) diabetes research, carried out with the U.S. National Institutes of Health and the Osaka University School of Medicine; (2) the use of chemo-prophylaxis for tuberculosis, in a joint project with the U.S. Public Health Service; and (3) a study (with a group from Cleveland, Ohio) of air pollution in the Osaka area, at a time when air pollution was only beginning to be a major concern worldwide.

In 1969 the Japanese government awarded the Fourth Order of the Sacred Treasure posthumously to Dr. Bush, who had died suddenly, at age forty-nine, of a coronary occlusion. The award was in commendation of his medical research activities in Japan in neonatal blood exchange transfusions, in tuberculosis prevention, and in atmospheric pollution, and for his service during the Ise Bay Typhoon.

YCH staff have published a large number of papers in American and Japanese medical journals and have lectured at medical meetings in the United States, Germany, India, Taiwan, Hong Kong, Korea, and other countries, as well as in Japan.

Hospice

The program of "Organized Care for the Dying Patient" (OCDP) began in 1973. YCH psychiatrist Dr. Tetsuo Kashiwagi, who later became a leader in the international hospice movement, pioneered in providing hospice care to YCH patients and in developing a research study program of the needs of the terminally ill. The *Japanese Christian Quarterly* described the program as follows:

> Dr. Kashiwagi began with an interdisciplinary team . . . [which] included doctors, nurses, chaplains, medical social workers and others on the hospital staff. In a hierarchical society like Japan, the gathering of this widely diverse group to exchange opinions and ideas on an equal footing was a revolutionary concept in itself. Meeting at least once a week in the beginning, they considered, besides the obvious physical needs, other basic psychological, social, spiritual, and practical needs of their patients. They also provided a coordinated program of supportive care. It was soon clear that this program not only greatly benefited the patients, but their families as well.[18]

This new concept (in Japan) was followed with interest by the medical community. Similar programs were developed in other institutions, and in 1990 the government recognized the value of the hospice approach by authorizing medical insurance coverage for such care.

Plans for a hospital-based hospice at YCH were approved in the fall of 1981 and a local fund-raising effort miraculously produced the $800,000 needed for the construction of the twenty-four-bed unit. Construction of this unit, the second hospice to be built in Japan, began in 1983. The YCH brochure proclaimed:

> Our Hospice aims at genuine care with warmth and love, not taking a negative approach to death, but promoting the quality of life in the

The Yodogawa Christian Hospital in 1983. Photograph from Yodogawa Christian Hospital brochure.

face of death. It aims at respecting the needs of patients and their families. Because of this, hospice staff are always seeking to extend their cooperative efforts to patients [and their families] sharing God's love so that patients can have peace of mind, living out their last days with God-given dignity and worth.[19]

A report made in April 1964 by the Medical Survey Committee, consisting of Drs. L. Nelson Bell, Warfield M. Firor, and Theodore D. Stephenson (see Korea), summarizes the remarkable influence of YCH:

In a country where the practice of medicine is strictly big-business, the concept of it as a ministry of healing is unknown. This is precisely what makes the YCH unique. In Japan consultations with doctors in other specialties is not done, hence the co-operative contributions of Dr. Bush and Dr. Brown, such as the introduction of exchange transfusions, have added further to the reputation of this hospital. One Japanese professor told us that the YCH is a show-case for Japanese medicine.[20]

Social and Community Outreach

The hospital's Department of Medical Social Work (MSW) was developed by June Lamb, a medical social worker, with the help of Teruko Ohashi (Mrs. Sugimoto), a U.S.-educated medical social worker.[21] June Lamb was also a certified X-ray technician and helped establish the hospital's radiology department. She had previously served for two years with the Atomic Bomb Casualty Commission at Hiroshima and Nagasaki.

A unique feature of the MSW department was the development of the psychiatric aspects of social work using psychiatric consultants from a local university. In time, as YCH grew, this psychiatric concern led to the establishment of the psychiatric department at YCH, headed by Dr. Tetsuo Kashiwagi, the founder of the Hospice Program.

As early as 1958 the MSW department at YCH was singled out in a feature article in one of Japan's large newspapers as one of the few such departments to do more than arrange for payments from the patients. The article advised those with certain personal or family problems to go to YCH for help.[22]

June Lamb and Teruko Ohashi also provided leadership to the local welfare department. They helped organize the Medical Social

Workers Association for the Osaka area, an organization that met regularly to encourage the professional development of social workers. Upon her retirement from Japan in 1968, June Lamb received a citation from the mayor of Osaka for her contributions in the field of medical social work.[23]

One of these contributions was the introduction of the use of volunteers in a service similar to the "pink ladies" commonly found in American hospitals. This activity started in 1962 when three young cosmetologists volunteered their time to help women patients shampoo and fix their hair. Eighteen charter members then organized what became a distinctive and important program at the hospital. Volunteers assisted patients in various ways, prepared medical linen supplies, operated a snack shop, and played a conspicuous part in raising funds for the hospital. This new concept in Japanese hospitals was later replicated in other institutions all over the country.[24]

Evangelistic Outreach

The evangelistic department, or chaplaincy, was an integral part of the program at Yodogawa Christian Hospital. Until 1970 the department was headed by the Rev. Lardner C. Moore, who was born in Japan to a family that had had missionaries in Japan for four generations. Moore spoke fluent Japanese and had a strong empathy with and affection for the Japanese people. He was also a gifted musician. His work was directed at strengthening the Christian outreach among the staff as well as witnessing to the patients.

Among the activities of the evangelistic department were daily morning worship for the staff, broadcasting of religious programs to the patients' rooms, visitation with inpatients and outpatients, special ministry in the children's wards, and programs to which neighborhood people were invited.

Lardner Moore was greatly assisted by his wife, Mollie. She taught English classes to hospital staff, cultivated warm relations with patients and staff (especially the nurses), and hosted many social events. Mollie Moore also served as "language secretary" for the doctors, helping with their correspondence and their preparation of papers in English for publication.

Lardner and Mollie Moore, until their retirement in the 1990s, were the only representatives of the PCUS on the YCH staff. Their personal warmth, deep understanding of the Japanese, and sensitivity to the niceties of the culture not only enhanced the relationship with the American church but helped strengthen the Christian focus of the institution.

In time YCH also developed an international outreach, especially to Asian countries. Sister relationships were established with several mission hospitals in South Korea including the Christian Children's Hospital in Pusan, the Wilson Leprosy Center in Soonchun, and the Presbyterian Medical Center in Chonju. Doctors and nurses from Taiwan, Thailand, Bangladesh, and South Korea came for study. A number of doctors and nurses from Yodogawa were appointed through the Japan Overseas Christian Service and other agencies to be missionaries in South Korea (at Wilson Leprosy Center), Bangladesh, Nepal, and Thailand.

Conclusion

The story of Yodogawa Christian Hospital from its founding in 1955 until 1983 can be described from the PCUS point of view as a "mission accomplished." It began as the PCUS expression of Christian service in the land of a former enemy and grew into an independent, sophisticated institution under Japanese administration. During this period Japan developed from a devastated land into a vibrant modern state. The YCH had a real influence on the medical community and a reputation throughout the country for professional quality and a compassionate human concern. It also developed an outreach to regional and international communities.

The PCUS responsibility for the YCH essentially ended when Frank Brown retired in 1976. As a self-supporting nonprofit institution operating under a Christian board of directors, YCH proudly upheld the principles on which it was founded. As its brochure proclaimed:

> The Yodogawa Christian Hospital is dedicated to the glory of God and the salvation of man through the ministry of healing, bringing the power of love and the highest competence of modern science to bear on the social, physical, mental, and spiritual needs of patients, in the conviction that healing will not be complete until, through Christ, the person is reconciled to God.[25]

Dr. Frank Brown, 1980, wearing the Third Class of the Order of the Sacred Treasure presented by the Japanese government in commendation for his distinguished service and leadership. Photograph from Yodogawa Christian Hospital brochure.

Dr. and Mrs. Brown returned to Japan in May 1980 when YCH celebrated its twenty-fifth anniversary. During the anniversary celebration the Japanese government awarded Dr. Brown with the Third Class of the Order of the Sacred Treasure in "commendation of his distinguished services and leadership in the work of a general hospital in the Osaka area, including activities in neonatal blood exchange transfusions, medical assistance following the Ise (Bay) Typhoon, and medical assistance as the official hospital for foreign visitors to Expo '70."[26]

At the celebration Dr. Brown received a bouquet from a university student, Yasuki Muraya, the first baby to receive a Rh-negative blood exchange transfusion. Dr. Brown had donated the blood.

This celebration occurred only months before Dr. Brown was diagnosed with a brain tumor. During his illness and before his death in January 1981, a delegation of seven representatives from YCH (including Dr. Shirakata), in a typical Japanese gesture, went to Atlanta to "comfort" him and pay their respects. They brought with them 2,000 folded paper cranes, a traditional expression of encouragement for one who is suffering. These cranes were made "with prayer" by the staff of each department of the hospital.[27]

Notes

1. Frank A. Brown, M.D., "Mission Hospital for Japan?" *Presbyterian Survey*, Feb. 1953, 36.

2. Margaret H. Taylor, "Missionary Extraordinary," (Japan: booklet published by Shikoku Christian College, 1955).

3. Frank A. Brown, "Medical Conditions and Opportunities in Japan: Survey Report," (Minutes of the 57th Annual Meeting of the Japan Mission, January 1950); and "Charity Medical Care for Japan," *Presbyterian Survey*, March 1955, 14–15.

4. "Yodogawa Christian Hospital History," typescript printed by the hospital, 1985.

5. Mollie B. Moore, letter, Jan. 22, 1994.

6. Lyle W. Peterson, (member of the board of directors) correspondence, Dec. 1993.

7. Ann V. Brown, R.N., (Mrs. Frank), interview, fall 1984.

8. Mollie Moore, letter, Dec. 11, 1993.

9. Ibid.

10. Ibid.

11. Brown, "Mission Hospital for Japan?" 36–37.

12. Annual Report (Minutes of the PCUS General Assembly, 1958), 93.

13. "Yodogawa Christian Hospital History."

14. Marion Powell, M.D., telephone conversation, Feb. 1994.

15. Peterson, correspondence, 1994.

16. Patricia Houck Sprinkle, *The Birthday Book: First Fifty Years* (Atlanta, Ga.: PCUS Board of Women's Work, 1972), 49.

17. "Yodogawa Christian Hospital History."

18. Mollie and Lardner C. Moore, "Yodogawa Christian Hospital: A Ministry to the Whole Person," *Japanese Christian Quarterly*, Spring 1991, 93.

19. "Yodogawa Christian Hospital History."

20. L. Nelson Bell, M.D., Warfield M. Firor, M.D., and Theodore D. Stevenson, M.D., "Yodogawa Christian Hospital at Osaka," (Survey Committee Report, April 1964), 8.

21. Teruko Ohashi, M.S. in social work from the University of Michigan.

22. Annual Report, 1958, 93.

23. June Lamb, interview, Aug. 1994.

24. "Yodogawa Christian Hospital History."

25. Ibid.

26. Ibid.

27. Ann Brown, interview, Jan. 1996.

—————————— *Chapter Thirteen* ——————————

Taiwan
(1953–1983)

Taiwan, a province of China, became a colony of Japan after the end of the Sino-Japanese War in 1895. In 1945, under the terms of the Declaration of Cairo issued by Roosevelt, Churchill, and Chiang Kai-shek in 1943, Taiwan was returned to China. An embryonic movement for an independent Taiwan was brutally suppressed in 1947 by the Nationalist government. This suppression soured relationships between the Taiwanese and the Chinese mainlanders and left animosities that remain to this day.[1]

After the Communist victory on the mainland in 1949, Chiang Kai-shek, accompanied by a large segment of his army and many refugees, withdrew to Taiwan. He made Taiwan the seat of administration for the ousted government of the Republic of China. The government remained firmly in the hands of the Nationalists (Kuomingtang [KMT] Party).

Under Japan's fifty-year rule, Taiwan had been a largely undeveloped agricultural society with a high rate of illiteracy and low standard of living. During World War II it had acted as, what has been described as, Japan's "largest aircraft carrier" outside Japan.

Since 1945 the population has grown from five million to an estimated eighteen million (1985). The influx of educated, sophisticated, and, in some cases, wealthy mainlanders revolutionized society. The literacy rate is now 95 percent and the population, which has become industrialized and urban, enjoys a standard of living in Asia second only to that of Japan. Political insecurity vis-a-vis Red China and tension between the mainlanders and the Taiwanese have resulted in sometimes oppressive measures and repressive regulations. Nevertheless, thanks to dynamic economic growth over the years,

410

Taiwan has become one of the so-called mini-tigers of Asia.

Presbyterian missionary activity in Taiwan began in 1865 with the arrival of the English Presbyterians; Canadian Presbyterians arrived in 1872. In 1949, the Taiwanese Presbyterian Church and the Canadian Presbyterian Mission invited the PCUS missionaries who had been forced to evacuate China to join the work in Taiwan. As a result, the Taiwan Mission, established in 1953 with twenty-one "China missionaries," became a new opportunity for PCUS mission activity. The PCUS medical contingent, consisting of Joseph (M.D.) and Estelle (R.N.) Wilkerson and Charlotte A. Dunlap, R.N., arrived in 1953 and shortly thereafter were assigned to the Changhua Christian Hospital.

CHANGHUA CHRISTIAN HOSPITAL
Changhua

Changhua city is located in the center of the most densely populated rural area of Taiwan, some 100 miles southwest of the capital, Taipei. Changhua Christian Hospital was founded in 1896 by the English Presbyterian Church under the leadership of Dr. David Landsborough Sr., and was turned over to the Presbyterian Church of Taiwan in 1937. It is one of three hospitals of the Presbyterian Church of Taiwan and is administered by a board of directors appointed by the General Assembly of the church.

After World War II five mission boards (English and Canadian Presbyterian, Reformed Church of America, Methodist, and the PCUS) contributed personnel and funds to the Changhua Christian Hospital. The hospital became an example of successful union (ecumenical) effort. Dr. David Landsborough Jr., son of the founder, joined the staff in 1952 and served as superintendent from 1954 to 1980. Dr. Landsborough, an internist, developed the Department of Neurology; Jean Connan Landsborough, his wife and also a physician, headed the OB/GYN department. Dr. Landsborough was followed by Dr. Wu Chen-Chun, a capable leader who maintained the hospital's reputation of high-quality medical practice and strong Christian witness.

The story of the thirty-year (1953–83) PCUS involvement at Changhua Christian Hospital can be told through the work of three people: Joseph (Joe) L. Wilkerson, M.D., William E. Rice, hospital administrator, and Allen L. Haslup, a graduate of George Washington

University (M.D., 1950). From 1953 to 1980 Dr. Wilkerson helped develop Changhua Christian Hospital into a multispecialty teaching hospital with high standards of practice and a highly respected training program for interns, residents, and nurses. Between 1968 and 1973 William Rice organized the administration into a fiscally sound operation. From 1978 to 1983 (and beyond) Dr. Haslup helped facilitate the transformation of the institution from a "Mission" hospital into a "Christian" hospital run entirely by Taiwan nationals.

Joseph L. Wilkerson, M.D.

Dr. Wilkerson agreed to head the surgical department and to act as vice-superintendent on condition that Charlotte Dunlap, R.N. (see Zhenjiang, China), also be assigned to the Changhua Christian Hospital. Dr. Wilkerson, following his release from Communist imprisonment in China (see Jiaxing, China), returned to the United States and spent two years of surgical residency at the Herrick Memorial Hospital in Berkeley, California. On his furlough (1958–60) he completed the requirements and became board-certified in surgery. He was board-eligible in thoracic surgery but returned to Taiwan rather than spend the extra time in the United States needed for certification in this subspecialty. Charlotte Dunlap, in the meantime, had studied to become a certified nurse-anesthetist at the Medical College of South Carolina in Charleston. Together they were able to develop an outstanding surgical service at Changhua Christian Hospital and to offer training to Chinese residents and nurses. The 1954 annual report noted that Dr. Wilkerson's "fame as a diagnostician and surgeon has spread all over Taiwan."[2]

Because World War II left the fifty-bed hospital plant in shambles, renovation was the first order of business. An indication of the condition of the hospital is evident from the same 1954 annual report, which rejoiced that, thanks to White Cross supplies, it was at last possible to provide bedding to the patients rather than have them bring their own. The PCUS contributed toward a new X ray and new buildings that, over the next ten years, completely replaced the original facilities. In 1983 Changhua Christian Hospital was a 378-bed institution.

At first, Changhua Christian Hospital was the only hospital in the area where modern medicine was practiced. By the early 1960s the level of medicine in Taiwan had begun to improve, as young physicians received training both locally and abroad. The level of medicine

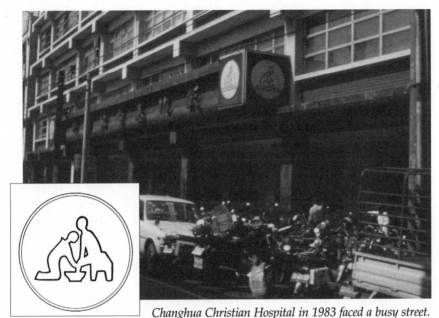

Changhua Christian Hospital in 1983 faced a busy street.
The logo depicts Jesus washing his disciples' feet. Photograph courtesy of Paul S. Crane.

continued to improve until Taiwan could no longer be said to be medically deprived.[3]

During this time of medical advance, Changhua Christian Hospital was recognized for practicing an international standard of medicine. The PCUS personnel were highly qualified in their specialties. At the same time, the hospital's logo, portraying Jesus washing the feet of his disciples, proclaimed the Christian principles of service and compassion on which the institution was founded.

Training remained a major element in the Changhua program. The intern-residency program was accredited to receive graduates from (at first) four medical schools (later ten). By 1980 training was offered in surgery, internal medicine, OB/GYN, pediatrics, neurosurgery, dermatology, ENT, and ophthalmology.[4] Most of these services were headed by well-trained Chinese physicians, and eventually some twenty interns and sixty residents were in the training program. A number of graduates went to the United States for further training.

Estelle Wilkerson, R.N., provided leadership in the training of nurses. She began by operating an LPN (licensed practical nurse) training program for women with junior high school education. In 1967 she began an affiliation with three (later seven) local nursing schools who posted students to Changhua Christian Hospital for their clinical training. Students served from six months to one year. Standards were kept high and graduates of the program were in high demand. Eva C. Haslup, R.N., became the director of student education after Estelle Wilkerson retired in 1980. At that time, there was no program in Taiwan offering a degree in nursing, and Eva Haslup worked to raise the professional level of nursing education to a degree program.[5]

Dr. Wilkerson devoted a major portion of his time to patients suffering from orthopedic problems, most of which resulted from vehicular accidents, polio, congenital deformities, leprosy, or tuberculosis of bones and joints. The arrival in 1963 of Hilda Ilten, a nurse who was also a Harvard-trained certified physiotherapist (P.T., 1940), led to the opening of an Orthopedic Clinic and the Department of Physical Therapy. Hilda Ilten established a nine-month training program for six student therapists. After ill health forced Hilda Ilten to leave, Lavonne Slusher (1967–68) and Ann Damsbo (1968–69), both certified physiotherapists, continued the work of the department. Mr. (Andrew) Kuo Wen-Long, who earned a master's degree in physical therapy at Duke University through a PCUS scholarship, eventually headed the department.

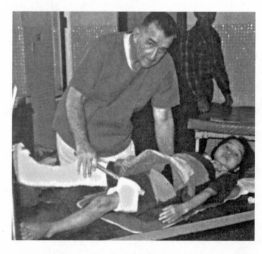

Joseph L. Wilkerson, M.D., cares for a young orthopedic patient. Photograph courtesy of Joseph L. Wilkerson.

A dental department was established in 1963 by Robert A. Bagramian (Temple University, D.D.S., 1960). In addition to carrying on an active practice, Dr. Bagramian taught at the local dental college, trained interns, and went out to remote areas with mobile clinics. Dr. Bagramian later became head of the dentistry department at the University of Michigan.

George H. McDonald, D.D.S., arrived in Taiwan in 1964 but did not join the staff of the Changhua Christian Hospital. Instead, at their request, he was assigned to the Kaohsiung Presbytery of the Presbyterian Church of Taiwan and practiced dentistry for eight years at the St. Paul's Clinic, an Episcopalian-run clinic in the southwestern city of Kaohsiung.

William E. Rice

By the mid-1960s Changhua Christian Hospital had a good physical facility and a good medical team, but its administration remained deplorable. The "business manager" had a third-grade education; bookkeeping was nonexistent; the only place where any inventory control was evident was in the control of narcotics (a system required by the government); laundry was given out on concession to five small companies, and some of it was washed by hand in the river.[6]

William Rice, a businessman turned missionary, served in Taipei as mission treasurer for four years (1963–67), during which time he introduced sound business procedures to mission financing. Among other things he set up the Interboard Treasurer's Office, which consolidated the business operations of the seven main Protestant missions in Taiwan. For a year and a half, Rice spent several days a month at Changhua Christian Hospital where he set up a double-entry bookkeeping system and trained a young Taiwanese accountant (Mr. Lu) in its use.

The Changhua Christian Hospital requested that Rice return to Changhua as hospital administrator after his furlough in 1967–68. In preparation for the new assignment, Rice spent his furlough year in a residency in hospital administration at the City of Memphis (Tennessee) Hospital. He was night administrator at this hospital the night that Martin Luther King Jr. was shot and he was involved in handling the many problems that resulted from that event.

At Changhua Christian Hospital, William Rice took an institution with little or no administrative organization and created for it a fiscally responsible structure administered by capable nationals. He set up departments in accounting, purchasing, personnel, general supply, maintenance, medical records, laundry, dietetics, and financial counseling for patients. Qualified university-trained persons headed the departments. He introduced a quality control system and a medical audit (peer review of cases).

Under Rice's supervision, hospital buildings were remodeled and renovated and a new six-story outpatient building was built. By 1973 the original property was completely filled by hospital buildings fronting on one of the major thoroughfares of the city. Its location near the railroad station provided easy access for patients from rural areas. The outpatient department grew from 300 to over 1,000 patients each day. Inpatients numbered around 400.

Meanwhile, in the early 1970s, the PCUS sent (Paul) Wang Yung-Ming, a young Taiwanese lawyer, to the United States for training in hospital administration.[7] He became eminently qualified to fill the position after Rice completed his term in 1973.

In addition to handling the administrative work, Rice helped develop a number of paramedical services: in social work, public health, and pastoral counseling.

The Department of Social Work

The Department of Social Work, the first on Taiwan, was headed by Mary Ann McGirt (1968–75) and became recognized as the "best on the Island."[8] The department received 10 percent of the hospital's gross receipts to pay for charity cases. Eventually the staff included five full-time university graduates, two of whom had studied in the United States. Competition for entrance into the accredited intern program remained high.

The Department of Public Health

The Department of Public Health was designed to increase community involvement through a program of preventive medicine and health education. Changhua Christian Hospital also provided visiting staff for small clinic/hospitals in the fishing village of Erlin and the mountain village of Jyuju.

The Department of Pastoral Care

The Department of Pastoral Care in 1970 had two full-time ordained (male) ministers and three women assistants to carry on a full program of services for patients and for the staff. The staff of the hospital averaged about 85 percent Christian (50 percent of the doctors and about 95 percent of the other staff). A program in pastoral counseling trained eight to ten pastors in a ten-week course. Openings for the program were filled a year in advance.[9]

Allen L. Haslup, M.D., F.A.C.P.

In 1978 Allen Lee (M.D.) and Eva Copley (R.N., A.D.A.) Haslup accepted the call to work at the Changhua Christian Hospital. Dr. Haslup, a board-certified internist, left a seventeen-year private practice in St. Petersburg, Florida, to work in Changhua. The retirement in 1980 of Drs. David and Jean Landsborough and the Wilkersons seriously reduced the professional staff at the hospital.

Dr. Haslup reports that his missionary experience turned out to be quite different from what he expected. Instead of conducting a busy medical practice and training interns and residents, he found himself primarily assisting in the transition of the hospital from a "Mission" hospital, run by missionaries, to an independent "Christian" hospital, under the leadership of Taiwan nationals appointed by the hospital board. This transition was successful, and Dr. Haslup made a significant contribution to its success. His official position was medical vice-superintendent (equivalent to chief of staff). He served on many committees, took care of English correspondence, acted as ceremonial head of the hospital in Dr. Wu's absence, and helped serve as liaison between the Presbyterian Church of Taiwan and the hospital's board of directors. He helped to maintain high standards by helping to start a quality control committee and a medical records committee.[10]

Dr. Haslup also helped recruit specialists from the United States who volunteered for limited periods of time, helped them adjust to an unfamiliar culture, and maximized the use of their time and talents. Among those who served in this way was Donald Eitzman, M.D., a neonatologist, whose two-year stay upgraded the care of infants.

The Haslups eventually moved some twenty to twenty-five miles away to Erhlin to help develop a primary health facility with a strong emphasis on health education and preventive medicine. Erhlin was a

The completed ten-story new hospital. Photograph courtesy of Changhua Christian Hospital.

farming and fishing township of around 90,000 people whose standard of living was well below the average in Taiwan. Changhua Christian Hospital had for many years cooperated with the local presbytery in providing visiting staff and medical supplies to a small hospital/clinic in Erhlin. In 1980 the property was turned over to the Changhua Christian Hospital, and the Erhlin Branch, as it was known, became the major outreach project for the hospital through regular funding, medical supplies, and visiting staff. The isolation and poor schooling for children of the staff made it difficult to recruit permanent staff for Erhlin.

Conclusion

In 1983, at the time the PCUS was phased out of existence, Changhua Christian Hospital faced a serious problem. The facility was totally inadequate for the large patient load. Competition from modern hospitals in the area made it necessary to modernize and

expand. Under Dr. C. C. Wu's
leadership and with the administrative assistance of Dr.
(Paul) Wang Yung-ming, a building
program was initiated to make
Changhua Christian Hospital a
thoroughly modern tertiary
medical center. Plans were developed for a twelve-story building
on former mission property (a
half-mile away) to be known as
the Nangkuo Medical Center.

Remarkably, the hospital
financed this ambitious building
program entirely through locally
generated funds: from its own
operation, by good credit with
local banks, and from private
donations. No appeal was made
to the United States or to

Dr. Wu Chen-Chun became director of the Changhua Hospital in 1980. Photograph from Changhua Hospital 1986 annual report.

Germany for building funds. Dedication of the first phase of the
impressive medical center in June 1986 was attended by many of
the former missionaries who had been associated with the
hospital.

The thirty-year story of the medical work of PCUS in Taiwan
(1953–83) can be summarized as beginning in a medically deprived,
totally underserved, poor community and ending in an affluent,
medically sophisticated, materialistic society. The ability of the
Taiwanese staff to proceed on their own with the development of the
new medical complex is a tribute to the soundness of the PCUS's
medical mission's emphasis on high training standards for its
personnel. Goals evolved with the changing conditions but the
constants, as articulated in "The Aims of the Hospital" in a report
published by the new hospital in 1986, are remarkably the same: (1) to
provide the best possible medical care for sick people; (2) to bring the
gospel to the people; (3) to give free treatment as needed for those in
poor circumstances; and (4) to train doctors, nurses, and other paramedical personnel.[11]

Notes

1. General information on Taiwan accumulated by author on January 1985 trip to Taiwan.
2. Annual Report (Minutes of the General Assembly, PCUS, 1954), 92.
3. Ibid., 1960, 77.
4. Joseph L. Wilkerson, M.D., interview, April 3, 1984.
5. Eva C. Haslup, R.N., interview, Jan. 19, 1985.
6. William E. Rice, interview, Dec. 12, 1984.
7. (Paul) Wang Yung-ming, Georgia State University (M.H.A.); Northside Hospital in Atlanta, Georgia, (residency); Houston, Texas (Ph.D.).
8. Rice, quoting the dean of the Sociology Department of the National University, interview, Dec. 12, 1984.
9. Ibid.
10. Allen L. Haslup, M.D., interview, Jan. 19, 1985.
11. Changhua Christian Hospital, 1986 Report, 6.

PART VI
Bangladesh and Haiti

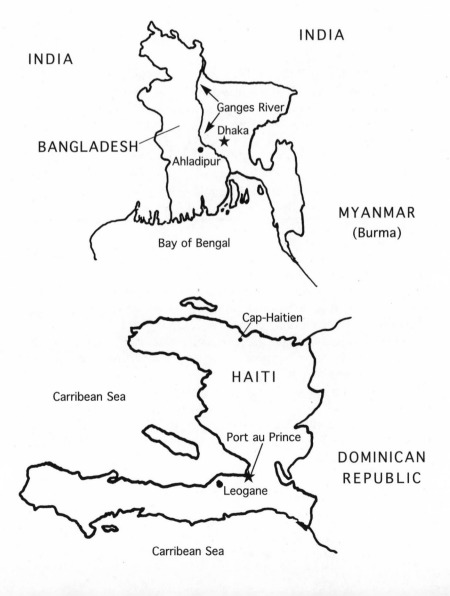

Part VI

In the 1970s the PCUS initiated its final two overseas medical programs, in Bangladesh and Haiti. The two countries resembled each other in many ways. Burdened by overpopulation, unemployment, illiteracy, and disease, both were among the poorest countries in the world. Both suffered from governments that either could not or would not address the problems of the people. And, finally, the PCUS became involved in both countries because of the efforts of individuals who were appalled by the hopeless conditions they found while on trips to the area: in Bangladesh it was Dr. Herbert A. Codington; in Haiti, the Rev. Marion Huske.

The two programs began after a major reorganization of the PCUS in which the church headquarters and various agencies moved to a central location in Atlanta, Georgia. The Bangladesh and the Haiti work reflected a new team at work in the headquarters office. The Division of International Missions replaced the Nashville-based Board of World Missions. Ecumenical relationships were fostered, and partnership with national churches strengthened. The appointment of workers for short terms (rather than for life) became more common. In the mission's medical work the emphasis changed to preventive as well as curative care. This change grew out of a growing sense of responsibility for the improvement of a community's health by addressing basic public health problems such as clean water, sanitation, and nutrition.

—————————— *Chapter Fourteen* ——————————

Bangladesh
(1974–1983)

T he PCUS work in Bangladesh began in 1974 and, as previously noted, originated with the concern of one person, Dr. Herbert A. Codington, missionary to South Korea. He found a responsive ear in William E. Rice, former business manager of the Changhua Christian Hospital in Taiwan and newly appointed (1974) to the staff of the Division of International Mission (DIM) at the reorganized PCUS headquarter offices in Atlanta.[1] Many in the church at large were ready to respond to the tragic conditions in Bangladesh, which were then making headlines daily in the news media.

Bangladesh is a small country (about the size of Alabama) located on the delta of three mighty rivers: the Ganges, the Jamuna-Brahmaputra, and the Meghna. Much of the land is a luxuriantly fertile, alluvial plain, which, however, is subject to annual floods caused by the rivers, the heavy monsoon rains (50 to 200 inches a year), and the cyclones that form along the coast. An average year will find one-third of the cultivated land under water; in a bad year as much as 70 percent of the land may be flooded.

When Britain ended its colonial rule in India in 1947, the subcontinent was partitioned into two countries according to the religion of the majority of its people: India (Hindu) and Pakistan (Muslim). Pakistan, in turn, was made up of East and West Pakistan, areas separated geographically by over 1,000 miles, with only their religion in common. East and West Pakistan had different languages, cultures, ethnic backgrounds, and degrees of economic development; tensions between the two were inevitable.

In 1970 and 1971, two disasters devastated what was then East Pakistan. The first was the cyclone/tidal wave/flood that roared out of the Bay of Bengal in November 1970, the "worst storm in centuries." It killed between 250,000 and 500,000 people and left thousands homeless and destitute.[2] A few months later came the nine-month brutal civil war with West Pakistan. With India's help, the armies of West Pakistan were defeated and, in December 1971, East Pakistan became the newly independent nation of Bangladesh. An estimated three million Bengali were killed and more than a million became refugees as a result of this war. Transportation, communication systems, and industries were in shambles.

Effective government was not easy to establish in the new nation. The first president, Sheikh Mujibur Rahman, was assassinated in 1975. His relatively open, secular government was followed by a series of military one-party dictatorships that became ever more dominated by Muslim fundamentalists. Islam was made the state religion in 1975 and in 1988 (beyond the bounds of this account) Bangladesh became an Islamic state.

Bangladesh, or Bengal as it was then known, was the area in which William Carey, the recognized father of the Protestant missionary movement, worked from 1793 to 1834. Today, however, Christians are a minuscule 0.25 percent of the population; 85 percent are Muslims and 13 percent are Hindus.[3] Although Christians are proud of their heritage (some families trace their religious affiliation back to the time of William Carey), the Christian church in Bangladesh is fragmented and fragile.

In March 1974 the PCUS responded to the desperate needs in Bangladesh by initiating health care and community development projects. Between 1974 and 1983 the PCUS established and developed three programs: The Presbyterian Fellowship of Bangladesh (PFB), an office in the capital, Dhaka, to provide administrative and logistical support; the Tongi Clinic, in a refugee camp near Dhaka; and the Christian Health and Agricultural Project (CHAPA) in Ahladipur, a remote rural area west of the Ganges River.

THE PRESBYTERIAN FELLOWSHIP OF BANGLADESH (PFB)
Dhaka

The PCUS began work in Bangladesh in 1974 with the assignment of two couples: Dr. Herbert Codington and his wife, Page Codington, R.N., from South Korea and Joseph Sursavage, an agriculturalist, and his wife, Mary Sursavage, R.N. They began their service by enrolling in language school. After two years, for a variety of reasons, the Sursavages decided to return to the United States.

In 1976 the PCUS organized its mission into the Presbyterian Fellowship of Bangladesh (PFB) with an administrative office in Dhaka to deal with government regulations and to handle such matters as finance, personnel, and import of supplies. Cooperative relationships were maintained between the PFB and other Christian bodies.

Partner churches in Asia (South Korea, Japan, Taiwan) were invited to join in the PCUS mission. For example, two Japanese physicians, Dr. Meiko Yoshino and Dr. Kentaro Hatano, were funded as "Partners in Mission" by the Japan Overseas Christian Medical Cooperative Services and the PCUS. Dr. Hatano performed rehabilitative hand surgery at the Christian Leprosy Center (a Baptist mission project) in Chandraghona in the eastern hill-tract region of Bangladesh. The PCUS also funded a beggar rehabilitation center and a hospital visitation program.

Stuart Bridgman, treasurer of the Taiwan Mission, transferred to Bangladesh in 1976 to set up the PFB. In addition to handling his administrative duties in Dhaka, Bridgman helped negotiate the acquisition and renovation of the property for the CHAPA project at Ahladipur.

Among the PCUS personnel in Dhaka were Charlotte Brown, secretary, and Petrie Mitchell and his wife, Mary Belle, former missionaries in South Korea who covered the office while the Bridgmans were on leave in the summer of 1978. In 1981 Cary March followed Bridgman as administrator of the PFB. Dawkins Hodges and his wife, Carolyn, spent his seminary intern year assisting in the work of the office. Page Codington made important contributions to the PFB by serving as mentor to the younger missionaries and by hosting numerous guests.

Working with the Bangladeshi government proved to be time-consuming and frustrating. A crisis developed when the Foreign Donations Act of 1978 required all foreign agencies with people living and working in Bangladesh to register with the Social Welfare Department of the government. This seemed reasonable enough because of the massive influx of foreign aid agencies after 1971. However, in 1980 the PFB application for registration was turned down, and the staff were told to close down their work and leave Bangladesh. After considerable negotiation, this matter was resolved in 1982, and the PFB was given a quota allowing seven "units" to work in Bangladesh (a married couple was considered one unit).[4]

Bangladesh was not an easy country in which to live and work. The heat and humidity were oppressive, and the daily life was difficult. The hostility that government officials generally exhibited, however, was not typical of other local people. In fact, at CHAPA, where the missionary residences were accessible to the public, life was complicated by the local people's (usually) friendly curiosity and by the lack of privacy. In addition, the constant pressure of problems for which there were no solutions were physically and emotionally wearing. The Muslim culture was especially hard on the missionary women, many of whom felt isolated. Most chose to wear the sari and avoided public gatherings when possible. "I almost wish I didn't understand what they are saying about me," commented one of the nurses.[5]

To relieve the tension and to maintain physical and emotional health, the PCUS adopted a personnel policy unique to Bangladesh: each missionary was required to take two weeks' vacation semiannually. To facilitate this break in routine, they were paid per diem plus a sum equal to round-trip airfare from Dhaka to Bangkok.[6]

TONGI CLINIC
Dhaka

The Tongi resettlement camp came into existence when the city of Dhaka sought to solve its refugee problem by rounding up some 12,000 homeless people and transplanting them to a desolate area twelve miles north of the city. Basic facilities were nonexistent, and conditions were deplorable. Overcrowding, malnutrition, and sickness were rampant.

Dr. Codington learned of the Tongi camp and felt a compelling call to respond to the needs in this particular place. In January 1975 he began medical relief services on the most basic level. Before long he had acquired space in an abandoned estate that had been burned during the war for independence, and the Tongi Clinic (officially titled the Christian Health Services, Bangladesh) came into being. Over time it developed a staff (most of whom were Bengali) that included three doctors, three nurses, a laboratory technician, pharmacists, business

The Tongi refugee village. Photograph courtesy of Paul S. Crane.

personnel, and two chaplains (a man and a woman). The staff commuted each day from Dhaka.[7]

A unique feature at Tongi was the inclusion on the staff of two "Partners in Mission" from the Presbyterian Church in South Korea. (John) Lee Yong-Ung, M.D., who had completed a medical residency at the Presbyterian Medical Center (PMC) in Chonju, and Park Hae-In, R.N., a graduate of the Margaret Pritchard School of Nursing in Chonju, arrived in 1979. Charlotte March, R.N., wife of the PFB administrator, was the only full-service PCUS missionary other than Dr. Codington assigned to Tongi Clinic before 1983; Julia Codington, daughter of Dr. and Mrs. Codington, worked at the clinic while studying language in preparation for the opening of CHAPA. The internationalization of the staff introduced an interesting, and sometimes difficult, blend of three cultures: Bengali, Korean, and American.

Tongi Clinic remained a facility geared to meet the basic medical needs of the refugee community. The refugees were landless laboring-class Muslims who were constantly on the move, and the refugee camp only gradually acquired the coherence of a village structure. Other aid agencies (Southern Baptists, Salvation Army) dealt with problems of sanitation, clean water, food, and shelter. Job opportunities and education finally became available.

Immunizations, oral rehydration for diarrhea, and treatment of skin and other infections were typical problems dealt with at the Tongi Clinic. MBF's gift of a portable X ray made it possible to begin a tuberculosis identification and treatment program. Patients needing hospitalization were taken to a patient hostel in Dhaka where two Christian social workers helped facilitate admission into Dhaka Medical College Hospital. Charlotte March and Park Hae-In began an outreach program and were especially successful in the training of midwives.

In 1983, Tongi Clinic was a medical relief project serving the poorest of the poor. The facilities and technology were simple. Dr. Codington, the "father" of the PCUS involvement in Bangladesh, continued at Tongi Clinic until his retirement in 1985. He maintained a broad concern for the poor and for all aspects of Christian witness.

After his retirement Dr. Codington continued to return to Bangladesh to oversee a privately funded clinic set up to care for the street cleaners of Dhaka. In the opinion of the author, if the Presbyterian Church were ever to canonize its saints, the name of Herbert Augustus Codington, M.D., would head the list.

CHRISTIAN HEALTH AND AGRICULTURAL PROJECT (CHAPA)
Ahladipur

In 1975, when the PCUS made the decision to develop a "comprehensive village health care and rural development ministry" in Bangladesh, no funds were available, no personnel had been lined up, and no site had been chosen.[8]

The breakthrough for funding came when the PCUS Women of the Church selected this project for one-half of their 1976 Birthday Offering. Again, as they had done for the Yodogawa Christian Hospital in Japan, the Presbyterian Medical Center in Korea, and the Good Shepherd Hospital in Zaire, PCUS women provided the seed money that brought CHAPA (the Christian Health and Agricultural Project in Ahladipur) into being. Other major sources of funding, which totaled approximately $400,000, came from St. John's Presbytery (Florida) Hunger Project and from an MBF grant.

A twenty-seven-minute color/sound motion picture titled "Golden Bangladesh" was produced to assist with fund-raising. This film presented the poetry and beauty, the poverty and despair, and the opportunities open to the PCUS in this newly independent and tragically poor Asian nation. The CHAPA share of the Birthday Offering amounted to $217,244.[9]

After extensive consultations and village surveys, the Ahladipur site in the Faridpur District was selected. In line with the principle that work be done ecumenically with Christian groups in Bangladesh, an agreement was made with the Bangladesh Baptist Union (BBU) to cooperate in this venture. The BBU helped locate and negotiate the rental of the property in Ahladipur, agreed to serve on working committees for the project, and, through the Faridpur Baptist Church and District Union, took responsibility for supervising religious activities. The PCUS agreed to provide the missionary personnel and the funds to implement the project.

Ahladipur is a small, impoverished village sixty miles west of Dhaka on the main road to Faridpur, reached by four or more hours' driving plus a ferry ride across the Ganges River. The land is flat and fertile. Most homes are of mud and thatch and, because of flooding, are built on elevated platforms; most had a boat in the yard.

The Ahladipur site, which had formerly been occupied by the Southern Baptist mission, consisted of six acres with a small building that had been used for a clinic. CHAPA began preparing the site for use during the summer of 1977. A number of American college and medical students, under the PCUS Youth for Mission program, helped to clear the land. Construction included a two-story stucco building with an apartment for nurses on the second floor; a one-story, open-air, thatched-roofed clinic partitioned with bamboo screens; storage facilities; and a residence for missionaries. Rice patties were converted into vegetable gardens and into plots for agricultural experimentation and demonstration. A sturdy wire fence was installed around the property.

Dr. Walter "Ted" Kuhn (Pennsylvania State University, M.D., 1974) was named the medical director, and Stuart Bridgman, the project coordinator. Bridgman, the PFB business manager whose twelve years in Taiwan included experience in development projects, invested a great deal of time and thought in planning CHAPA. Missionary personnel at CHAPA were young, enthusiastic, well trained, and energetic. In 1978 they moved to Faridpur, where they lived in Baptist mission housing while supervising preparation of the Ahladipur facilities some twelve miles away. CHAPA officially opened on March 3, 1979.

Medical leadership at CHAPA until 1983 was provided by two sets of missionary personnel. The first consisted of Dr. Ted Kuhn and his wife, Dr. Sharon Kuhn (Pennsylvania State University, M.D., 1976). The nurses were Melanie Smith, R.N., Julia Codington, R.N., Margaret Hopper, R.N. (one year), and Kaye Wilson, R.N. (one year). Dr. Patricia Lee "Patty" June (Emory University, M.D., 1975) followed the Kuhns in 1981. Carol McLean, R.N., a public health nurse with experience in Cameroon, Africa, and with the West Virginia Department of Welfare, joined Melanie Smith in the nursing department.

Scott Smith, the agriculturalist who was working on his master's degree in agronomy from Texas A & M University, arrived in Bangladesh in August 1977. He met and then married Melanie Sharpe, a British nurse/midwife who was working in a Bengali refugee camp. Except for a year of furlough, Smith headed the agricultural component of the CHAPA program throughout the years of PCUS involvement. The Smiths lived Bengali style in the nearby village of Khankhanpur.

Drs. Ted and Sharon Kuhn

The Kuhns brought with them enough medical equipment, it was said, to open a small hospital.[10] Processing these supplies through customs and providing adequate storage proved to be no small matter. In fact, one of the real challenges at CHAPA was to restrict the medical component of the program to the intended level—that of only a primary care medical facility. Patients abounded, hospital care in the area was limited and of very poor quality, and the pressure to expand the medical services to better meet emergency medical needs was great.

The approach devised by Scott Smith for the agricultural aspect of the CHAPA program provided a vehicle for developing the public health outreach as well. A target population of some 300 marginal farming families within five miles of CHAPA were selected to take part in a program that would enable them to become self-sustaining. The organization of these target families into small groups helped the farmers work together to seize marketing opportunities and to deal with crisis situations. Assistance included advice in the use of seeds and fertilizers, instruction in irrigation using tube wells, demonstration of fish ponds, improvement of poultry and goat production, and

A well-baby clinic in a village home. Photograph courtesy of Paul S. Crane.

information on using government-supplied material and services. After a specified time a new set of "target families" was selected.

In 1980 while the Smiths were on leave in the United States (and Scott was finishing his master's degree at Texas A & M), Craig and Sharon Meisner headed the agricultural services at CHAPA. Sharon started a literacy program that was well received. Young illiterate farmers were especially grateful for a chance to learn to read and write.

The "target family" approach was also used in the organization of village health extension programs. Melanie Smith, Kaye Wilson, and Carol McLean concentrated on this outreach work. Village health workers were trained to work with the CHAPA staff in immunizations, pre- and postnatal care, well-baby clinics, family planning, parasite control, sanitation, and nutrition education. Health fairs were well-attended, festive occasions.

Dr. Patty June

Dr. June[11] described CHAPA as a rural outpatient clinic with treatment facilities that were good but probably more than needed for a primary health care facility. However, a second physician was badly needed because it was impossible for Dr. June to see all the patients who came.

The practice of medicine at CHAPA, Dr. June noted, was limited by time constraints and the lack of sophisticated diagnostic tools;

William Rice (far left) at a health fair at CHAPA. Photograph courtesy of Paul S. Crane.

much was empiric. Many diseases were inadequately treated (chronic osteomylitis, fractures requiring open reduction, meningitis etc.); referral facilities were inadequate.

Medical problems included tetanus, diphtheria, rabies, scabies and impetigo, malnutrition and some starvation, severe rheumatic heart disease, glomerulonephritis, peptic ulcer disease, much tuberculosis, ever-present intestinal parasites (ascaris and hookworm), malaria, kala-azar, infantile pneumonitis, diarrhea, Pott's disease, and one case each of leprosy, congenital syphilis, and neurosyphilis.

Dr. June found the treatment of neonatal tetanus a major concern and, when successful, the most rewarding. Patients were given nasogastric valium and breast milk. Penicillin and antitetanus immune globulin were given intravenously. By contrast, in the United States, the child would temporarily be paralyzed, put on a respirator, and given intravenous medicines and hyperalimentation.

The health extension program was a good one. In the target families little severe diarrhea was seen in infants and in three years the infant mortality rate was halved. Birth control and the training of midwives were the least successful parts of the program. The midwife

A patient arrives at the clinic. Photograph courtesy of Paul S. Crane.

training program was a complete flop at CHAPA, where relatives do most of the deliveries, but was successful at Tongi.

Training was always an important part of the work. Most satisfying was the informal on-the-job teaching of paramedics. Bengali nurses, physician assistants, and technicians were important permanent members of the CHAPA staff. Efforts to find a Bengali doctor willing to stay at CHAPA were unsuccessful.

Supplies were generally adequate, although at times there were problems in procurement and some supplies were spoiled or eaten by rats. Most drugs were available locally, but certain types of intravenous fluids were hard to get. Patients kept their own records and did a good job of it. Disposable syringes, needles, and blades were autoclaved and could be used about four times.

When asked to evaluate the level of medicine practiced at CHAPA, Dr. June raised questions that trouble all who are engaged in mission medical work:

> Sure [the practice of medicine] can be improved. The question is how much improvement and how much money are we willing to

spend versus the amount of benefit from the same dollars spent in primary care prevention programs. Are we willing to give dollars for both? The potential in either direction is almost limitless . . . The real problem is the balance between the two.

The other question is paternalism. Are we trying to set up something that nationals can afford to take over or something we will always [for the foreseeable future] run? . . . The poor, who are the vast majority, cannot afford [what we offer]. Do not take this to mean that I feel we should only supply what the poor can afford. I think we decided as a group that this is not acceptable.[12]

In June 1983 when the PCUS ceased to exist, CHAPA had been operating for five years. This comprehensive public health and community development project, as previously noted, had as a primary objective the training of local leadership in the skills needed to sustain an adequate and dignified standard of living for people in a desperately needy area. These first five years of the project might be best described as CHAPA's birth and infancy; the evolution into a self-sufficient and Bengali-run program was yet to be completed.[13]

The work had not been easy. In addition to difficult living and working conditions, the project faced hostility from government officials who, as noted, threatened in 1980 to close down the PCUS presence in Bangladesh; this matter was resolved in 1982. Moreover, the task of defining goals and principles, particularly in relation to the Bengali church partner required many meetings (thirty between 1978 and 1983) in which the participants struggled with basic long-term questions.

At the same time, CHAPA had impressive accomplishments. In 1983 a missionary staff of four (a physician, an agriculturalist, two nurses) and a Bengali staff of fifty-three were engaged in medical, agricultural, health extension, and adult education programs at CHAPA. A total of 25,000 patients were seen in the clinic that year, and 165 tuberculous patients were under treatment. Three out of four villages increased self-sufficiency by 70 to 80 percent. Infant deaths among "target families" had been cut in half. Training of paramedics and village health workers continued as a major emphasis.

A typescript titled "CHAPA History," by Melanie Smith, R.N., ends with this summary:

Years of plodding on without a clear direction, without definite goals or a clear line of authority. Years of changing PFB personnel, of changing ideas. But through all this, despite unsure foundations, CHAPA stands. Stands for what? Stands for a joint work between the [PCUS] and the BBF [Bangladesh Baptist Fellowship] and for the glory of God.[14]

Conclusion

In 1983 when the PCUS ceased to exist, the experiment in primary health care in Bangladesh could best be described as still in a formative stage. Considerable funds and the energies of talented, well-trained young people had been invested in the effort. Whether this approach could be maintained by the Bengali without a missionary presence and a hospital base remained to be seen.

Notes

1. William E. Rice gave the author a number of interviews and generously shared his files, thereby contributing substantially to this chapter.
2. Jason Laure, *Bangladesh: Enchantment of the World* (Chicago: Children's Press, 1992), 15.
3. David B. Barrett, *World Christian Encyclopedia* (New York: Oxford University Press, 1982), 164–65.
4. William E. Rice, interview, Feb. 22, 1985; Melanie Smith, "CHAPA History," typescript, 1986.
5. Angela Carter, R.N., PCUS missionary in Bangladesh, 1984–86.
6. Rice, interview.
7. Herbert A. Codington, M.D., interview, Feb. 1984.
8. Rice, interview.
9. *Report*, Division of International Mission, 1975.
10. John T. Nonweiler, M.D., PCUS missionary at CHAPA 1983–87, interview, Feb. 8, 1985.
11. Patty June, M.D., interview, Nov. 10, 1985.
12. Ibid.
13. Melanie Smith, R.N., "CHAPA History," typescript, March 1986.
14. Ibid.

Chapter Fifteen

Haiti
(1972–1983)

I n January 1972 Rev. Marion Huske, an eighty-four-year-old minister from Charlotte, North Carolina, flew to Haiti to join a Caribbean cruise whose departure from the United States he had missed. He became deeply troubled by the hunger, poverty, and dire need he observed in this small country and near-neighbor to the affluent United States. When he returned home, Huske wrote to the PCUS Board of World Missions, on which he had once served, and offered a challenge gift if the PCUS would begin work in Haiti.[1]

Two circumstances contributed to the prompt response by the PCUS to this challenge. First, medical personnel were available because of the withdrawal of the PCUS from Mexico in 1972. Specifically, suitable placement was being sought for the mission staff from the Sanatorio La Luz in Morelia. Second, the Episcopal Church in Haiti desired help in operating its clinic in the city of Leogane. Contact with Monsignor Luc A. Garnier, bishop of the Episcopal Church of Haiti, resulted in an agreement for the PCUS to operate the Hospital St. Croix in Leogane as an ecumenical project in cooperation with the Episcopal Church of Haiti.

Haiti's sad history continues as an open sore in the social fabric of the Western Hemisphere. Occupying one-third of the island of Hispanola, the Republic of Haiti (the name means "high ground" or mountainous) is one of the most densely populated and least developed countries in the world; 95 percent of the people there are of African descent and 80 percent cannot read. A colony of France, Haiti was the second nation in the hemisphere (after the United States) to become an independent nation. The French Revolution sparked revolt among the huge majority of African slaves who, after a brutal fight, achieved independence in 1804. Since that time the country has been ruled by a series of unstable and exploitive dictators, who were not interested in the welfare of the people. A two-class society developed, with 90 percent black peasants and a small, educated, prosperous elite.

In 1915, because of the political, social, and financial chaos in Haiti and because of fear of German or French intervention during World War I, President Woodrow Wilson sent U.S. marines to restore order. The U.S. occupation lasted until 1934. Order was restored and the government strengthened; foreign debts were paid; highways, schools, and hospitals were built; a sanitation system was installed and yellow fever was eliminated. However, the U.S. presence was deeply resented.

During the period covered in this account, Haiti was ruled by Jean-Claude Duvalier ("Baby Doc"), son of Francois Duvalier ("Papa Doc"), who had ruled from 1957 to 1971. The Duvaliers maintained a stable but oppressive regime through a combination of military force and a secret police made up of brutal thugs (the *Tonton Macoutes*).

Leogane, a town of approximately 5,000 population, is located 26 miles west of the capital, Port-au-Prince, at the head of the rugged southern peninsula ("jaw") that juts 150 miles into the Caribbean. Leogane is the administrative center for a region made up of a coastal plain and steep mountains.

The development of the Hospital St. Croix can be divided into three stages: (1) 1973–77, the beginnings made by Dr. Rion Dixon and other transplants from the hospital in Morelia, Mexico; (2) 1977–81, construction and growth under Dr. Salvadore de la Torre; and (3) 1981–83+, progress under the directorship of Dr. David F. McNeeley. The Medical Benevolence Foundation (MBF) played a major role in what became known as one of the PCUS's "success stories."[2]

Discouraging aspects of the work in Haiti include the stultifying effect of the abysmal poverty; the language (a soft Creole based on the French of the earliest colonials); the heat (exhausting and enervating); and voodoo (the animistic religion that permeated the society—both Drs. Dixon and McNeilley report being hexed). At the same time, interaction with the people of Haiti was rewarding. As Dr. McNeeley put it, "The Haitians are a delightful people. . . . The isolated, illiterate (rural) people have a dignity and sense of self-worth that is very precious and needs to be preserved."[3] A poem by Virginia Coultas, a PCUS missionary from 1980 to 1982, evokes the country this way:

Haiti

Haiti assaults the senses
alternating delight
with despair

creating chaos
in the region
of the heart.[4]

HOSPITAL ST. CROIX
Leogane

The Dixon Era, 1973–1977

The team of former missionaries from Mexico was uniquely qualified to tackle the job in Haiti. Dr. Rion Dixon, a recent graduate of the
University of Michoacan Medical School in Morelia (M.D., 1969), had
formerly been a highly successful businessman; he brought administrative and organizational skills not normally found in missionaries.
Nurses included his wife, Ann Dixon, R.N., and Irma Astudillo, R.N.,
a graduate of the Dr. L. J. Coppedge School of Nursing in Morelia.
They were joined in August 1973 by Dorothy Liston (Descieux), R.N.,
who had a master's degree in nursing education.

The "Dixon Era" was a period of building, equipping, and training
personnel. Work began in the two-room shell of a clinic formerly run
by the Episcopal Church. There was no lack of patients; many
suffered from so-called preventable diseases[5] such as malaria, malnutrition, diarrhea, tetanus, and whooping cough. Tuberculosis was
very common.

Construction of a hospital began immediately with the help of the
MBF and of volunteers from the United States and Canada. Within six
months a twenty-five-bed hospital—with operating room, outpatient
clinics, and departments of surgery, medicine, obstetrics, and pediatrics—was completed. A home for doctors and accommodations for
nurses also were built. Medicines, supplies, equipment, and White
Cross linens poured in from many sources. A fully equipped 200-bed
army hospital was purchased for $2,500 from U.S. Army surplus and
delivered free of charge to Haiti. A Volkswagen bus for use as a

public health ambulance was donated by a member of a church in Corpus Christi, Texas. A formal dedication occurred early in 1974.[6]

The pattern of support from the MBF became established. In addition to raising funds and sending equipment, MBF recruited teams of volunteer doctors and dentists. These teams served for two weeks at a time and provided a high quality of medical practice. Dr. Dixon reported that during his stay in Haiti, the hospital was covered by visiting physicians or dentists for all but two days.[7]

The outreach program, for which the Hospital St. Croix became well known, was begun during the Dixon era. Dorothy Descieux, R.N., with the help of Madame Demas, a Haitian nutritionist, developed a training program for midwives to combat the problem of neonatal tetanus, one of the leading causes of death in the area. The local "traditional birth attendants," often illiterate women, were given in-service training twice a week for six months, after which they received a diploma from the Public Health Ministry. Graduates returned every two weeks to report on their work and receive further training, supervision, and encouragement. Dorothy Deisieux, during her seven years in Haiti, trained some 250 midwives.

After the Dixons returned to the United States in 1975, Dr. Andre, a Haitian doctor, served as interim director. The work continued with the help of the two nurses (Dorothy Deisieux and Irma Astudillo), the visiting MBF personnel, and Mr. Rhine Fecho (part-time business manager, 1974–79). Mr. Fecho was an industrial engineer assigned to Haiti to start vocational/agricultural trade schools in Port-au-Prince, Cap Haitien, and Terrier Rouge. His expertise helped broaden the mission of the Hospital St. Croix to reflect concern with community issues such as sanitation and clean water.

Jesus Salvadore Garcia de la Torre, M.D., 1977–1981

The de la Torre period at the Hospital St. Croix had a romantic beginning. Irma Astudillo, the Mexican nurse who participated in the founding of the PCUS medical work in Haiti, returned to Mexico in 1976 on furlough. There she met and married Salvadore Garcia de la Torre, a graduate of the University of Mexico (M.D., 1974). Their Caribbean honeymoon included a stop in Haiti, where she introduced him to the work at the Hospital St. Croix. The result was his appointment in 1977 by the PCUS to be the next director of the Haiti project.[8]

Dr. de la Torre carried forward the three features that came to distinguish the PCUS work at the Hospital St. Croix: the upgrading of

*Hospital St. Croix,
Leogane. Photograph
courtesy of Paul S.
Crane.*

the physical plant, the program of visiting specialists from the United
States, and the development of the public health program.

In 1977 the Hospital St. Croix was a simple, primitive operation. It
had three rooms for patients (men, women, pediatrics), a small
surgical suite, and laboratory, but no X-ray machine and no autoclave.
A pressure cooker was used for sterilizing, and spinal anesthesia was
the primary modality used for anesthesia. The MBF raised $300,000 to
remodel and expand the facilities. In 1981 David and Floy Altenbernd,
who served in Zaire from 1974 to 1980, were assigned to supervise the
construction. The result was an attractive seventy-five-bed hospital
with a new wing, two-room surgical unit, delivery room, laboratory,
pharmacy, outpatient clinic, and two X rays (one portable). The
hospital had electricity and was air-conditioned.

The accessibility of Haiti, combined with the desire of many PCUS
physicians and dentists to contribute their skills to the underserved
and needy, enabled the Haitian hospital to be professionally staffed at
first almost entirely by teams of volunteers from the United States—an
unusual practice in PCUS medical work. For ten years (from 1974 to
1984) teams averaging two to six persons went to Haiti regularly on a
rotating basis. Not only did these specialists help in covering the work
and maintaining high standards, but their enthusiasm raised the level
of interest and support in the PCUS churches in the United States.

The work of Dr. Gardner Landers, an ophthalmologist, and his
wife, Frances, of El Dorado, Arkansas, exemplifies what these

volunteers did. Between 1977 and 1982 the Landers traveled ten times to the Hospital St. Croix, taking with them a team that included Thanna Parks (assistant and surgical nurse) and their sons Bill (an optometrist) and Jim (also an ophthalmologist). Frances Landers was the organizer, administrator, supervisor, treasurer, fund-raiser, public relations person, and "preacher" for the team. A fellow missionary reported:

> In the beginning [Dr. Landers] treated many simple eye conditions. The demand became so great that now he sees only the blind or nearly blind. They come from all parts of Haiti by tap-tap, donkey, or on foot. Of the patients he sees, 75% can be helped. . . . Dr. Landers gives the following advice to volunteers: "It is *not* a vacation! Forget how you do it at home. Bring your supplies. Develop a high frustration threshold."[9]

Until 1980, when a guesthouse was built, visiting specialists were housed in the home of the de la Torres, an experience that Irma de la Torre described as "rewarding but sometimes exhausting."[10]

The public health outreach was a priority with Dr. de la Torre, and one of the most satisfying tasks. Malnutrition, diarrheas, infectious diseases, and tetanus in the newborn were conditions that responded well to the public health approach. Satellite clinics were established and visited regularly by teams that included a nutritionist, a driver/vaccinator, and a nurse's aide. The training of the traditional birth attendants in midwifery techniques continued to be rewarding. As Dr. de la Torre noted, "The incidence of infant mortality and neonatal tetanus was brought under control in the Leogane area."[11]

Design at entrance to the Community Health Training Center. Photograph courtesy of Paul S. Crane.

Public health nurses head out to the country. Photograph courtesy of Paul S. Crane.

In addition to the volunteers supplied by MBF, the PCUS assigned a number of people for short periods to do specific jobs. Harvey A. Musser and his wife, Doris (R.N.), transferred from the Brazil Mission (1979–80) in order to follow Rhine Fecho as business manager. In addition to his duties in the business office, Musser improved the hospital grounds by landscaping and plantings; he also worked with Church World Service in village development programs that installed tube wells and built roads, among other things. Doris Musser worked in the nursing program.

Mrs. Julia Maulden (1980–81), a retired schoolteacher from Charlotte, North Carolina, and a friend of the Huske family, took charge of the newly completed guesthouse. She also helped in the business office.

The Rev. Day Carper and his wife, Blanche (R.N.), former missionaries in Congo/Zaire (1940–72), went to Haiti to provide on-the-job training to the newly appointed chaplain, Father Jean Albert. The work of the chaplain at the hospital had been performed on a part-time basis by the parish priest of the Leogane Episcopal Church. In 1980 Father Albert, a Haitian, was assigned as a full-time chaplain, and he greatly enhanced the Christian witness of the hospital. He lived at the hospital and visited the public health outposts.

David McNeeley, M.D., 1981–1983+

David F. McNeeley, M.D., was the third director of the Hospital St. Croix. Under his leadership, the hospital came to fulfill the expectations for which it was founded. It also became recognized in international public health circles for conducting a highly successful model of a cooperative regional health care program.

Dr. McNeeley, who is an Episcopalian, traces his interest in Haiti to when, at age six, he acquired a pen pal who was a student at the Holy Trinity School in Port-au-Prince. At age seventeen McNeely began summer volunteer work there and served as manager of the music camp for the renowned youth symphony orchestra of that school. During this time he acquired fluency in French and in the Creole language commonly used in Haiti. He met Dr. Rion Dixon in 1973 and served as his interpreter from January to August of 1974.[12]

David McNeeley decided to become a medical missionary while attending college at the University of the South in Sewanee, Tennessee (B.A., 1974). He went to Tulane Medical School, acquiring degrees in medicine and in public health (M.D., M.P.H., 1978), completed a residency in preventive medicine and in pediatrics, and became board certified in pediatrics. He described his assignment to Haiti as the "natural outcome of years of association with that country," and like "stepping into an old shoe." His affiliation with the Episcopal Church was an asset; his relations with the PCUS, while requiring some adjustment and education, were "comfortable."[13]

Dr. McNeeley further developed the three basic aspects of the program at the Hospital St. Croix: the hospital, the use of volunteer specialists from the United States, and the public health services. He also fostered and expanded cooperation between churches and church agencies (PCUS, Episcopal Church of Haiti, MBF, presbyteries, etc.) and with nonchurch national and international agencies such as U.S.AID, Rotary International, and UNICEF. He worked closely with the Haitian Public Health Department developing health policies that would help that department reach its goals. He emphasized the training of the Haitian staff who eventually assumed responsibility for most of the day-to-day operation of the institution.

The Hospital St. Croix, in 1983, was a sixty-three-bed general hospital offering outpatient primary health services and inpatient general medical, surgical, urologic, gynecologic, obstetric, and pediatric services to the Leogane region. Its now largely Haitian staff of about seventy employees included physicians, nurses, nurse anesthetists, laboratory and radiology technicians, and administrative and service personnel. The level of practice was generally good though technically not sophisticated. Mortality rates, according to Dr. McNeeley, were "equal to or better than those seen at Charity Hospital in New Orleans." The Hospital St. Croix was considered one of the best hospitals in Haiti.[14]

Administration of the hospital was one of the more difficult aspects of the work. The PCUS (Division of International Mission) invested $15,000 in training a Haitian administrator and reorganizing the systems of accounting, auditing, inventory, and purchase control.[15] The annual reports and audit went to the Episcopal Church of Haiti, the owners of the hospital's internal control process. Support from the PCUS and the MBF averaged about $200,000 a year; more was needed to carry out the program as it should be. The budget was a hand-to-mouth operation with a very narrow margin.[16]

As the Haitian staff became more competent, the medical visitor program was revised in order to concentrate on training Haitian medical personnel. The visitors continued to provide specialty services not otherwise available but shifted emphasis to that of a teaching mission. The visiting teams reduced their visits to approximately twenty weeks each year.

Scott Jordan, a pharmacist, and his wife, Edna, were special two-year appointees (1981–83). He trained a Haitian pharmacist, while she ran the guesthouse.

By 1983 the public health services were organized into an effective program and the Hospital St. Croix, at the Haitian government's request, assumed responsibility for the Leogane district, which had a population of 95,300. (The hospital drew from a wider community of some 300,000.)[17] A pyramidal health care structure was devised, with the Hospital St. Croix at the top, a number of satellite clinics (eight in 1983) and "rally posts" (twenty-five in 1983) in the middle, and a network of village health workers and village midwives at the base.

Satellite Clinics
The satellite clinics, in remote locations throughout the region, provided primary care, health education, and support to resident village health workers. Each satellite clinic had several "rally posts" providing immunizations, nutrition education, surveillance of the under five-year-olds, prenatal classes, and family planning services. These rally posts often consisted of no more than a crossroads location where people met the health team at regular specified times. Many posts were accessible only by horseback.

Village Health Workers
The village health workers (forty in 1983) were trained to counsel villagers about health, sanitation, and the construction and maintenance of clean water supplies. They could prescribe simple remedies and could recognize criteria for referring patients to clinics or to the hospital. These *Agents de Sante* were selected by their local community

David F. McNeeley, M.D., goes by horseback to a health post. Photograph courtesy of Paul S. Crane.

councils and trained by the International Nursing Service
Association. They were supervised by a monthly meeting at the
hospital, monthly site visits by two supervisors, and on-site supervision by hospital personnel.

Village Midwife Program

A village midwife program trained traditional birth attendants
(188 in 1983) using a government-approved curriculum. Supervision
was provided by hospital personnel on their monthly visits to the
rally posts and clinics.

An article printed in 1984 in the *Journal of the American Medical
Association* (*JAMA*) titled "A Cooperative Model for Provision of
Regional Health Services in a Developing Nation," by David
McNeeley and C. D. Bessinger, M.D., describes the Hospital St. Croix
and the policies that made its program so successful:

> The development of health care in the Leogane region of Haiti has
> been a ten-year story of the international cooperation among health
> professionals, of closely targeted assistance, and of policy coordina-
> tion between assisting private agencies and the Haitian government.
> The broadly based health care program of [the Hospital St. Croix] of
> Leogane is presented as a model of a cooperative effort that has
> resulted in rapid regional care development and as an encourage-
> ment to the many differing types of groups responding to a world in
> medical need.[18]

Conclusion

The PCUS venture in Haiti until 1983, as noted, has been described
as a success. The curative component in the Hospital St. Croix operated efficiently, and the community health outreach improved the
quality of life in the area around Leogane. The Leogane district is definitely a healthier place because of the PCUS presence. The infant
mortality rate has been reduced, neonatal tetanus has practically
disappeared, nutrition education has reduced malnutrition, preventive medical measures have curtailed the incidence of infectious
diseases, methods for acquiring fresh clean water supplies have been
introduced, and a network of village health workers provide regular

services in remote areas. While the expatriate presence remained strong, the training of Haitians anticipated more Haitian involvement and assumption of responsibility.[19]

Until 1983 the government in Haiti was stable though oppressive. It was in January 1986, beyond the scope of this document, that revolution took place, and Haiti became a very unstable place. The Hospital St. Croix performed magnificently, during the crisis, treating the wounded from all political persuasions. At one point the hospital's vehicles were the only ones able to travel unmolested on the Leogane/Port-au-Prince highway.[20]

Haiti's future remains uncertain. How best to demonstrate a loving God's concern for hurting people through medical work continues to challenge God's people.

Notes

1. *The Charlotte Observer*, April 30, 1973, 2C.
2. William Rice, interviews, Feb. 1985 and Sept. 1993.
3. David McNeeley, M.D., interview, April 1986.
4. Virginia Coultas, "Sketches of Haiti," typescript.
5. C. D. Bessinger Jr., M.D., and David F. McNeeley, M.D., "A Cooperative Model for Provision of Regional Health Services in a Developing Nation," *JAMA* (vol. 252, 1984), 3149.
6. "How Does God Put Together a Mission Hospital?" (First Presbyterian Church, Corpus Christi, Tex.: bulletin, April 13, 1973).
7. Rion Dixon, M.D., interview, 1993.
8. Salvadore G. de la Torre, M.D., interview, March 1986.
9. Harvey and Doris Musser, missionary correspondence letter, May 1982.
10. Irma de la Torre, R.N., interview, March 1986.
11. Salvadore de la Torre, interview.
12. McNeeley, interview.
13. Ibid.
14. Ibid.
15. Rice, interview, Sept. 1993.
16. McNeeley, interview.
17. Bessinger and McNeeley, "A Cooperative Model."
18. Ibid.
19. Ibid.
20. McNeeley, letter, May 23, 1986.

Epilogue

I n all probability the demise in 1983 of the PCUS (Presbyterian Church in the United States) when it merged with the UPUSA (United Presbyterian Church) to form the Presbyterian Church (U.S.A.) was hardly noticed in its varied medical facilities around the world. Medical missionaries continued their work, sick people continued to find health and hope, young people continued to be trained in the medical professions, and Christ continued to be proclaimed through the compassionate practice of modern medicine.

Two themes dominate this history of the one hundred years in which PCUS carried out its medical mission in nine countries around the world.

First, Western medicine, through an astonishing scientific revolution, was able, for the first time, to offer effective cures for many of the ills that afflicted mankind. The medical missionary had the privilege and the satisfaction (even the excitement) of being an agent for scientific medicine among those who had no access to modern care. In some instances, the missionary was able to make a contribution to new medical knowledge. The training of nationals in medicine was a natural progression. The appeal of medical work lay in its ability to meet specific needs with tangible results. Members of the home church found satisfaction in supporting specific opportunities that mission medicine had to offer.

Second, the enormous political and social changes during this period had its effect on each of the mission fields and on the PCUS home base. Major upheavals, to name but a few, included the Boxer Rebellion in China, the Great Depression, World War II, the Korean War, independence in Congo/Zaire, and the Vietnam War. While many countries became "developed" societies, some (Congo/Zaire, Haiti, and Bangladesh) benefited little from the fruits of positive change.

It is interesting to note the different ways in which, at first, the medical missioanry was greeted in various localities. In China there was hostility, including the widespread rumor of the killing of children for their blood and organs (one speculates how the terminology of the communion sacrament may have contributed to this rumor). In Korea physicians were overwhelmed by the volume of patients. In Congo the doctor was said to sit under a tree and no one came. In Mexico and Brazil opposition stemmed principally from the Catholic Church. By 1983 Western medicine was well accepted around the world. A new phenomenon was the participation of governments and secular bodies in international health.

This account does not emphasize the biographical portrayal of the individual missionary, largely because of the limitations of space. Among the medical personnel were many well-educated, highly motived, hardworking, interesting personalites. The role of women (the physicians in China and Korea and the "super nurses" elsewhere) was important. A generalized observation would be that the biggest impact was made by those who served for long periods of time (ten years or more), learned the language, and immersed themselves in the culture.

Underlying all else was the Christian motivation to present the good news of the compassionate Christ. The medical mission concern for "the whole person" best crystalizes this motivation.

A Legacy
Remembered

Appendices

PCUS
Missionary Personnel

M edical missionaries appointed by PCUS are listed in alphabet-ical order by occupation. Dates are not precise. A plus sign after 1983 indicates that service continued under the newly formed Presbyterian Church (USA).

Appendix A—Physicians

Alexander, Alexander John Aitcheson, *Korea*, Kunsan, 1902–1903 (2 months).

Allyn, Rev. Horace Selden, *Brazil*, 1896–1925.

Anderson, Stuart H., *Congo/Zaire*, Bulape, 1976–1978.

Bell, (Lemuel) Nelson, *China*, Huayin, 1916–1941.

Birdman, Ferdinand Henry, Korea, Mokpo, 1908; Chonju, 1908–1909.

Blamoville, Hulda Claudine, *Congo/Zaire*, IMCK, 1970–1971.

Boggs, Lloyd Kennedy, *Korea*, Chonju, 1925–1940.

Boyce, Rev. James Reid, *Mexico*, Mexico City, 1941–1951, Ometepec, 1951–1971.

Bradley, John Wilson, *China*, Suqien, 1901–1929.

Brand, Louis Christian, *Korea*, Kunsan, 1924–1929; Kwangju, 1929–1938.

Bridgman, Albert Henry, *Korea*, Kwangju, 1972–1975.

Brown, Frank Augustus, Jr., *China*, 1947–1949; *Japan*, Osaka, *1950–1976*.

Brown, Richard Coleman, *Congo/Zaire*, Bulape, 1973–1977.

Browne, Earl Zollicoffer, *Mexico*, Morelia, 1925–1926.

Buckingham, Edwin Wheeler, *China,* Jiaxing, 1921–1927.
Bush, Ovid Bern, *Korea,* Chonju, 1949–1952; *Japan,* Osaka, 1953–1967.
Butler, Rev. George William, *Brazil,* 1882–1919.
Butman, Burton B., *Korea,* Chonju, 1975–1981.
Chapman, Jeff Watson, Congo/Zaire, Bulape, 1929–1930, 1932–1939.
Chu, David Bao-shan, *Korea,* Chonju, 1967–1983+.
Chun, John Jung-Youl, *Korea,* Chonju, 1976–1979.
Codington, Herbert Augustus, *Korea,* Kwangju, 1950–1974; *Bangladesh,* Dhaka, 1974–1983+.
Coppedge, Llewellyn Jackson, *Congo/Zaire,* Luebo, 1906–1918; *Mexico,* Morelia, 1921–1948.
Cousar, George Richard, *Congo/Zaire,* Mutoto, 1924–1925; Lubondai, 1925–1954; Bibanga, 1954–1960.
Crane, Paul Shields, *Korea,* Chonju, 1947–1969.
Crawford, Frances Randolph, *China,* Jiangyin, 1914–1917; Jiaxing, 1917–1932.
Daniel, Thomas Henry, *Korea,* Kunsan, 1904–1909; Chonju, 1910–1916; Seoul, 1916–1917.
De la Torre, (Jesus) Salvadore Garcia, *Haiti,* Leogane, 1977–1981.
Dickerson, Melford Sherman, *Congo/Zaire,* Moma, 1956–1960.
Dietrick, Ronald Burton, *Korea,* Chonju, 1958–1961; Kwangju, 1961–1983+.
Dixon, Rev. (Woodward) Rion, *Mexico,* Morelia, 1966–1972; *Haiti,* Leogane, 1973–1975.
Douglas, Robert Arnold, *Congo/Zaire,* Bulape, 1970–1973.
Drew, (Alesandro) Damer, *Korea,* Kunsan, 1896–1901.
Dunn, (William) Robert, *Congo/Zaire,* Lubondai, 1955–1956; Bulape, 1956–58.
Eitzman, Donald Vern, *Taiwan,* Changhua, 1981–1983.
English, Hugh Gaston, *Congo/Zaire,* Mutoto, 1952–1953; Lubondai, 1954–1955.
Farrior, Hugh Lanier, *Congo/Zaire,* Mutoto, 1958–1959; Bibanga, 1959–1960, 1962–1965; IMCK 1967–1971.
Fishburne, Richard Baxter, *China,* 1881–1883.
Forsythe, Wiley Hamilton, *Korea,* Chonju, 1904–1905; Mokpo, 1909–1911.
Frist, John Chester, *Korea,* Soonchun, 1974–1975.
Gieser, (Paul) Kenneth, *China,* Huayin, 1934–1939; Zhenjiang, 1940.

Gilmer, William Painter, *Korea,* Mokpo, 1922–1926; Kwangju, 1926–1927.
Gordon, Alan Gary, *Brazil,* Dourados, 1972–1978; Sao Paulo, 1979–1983+.
Graybill, J. Walton, *Mexico,* 1881–1883.
Grier, Henrietta Donaldson, *China,* Xuzhou, 1897–1940.
Harding, Maynard C., *Korea,* Mokpo, 1911–1913.
Haslup, Allen Lee, *Taiwan,* Changhua, 1978–1983+.
Henning, (Arthur) Jack, *Congo/Zaire,* IMCK, 1975–1977.
Hewett, Julius Winch, *China,* Yencheng, 1916–1927.
Hollister, William, *Korea,* Mokpo, 1927–1931; Kunsan, 1931–1936.
Hull, Walter Baird, *Congo/Zaire,* Bibanga 1970–1973; IMCK, 1974–1983+.
Hutcheson, Allen Carrington, *China,* Jiaxing, 1909–1917; Nanjing, 1917–1927.
Ingold, Mattie B. (Tate), Korea, *Chonju,* 1897–1928 (evangelistic after 1905).
Iverson, Lalla, *China,* Jinan, 1947–1949.
Jefferson, Henry D., *Congo/Zaire,* IMCK, 1977–1978.
June, Patricia Lee, *Bangladesh,* CHAPA, 1980–1983+.
Keller, Frank Goulding, *Korea,* Chonju, 1955–1967.
Kellersberger, Eugene Roland, *Congo/Zaire,* Lusambo, 1916–1918; Bibanga, 1918–1940.
King, Robert Rogers, *Congo/Zaire,* Mutoto, 1915–1931; Luebo, 1944–1949; Moma, 1951–1955.
Kuhn, Sharon Clodfelter, *Bangladesh,* CHAPA, 1977–1981.
Kuhn, Walter F. "Ted," *Bangladesh,* CHAPA, 1977–1981.
Leadingham, Roy Samuel, *Korea,* Mokpo, 1912–1920; Seoul, 1921–1923.
Lee, Jane Varenia, *China,* 1899–1937.
Lee, (John) Young–Ung, *Bangladesh,* Dhaka, 1979–1983+.
Malcolm, William, *China,* Huayin, 1910–1912; Yencheng, 1913.
McFadyen, Archibald Alexander, *China,* Xuzhou, 1904–1941.
McGill, Kenneth Harwood, *Congo/Zaire,* Bibanga, 1968–1978; Bulape, 1980–1983+.
McIntosh, (William) Grant, *Congo/Zaire,* Lubondai, 1961–1962.
McNeeley, David Fielden, *Haiti,* Leogane, 1981–1983+.
Miller, John Knox, *Congo/Zaire,* Luebo, 1950–1953; Lubondai, 1954–1961; Bulape, 1962–1964, 1967–1969; Bibanga, 1961–1962; IMCK, 1965–1967, 1970–1983+.

Miller, (Samuel) Houston, *China*, Huayin, 1915–1916.
Moffett, Alexander Stuart, *China*, Jiangyin, 1935–1940; Zhenjiang, 1947–1948.
Mooney, James Potter, *China*, Suzhou, 1911–1915.
Moore, Lynford L., *China*, Xuzhou, 1897–1902.
Moore, John William, *China*, Suzhou, 1922–1925.
Moore, (Ralph) Erskine, *Korea*, Soonchun, 1969–1971.
Morgan, Lorenzo Seymour, *China*, Huayin, 1905–1908; Haizhou, 1908–1934.
Morgan, Ruth Bennett, *China*, Huayin, 1905–1908; Haizhou, 1908–1934.
Mosley, Kirk Thornton, *China*, Huayin, 1931–1934; Yencheng, 1934–1936.
Nelson, Henry Sperry, *China*, Taizhou, 1948–1951; *Congo/Zaire*, Bulape, 1952–1953, 1960–1961; Luebo, 1953–1961; Lubondai, 1964–1967; IMCK, 1972–1974, 1978–1982, 1983+.
Newman, Henry Wade, *China*, Zhenjiang, 1923–1925.
Nolan, Joseph Wynne, *Korea*, Mokpo, 1904–1905; Chonju, 1905; Kwangju, 1905–1907.
Owen, Rev. Clement Carrington, *Korea*, Mokpo, 1898–1904; Kwangju, 1904–1909 (evangelistic after 1905).
Owen, Georgiana Whiting, *Korea*, Mokpo, 1900–1904; Kwangju, 1904–1923 (evangelistic/educational after 1904).
Patten, Robert Chester, *Korea*, Kwangju and Kojido, 1974–1978.
Patterson, Annie Houston, *China*, Suqien, 1893–1922; Tienshien, 1922–1936.
Patterson, Jacob Bruce, *Korea*, Kunsan, 1910–1924.
Patterson, Norman Guthrie, *China*, Huayin, 1929–1930; Suqien, 1930–1937.
Phillips, Robert Derrick, *Korea*, Chonju, 1956–1960.
Poole, Mark Keller, *Congo/Zaire*, Bulape, 1936–1937, 1942–1961; Luebo, 1938–1939; Bibanga, 1940–1942.
Preston, James Fairman Jr., *Korea*, Soonchun (intern), 1937–1939; Kwangju, 1940.
Price, Philip Barbour, *China*, Suzhou, 1926–1927, Jinan, 1929–1937; *Korea*, Mokpo, 1927.
Price, Robert Black, *China*, Taizhou, 1916–1941.
Rambo, (Victor) Birch, *Congo/Zaire*, Bulape, 1964–1972; IMCK, 1973–1983+.

Reed, John Hobart, *China*, Haizhou, 1932–1941.

Robertson, Moorman Owen, *Korea*, Chonju, 1916–1921.

Rogers, James McLean, *Korea*, Soonchun, 1917–1940.

Ross, (James) Hervey, *Mexico*, Mexico City, 1940–1945; Morelia, 1945–1967.

Rule, William, *Congo/Zaire*, Lubondai, 1940–1944, 1954–1964; Bibanga, 1946–1954; IMCK, 1964–1970; Bulape, 1977–1980.

Seel, David John, *Korea*, Chonju, 1954–1983+.

Shannon, Ralph Edwin, *Congo/Zaire*, Lubondai, 1964–1965; Bibanga, 1965–1968; IMCK, 1972–1983+.

Shaw, John Colton, *Korea*, Chonju, 1971–1983+.

Shields, Randolph Tucker, *China*, Suzhou, 1908–1909; Nanjing, 1909–1917; Jinan, 1917–1941.

Sich, Dorothea, *Korea*, Chonju, 1966–1970.

Simpson, (Wilfred) Laurence, *Korea*, Kwangju, 1958–1960, 1964–1967.

Smith, (James) Tinsley, Jr., *Congo/Zaire*, Mutoto, 1931–1962.

Smith, T. Joanne, *Korea*, Chonju, 1963–1966.

Smithwick, (Laura) Gladys, *China*, Xuzhou, 1925–1936; *Congo/Zaire*, Lubondai, 1950–1952; Mboi, 1953–1954; Luebo, 1955–1958; Bulape, 1959–1964.

Stixrud, Thomas Thomasson, *Congo/Zaire*, Luebo, 1914–1942.

Stephenson, Robert Mills, *China*, Yencheng, 1913.

Stuart, David Todd, *China*, Suzhou, 1907–1909.

Stump, Bonnie, *Congo/Zaire*, IMCK, 1981–1982.

Terrill, Charles, *China*, 1899–1900.

Threlkeld, William Logan, *Congo/Zaire*, Bulape, 1965–1968.

Timmons, Henry Loyola, *Korea*, Chonju, 1912–1913, 1922–1925; Soonchun, 1913–1916.

Topple, Stanley Craig, *Korea*, Soonchun, 1959–1981.

Topple, (Ane) Marie Amundsen, *Korea*, Soonchun, 1962–1981.

Venable, Wade Hampton, *China*, Jiaxing, 1895–1917; Guling, 1919–1927.

Vinson, (Thomas) Chalmers, *China*, Huayin, 1940–1941; 1947–1948; *Philippines*, POW, 1941–1945.

Voss, Charles Henry, *China*, Suqien, 1923–1925; Jiangyin, 1925–1926.

Watson, Keene Arnold, *Congo/Zaire*, Kananga, 1982–1983+.

Welton, Felix Burwell, *China*, Yencheng, 1931–1933; Suzhou, 1933–1937.

White, Carlton Benjamine, *Congo/Zaire,* Bibanga, 1950–1951; Luebo, 1952–1954.
Wilkerson, Joseph Leyburn, *China,* Jiaxing, 1948–1951; *Taiwan,* Changhua, 1953–1980.
Wilkinson, James Richard, *China,* Suzhou, 1894–1920.
Williams, Eddie M., *Congo/Zaire,* IMCK, 1978–1983.
Wilson, James Stevenson, *Korea,* Kunsan, 1939–1940.
Wilson, John Knox, *Korea,* Chonju, 1968–1971.
Wilson, Rev. Robert Manton, *Korea,* Kwangju, 1908–1928; Soonchun, 1928–1941.
Wolbrink, Adrian James, *Korea,* Kwangju, 1972–1975.
Woodbridge, Casper Ligon, *China,* Haizhou, 1923–1927.
Woodbridge, Mary Elizabeth Newell, *China,* Shanghai, 1915–1929.
Woods, Edgar, Jr., *China,* Huayin, 1888–1899.
Woods, James Baker, Jr, *China,* Zhenjiang, 1925–1940; *Korea,* 1927.
Woods, James Baker, Sr., *China,* Huayin, 1894–1941.
Worth, George Clarkson, *China,* Jiangyin, 1895–1936.
Young, Mason Pressly, *China,* Suzhou, 1915–1941; Jiaxing, 1947–1949.

Appendix B—Dentists

Bragramian, Robert Aslad, *Taiwan,* Changhua, 1963–1966.
Hillsman, John Lee, *Congo/Zaire,* IMCK, 1965–1972.
Jackson, Bernard Gordon, *Congo/Zaire,* Lubondai, 1958–1960.
Jung, Jean Baptiste, *Congo/Zaire,* Lubondai, 1952–1959, 1960–1964; Luebo, 1959–1960.
Koostianti, Sandra, *Korea,* Kwangju, 1982–1983.
Levie, James Kellum, *Korea,* Kwangju, 1923–1940, 1956–1959.
Marks, Sandy Coles, *Congo/Zaire,* Lubondai, 1948–1961.
McDonald, George Harrison, *Taiwan,* Kaohsiung, 1964–1976.
Nieusma, Dick H., *Korea,* Kwangju, 1961–1983+.
Shannon, Jack Alvin, *Congo/Zaire,* IMCK, 1971–1973.
Wilds, (Samuel) Hugh, *Congo/Zaire,* Luebo, 1919–1957.
Willard, Fred Bailey, *Korea,* Kwangju, 1971–1972.
Zanone, Robert Oliver, *Congo/Zaire,* IMCK, 1972–1976.

Appendix C—Dental Hygienists

Kane, Nancy Lynn, *Korea*, Kwangju, 1976–1978.

Appendix D—Nurses

Albaugh, Ida McKay, *China*, Jiangyin, 1908–1919.
Alderman, Flora S., *China*, Suzhou, 1904.
Aldrich, Margaret Ann, *Congo/Zaire*, Bibanga, 1972–1976.
Arnold, Hope Hoft, *Brazil*, 1963–1983+.
Bain, Mary Rachel, *Korea*, Mokpo, 1921–1926; Kwangju, 1926–1927.
Balenger, Rebecca Ann, *Korea*, Chonju, 1968–1978.
Bateman, Frances Davis, *Korea*, Taejon, 1967–1972.
Beaty, (Dorothy) Mildred, *Mexico*, Morelia, 1944–1948.
Bissett, Mary Stuart, *China*, Haizhou, 1919–1927.
Boyer, Elizabeth Ann, *Korea*, Chonju, 1955–1958; Kwangju, 1959–1963; Taejon, 1963–1983+.
Boyer, Sylvia Haley, *Korea*, Kwangju, 1959–1961, 1968–1977.
Bracken, Ruth A., *China*, Xuzhou, 1925–1927; Haizhou, 1929–1934.
Bridgman, Eleanor Galbraith, *China*, Taizhou and Yencheng, 1920–1940.
Brown, Ann Vertovsk, *China*, 1947–1949; *Japan*, Osaka, 1950–1976.
Brown, Doris Jean, *Mexico*, Morelia, 1964–1968.
Buckingham, Bessie Kenniger, *China*, Jiaxing, 1921–1927.
Butman, Eleanor Janet, *Korea*, Chonju, 1975–1981.
Carper, Blanche Wiggs, *Congo/Zaire*, Mutoto, 1951–1952; Bibanga, 1953–1956, 1963; Moma, 1963–1971; *Haiti*, Leogane, 1981.
Chapman, Mary Elizabeth Ayers, *Congo/Zaire*, Bulape, 1929–1930.
Chapman, Rachel Crawford, *Congo/Zaire*, Bulape, 1932–1939.
Chu, Gail Cooper, *Korea*, Chonju, 1967–1983+.
Clark, Janet Agnew, *Brazil*, 1963–1983+.
Codington, Julia Neville, *Bangladesh*, Dhaka, 1976–1978; CHAPA, 1977–1978.
Codington, Mary Littlepage Lancaster, *Korea*, Kwangju, 1954–1974; *Bangladesh*, Dhaka, 1974–1983+.
Comstock, Judith, *Congo/Zaire*, Bulape, 1974–1977.

Cooksey, Esther, *Korea*, Kwangju, 1974–1976.

Corriher, Elizabeth, *China*, Jiaxing, 1908–1927.

Coyer, Juanita Nan, *Korea*, Kwangju, 1961–1971.

Cumming, Virginia Kerr, *Korea*, Mokpo, 1927–1934; Kwangju, 1936–1938, 1950–1956.

Dale, Effie Lucille, *Congo/Zaire*, Bibanga, 1936–1937.

De la Torre, Irma Nimrod Astudillo, *Haiti*, Leogane, 1973–1976, 1977–1981.

Descieux, Dorothy Ann Liston, *Haiti*, Leogane, 1973–1979.

Dickerson, Mary Frances Condor, *Congo/Zaire*, Moma, 1956–1960.

Dickson, Anna Katherine, *Congo/Zaire*, Bibanga, 1959–1960; Lubondai, 1961–1967; Bulape, 1967–1973.

Diehl, Rubye Mae, *China*, Jiaxing, 1920–1927.

Dixon, Ann Stephenson, *Mexico*, Morelia, 1965–1972; *Haiti*, Leogane, 1973–1975.

Dixon, Margaret, *China*, Jiangyin, 1920–1925.

Dole, Alma Gordon, *Brazil*, 1968–1983+.

Dunlap, Charlotte Audrey, *China*, Zhenjiang, 1922–1941, 1946–1951; *Taiwan*, Changhua, 1953–1965.

Edhegard, Grace Miller, *Congo/Zaire*, Luebo, 1916–1919.

Eitzman, Mary Lou O'Toole, *Taiwan*, Changhua, 1981–1983.

Ellington, Joetta Brown, *Congo/Zaire*, Kinshasa, 1965–1983.

Fair, Elda May, *Congo/Zaire*, Luebo, 1913–1915; Bulape, 1915–1921.

Farmer, Nancy Smith, *China*, Suzhou, 1917–1918.

Farmer, Nina Lewis, *Congo/Zaire*, Mutoto, 1920–1931.

Folta, Ruth Humes, *Korea*, Chonju, 1977–1983+.

Fontaine, Janette Forrestier, *Congo/Zaire*, Luebo, 1924–1932.

Fulson, (Rena) Nannette, *Congo/Zaire*, Lubondai, 1952–1954; Mboi, 1955–1960.

Garza, Edna Iris, *Mexico*, Ometepec, 1964–1969.

Gordon, Alma Daugherty, *Brazil*, Dourados, 1972–1978; São Paulo, 1979–1983+.

Greer, Anna Lou (Walker), *Korea*, Kwangju, 1912–1913; Soonchun, 1913–1929; Kunsan, 1929–1935.

Grey, Annie Isabell, *Korea*, Kunsan, 1921–1925.

Grier, Lucy Henrietta, *China*, Suzhou, 1933–1940.

Guedes, Ann Frances Shearman, *Brazil*, 1963–1975.

Hampton, Julia Sprague, *Congo/Zaire*, Mutoto, 1941–1945; Mboi, 1946–1953; Lubondai, 1954–1955.

Haslup, Eva Copley, *Taiwan,* Changhua, 1978–1983+.

Heilig, Patricia Mae, *Korea,* Chonju, 1957–1960.

Henning, Pauline Dunford, *Congo/Zaire,* IMCK, 1975–1977.

Hewson, Georgiana Florine, *Korea,* Kwangju, 1920–1925; Mokpo, 1926–1930; Soonchun, 1931–1940.

Hoffman, Marilyn Vieth, *Korea,* Chonju, 1961–1966.

Hopper, Margaret Lois, *Bangladesh,* CHAPA, 1978–1979.

Innes, Agnes Violet, *China,* Suzhou, 1905–1906.

Jennings, Fern B., *Brazil,* 1972–1983+.

Johnson, Glenice Mae, *Congo/Zaire,* Bulape, 1971–1976.

Johnston, Quinnie Adelaide, *Mexico,* Morelia, 1924–1926.

Kaderly, Jane R., *Congo/Zaire,* Bibanga, 1973–1977.

Keller, Janet Talmage, *Korea,* Chonju, 1954–1976.

Kestler, Ethel Esther, *Korea,* Kunsan, 1905–1912; Chonju, 1912–1940.

King, Marguerite Van Leancourt, *Congo/Zaire,* Luebo, 1913–1916; Mutoto, 1916–1931.

King, Virginia Wood, *Congo/Zaire,* Mboi, 1954–1960, 1962–1965; Kananga, 1961–1962; Luebo, 1965–1970; Bibanga, 1970–1972, 1983+.

Kraakenes, Astrid, *Korea,* Chonju, 1952–1955; Kwangju, 1955–1959.

Kriner, (Bernice) Annette, *Congo/Zaire,* Bulape, 1969–1972; IMCK, 1974–1978; Mbuji Mayi, 1979–1982; Kinshasa, 1980–1983+.

Larson, Emma E., *Congo/Zaire,* Bulape, 1920–1928.

Lathrop, Lillie Ora, *Korea,* Mokpo, 1911–1919; Kunsan, 1919–1927.

Liston, Margaret Lapsley, *Congo/Zaire,* Lubondai, 1924–1946, 1954–1960; Mutoto, 1943–1946; Bibanga, 1946–1953.

Long, Mary Dalton, *Congo/Zaire,* Bibanga, 1954–1960; *Brazil,* 1962–1981.

Longenecker, Alice May, *Congo/Zaire,* Lubondai, 1946–1950, 1955–1959; Kakinda, 1951–1954.

Lundeen, Elizabeth Caroline, *Japan,* Osaka, 1957–1961.

March, Charlotte, *Bangladesh,* Dhaka, 1981–1983+.

Marks, Katherine Woods, *Congo/Zaire,* Lubondai, 1948–1960.

Matthes, Hazel Lee, *China,* Taizhou, 1930–1940.

Matthews, Esther Boswell, *Korea,* Kwangju, 1916–1920; Mokpo, 1920–1928.

Maxwell, Elizabeth Williamson, *Brazil,* 1960–1972.

McBee, Mary Kathryn, *Mexico,* Morelia, 1948–1972.

McCallie, Emily Cordell, *Korea,* Chonju, 1907–1910; Mokpo, 1910–1926.

McElroy, Lucille Stone, *Congo/Zaire*, Lubondai, 1945–1946, 1954–1964; Moma, 1947–1954; IMCK, 1964–1972; Bulape, 1979.

McElroy, Mary Etta Stixrud, *Congo/Zaire*, Kasha, 1947–1956.

McFadyen, Helen Murr Howard, *China*, Suzhou, 1912–1916; Xuzhou, 1916–1941, 1947–1948.

McLaren, Frances, *Congo/Zaire*, Bulape, 1925–1928.

McLean, Carol, *Bangladesh*, CHAPA, 1980–1983.

McMurry, Margaret Birch, *Congo/Zaire*, Mutoto, 1946, 1953–1954; Luebo, 1947–1952, 1955–1957; Mboi, 1958–1960.

Miller, Elizabeth, *Congo/Zaire*, Bulape, 1960–1961, 1964–1972; Kakinda, 1954–1960; Lubondai, 1962–1963; Bibanga, 1972–1973.

Moore, Laura Venable, *China*, Suzhou, 1922–1925.

Moore, Margaret Wood, *Congo/Zaire*, Bibanga, 1944–1945; Kasha, 1946–1947; Lubondai, 1948–1952; Mutoto, 1955–1960.

Morrison, Mary Salter Porter, *Congo/Zaire*, Luebo, 1922–1945, 1947–1955; Moma, 1945–1946.

Mosley, Corinne Daigley, *China*, Huayin, 1931–1939, 1947–1948.

Musser, Doris Ann Hinkle, *Brazil*, 1969–1979; *Haiti*, Leogane, 1979–1980.

Nelson, Kathryn Wolff, *China*, Taizhou, 1948–1949, *Congo/Zaire*, Bulape, 1952–1953, 1960–1961; Luebo, 1953–1960; Lubondai, 1964–1967; IMCK, 1972–1974, 1978–1983+.

Olson, Janice Feagin, *Brazil*, 1966–1970.

Park, Hae-In, *Bangladesh*, Dhaka, 1981–1983+.

Patten, Joy Blaney, *Korea*, Kwangju and Kojido, 1974–1978.

Pitts, Laura Mae, *Korea*, Chonju, 1910–1911.

Poole, Sara Dale, *Congo/Zaire*, Bulape, 1936–1937, 1942–1960; Luebo, 1938–1939; Bibanga, 1940–1942.

Price, Octavia Howard, *China*, Suzhou, 1926–1927; Jinan, 1929–1937.

Pritchard, Margaret Frances, *Korea*, Kwangju, 1929–1940; Chonju, 1947–1970.

Quinn, Edna Bryan, *Brazil*, 1963–1967.

Rambo, Margaret Gordon, *Congo/Zaire*, Bulape, 1964–1972; IMCK, 1973–1983+.

Reynolds, (Dora) Lena, *Congo/Zaire*, Bulape, 1927–1960.

Rickabaugh, Natalie Abbott, *Korea*, Chonju, 1964–1974; Seoul 1974–1980.

Robertson, Sheila J. S., *Congo/Zaire*, Bulape, 1973–1976.

Rogers, Ruby, *Congo/Zaire*, Bibanga, 1919–1936.
Ross, Nancy Jones, *Congo/Zaire*, Bulape, 1956–1983+.
Rutherford, Ann Martin, *Congo/Zaire*, IMCK, 1972–1980.
Savels, Martha Burke, *Congo/Zaire*, Luebo, 1924–1934.
Sawyer, Blanche, *Congo/Zaire*, Bibanga, 1939–1955; Kasha, 1956–1957.
Scott, Eleanor Caslick, *Korea*, Kwangju, 1953–1954.
Shepping, Elizabeth Johanna, *Korea*, Kwangju, 1912–1913, 1920–1934 (evangelistic); Kunsan, 1914–1918; Seoul, 1918–1920.
Shive, Jean Belle Setser, *Congo/Zaire*, Lusambo, 1920–1921; Mutoto, 1922–1924; Luebo, 1926–1929, 1936–1960; Lubondai, 1931–1935.
Sizer, Octavia, *Mexico*, Morelia, 1946–1948.
Smith, Catherine Minter, *Congo/Zaire*, Mutoto, 1931–1962.
Smith, Iona, *Mexico*, Morelia, 1948–1971.
Smith, Melanie Sharpe, *Bangladesh*, CHAPA, 1978–1983+.
Somerville, Virginia Bell, *Korea*, Mokpo, 1954–1968; Taejon, 1968–1983+.
Southerland, Pattye, *Mexico*, Morelia, 1923–1944.
Southern, Carol Ann, *Congo/Zaire*, Bulape, 1971–1972.
Steele, Barbara, *Korea*, Taejon, 1974–1977.
Stixrud, Carol Elaine Geraghty, *Congo/Zaire*, Bibanga, 1951–1955.
Stixrud, Mary Etta Parks (McElroy), *Congo/Zaire*, Luebo, 1917–1946.
Swenson, Nell Sophronia, *Japan*, Osaka, 1954–1963.
Talbot, Cassie Lee Oliver, *China*, Huayin, 1922–1942, 1947–1948.
Talmage, Mariella, *Korea*, Chonju, 1947–1952.
Threadgill, Dorothy Riggins, *Congo/Zaire*, Bibanga, 1968–1970.
Threlkeld, Joanne Stanfield, *Congo/Zaire*, Bulape, 1965–1968.
Thumm, Thelma Barbara, *Korea*, Soonchun, 1929–1931.
Torres, Haydee, *Brazil*, 1961–1966.
Torsch, Mary Ethel Edwards, *Brazil*, 1959–1972.
West, Paula Frances, *Mexico*, Ometepec, 1957–1971.
White, Elizabeth Yates, *Congo/Zaire*, Bibanga, 1950–1951; Luebo, 1952–1954.
Whitener, Patricia Anne, *Korea*, Chonju, 1962–1966.
Whong, Dixie Valorie, *Brazil*, 1967–1979.
Wilkerson, Estelle Isenhour, *China*, Jiaxing, 1948–1949; *Taiwan*, Changhua, 1953–1980.
Williams, Carrie Knox, *China*, Suqien, 1917–1918.

Williams, Katherine Ward, *Congo/Zaire*, IMCK, 1978–1983.
Wilson, Bessie Hancock, *Congo/Zaire*, Mboi, 1946; Mutoto, 1947–1948, 1955–1956; Bulape, 1949–1953; Luebo, 1954; Katubwe, 1958–1960; *Brazil*, 1961–1978.
Wilson, (Betty) Kaye, *Bangladesh*, CHAPA, 1979–1981.
Wilson, Edna Mae Newton, *Korea*, Kunsan, 1939–1940.
Wolbrink, Frances Schmidt, *Korea*, Kwangju, 1972–1975.
Wood, Margaret Poague, *China*, Suqien, 1936–1941; Huayin, 1946–1948; *Brazil*, 1951–1975.
Woods, Elizabeth Brown, *Korea*, Kunsan, 1937–1940.
Wright, Lillian F., *Congo/Zaire*, Kakinda, 1974–1980.
Yates, Ellen Baskervill, *China*, Huayin, 1909–1913; Huaian, 1913–1940.

Appendix E—Medical Technologists

Bush, Florence Callahan (bacteriologist), *Japan*, Osaka, 1953–1967.
Connell, Peggy, *Congo/Zaire*, IMCK, 1973–1975.
Hudgins, Charlotte, *Mexico*, Morelia, 1961–1967.
Lindler, Gene Nisbet, *Korea*, Chonju, 1949–1954.
McDonald, Nolie Kathaleen, *Congo/Zaire*, Bulape, 1949–1950; Mutoto, 1950–1952; Lubondai, 1953–1966.
Miller, Aurie Montgomery, *Congo/Zaire*, Luebo, 1950–1953; Lubondai, 1954–1960; Bibanga, 1961–1962; Bulape, 1962–1964, 1967–1969; IMCK, 1965–1967, 1970–1983+.
Norman, Nancy, *Congo/Zaire*, IMCK, 1980–1983+.
Patton, George Mallory, *Korea*, Chonju, 1964–1978.
Pipe, Virginia Lennox, *Mexico*, Ometepec, 1968–1971.
Respess, Ocie Eunice, *Korea*, Chonju, 1954–1964.
Seel, Mary Batchelor, *Korea*, Chonju, 1954–1983+.
Southerland, (Emma) Jane, *Mexico*, Morelia, 1950–1952.
Stevenson, Lucretia W., *Congo/Zaire*, Mutoto, 1957–1960.
Templeton, Elizabeth, *Congo/Zaire*, Bibanga, 1952–1960; Lubondai, 1961–1967; IMCK, 1967–1969.
Woods, Elinor Myers, *China*, Huayin, 1931–1940.
Worth, Ruth, *China*, Jiangyin, 1932–1938; Zhenjiang, 1947–1951; *Congo/Zaire*, Bulape, 1952–1969; IMCK, 1969–1975.

Appendix F—Pharmacists

Altland, Sarah Catherine, *Congo/Zaire*, Kananga, 1981–1983+.
Altland, William Roland, *Congo/Zaire*, Kananga, 1981–1983+.
Creasman, Mark Eugene, *Korea*, Chonju, 1973–1976.
Jordon, Scott, *Haiti*, Leogane, 1981–1983.

Appendix G—X-ray Technicians

Myhre, Corey, *Korea*, Chonju, 1953–1955.

Appendix H—Physiotherapists

Damsbo, Ann Marie, *Taiwan*, 1968–1969.
Hottentot, Robert C. G., *Korea*, Soonchun, 1968–1970.
Hottentot, Theodora Vriens, *Korea*, Soonchun, 1968–1970.
Ilten, Hilda, *Taiwan*, Changhua, 1963–1966.
McBryde, Sally Wilhoit, *Korea*, Kwangju, 1959–1968.
Slusher, Lavonne Weir, *Taiwan*, Changhua, 1967–1968.
Tillman, Ruby Theresa, *Korea*, Soonchun, 1963–1966.

Appendix I—Occupational Therapists

Shaw, Sharon Ulrich, *Korea*, Chonju, 1971–1983+.
Zelek, Susan Ellen, *Korea*, Chonju, 1982–1983.

Appendix J—Administrators

Boyer, Rev. Elmer Timothy, *Korea*, Soonchun, 1948–1965.
Bridgman, Stewart, *Bangladesh*, Dhaka, 1976–1980.
Durham, Clarence Gunn, *Korea*, Soonchun, 1969–1983+.
Grubbs, Merrill Howard, *Korea*, Chonju, 1961–1983+.
Harle, Antoine, *Congo/Zaire*, IMCK, 1974–1977.

Harris, Albert Marion, *Congo/Zaire,* IMCK, 1967–1971.
Johnstone, Donald Matthew, *Congo/Zaire,* IMCK, 1976–1981.
Linton, Elizabeth Flowers, *Korea,* Soonchun, 1961–1983+.
March, Cary B., *Bangladesh,* Dhaka, 1981–1983+.
Marvin, Oscar M., Jr., *Japan,* 1957–1960.
McBryde, John Malcolm, *Korea,* Kwangju, 1959–1968.
Murray, Marcia Berta, *Congo/Zaire,* Mbuji Mayi, 1979–1983+.
Rice, William E., *Taiwan,* Changhua, 1968–1973.
Simmons, (David) William, Jr., *Congo/Zaire,* IMCK, 1980–1983.
Smith, Howard Basil, *Korea,* Chonju, 1950.
Taylor, Thomas Wayne, *Korea,* Chonju, 1954–1959.

Appendix K—Business Office

Bradley, Lina Elizabeth, *China,* Huayin, 1934–1940.
Brown, Charlotte, *Bangladesh,* Dhaka, 1977–1978.
Cope, Martha Hadden, *Korea,* Chonju, 1978–1983+.
Dietrick, Bessie Brothers, *Korea,* Kwangju, 1961–1983+.
Fecho, Rhine G., *Haiti,* Leogane, 1974–1978.
Hodges, Carolyn, *Bangladesh,* Dhaka, 1978–1980.
Hodges, Dawkins, *Bangladesh,* Dhaka, 1978–1980.
Johnson, Edson, *Mexico,* Morelia, 1967.
Kinder, Cledith Bowling, *Korea,* Kwangju, 1971–1973.
Mackeprang, Lois Lee, *Korea,* Chonju, 1975–1976.
Maulden, Julia Watson, *Haiti,* Leogane, 1980–1981.
Mitchell, Mary Belle, *Bangladesh,* Dhaka, 1978.
Mitchell, H. Petrie, *Bangladesh,* Dhaka, 1978.
Musser, Harvey A., *Haiti,* Leogane, 1979–1980.
Nesbit, Sara A., *China,* Jiaxing, 1914–1920; Suzhou, 1920–1927.
Rogers, Carolyn, *Mexico,* Morelia, 1945–1949.
Satterfield, Ruby, *China,* Jiaxing, 1920–1927; Suzhou, 1929–1940.

Appendix L—Staff Associates

Moore, Mollie Boney, *Japan,* Osaka, 1956–1983+.

Appendix M—Medical Social Workers

Lamb, (Martha) June, *Japan*, Osaka, 1955–1968.
McGirt, Mary Ann, *Taiwan*, Changhua, 1968–1975.

Appendix N—Hospital Chaplains

Carper, Rev. Day, *Haiti*, Leogane, 1981.
Cervantes, Rev. David, *Mexico*, Morelia, 1969–1972.
Dysart, Anne E., *Mexico*, Morelia, dates n.a.
Grey, Katherine Clingman, *Mexico*, Morelia, dates n. a.
Huntley, Rev. (Charles) Betts, *Korea*, Kwangju, 1965–1983+.
Linton, Rev. (Thomas) Dwight, *Korea*, Kwangju, 1961–1965.
Mitchell, Rev. Irvine Grisson, *Japan*, Osaka, 1955–1956.
Moore, Rev. Lardner Charles, *Japan*, Osaka,1956–1983+.
Ross, Rev. Hervey Leonidas, *Mexico*, Morelia, 1961–1969.
Spencer, Rev. Homer A., *Mexico*, Morelia, dates n.a.
Wood, Rev. John Butler, *Mexico*, Ometepec, 1951–1964.

Appendix O—Agriculture Specialists

Dimmock, Frank Eugene, *Congo/Zaire*, Mbuji Mayi, 1979–1980.
Meisner, Craig, *Bangladesh*, CHAPA, 1980–1983+.
Smith, Scott A., *Bangladesh*, CHAPA, 1977–1983+.
Welch, Douglas Michael, *Congo/Zaire*, Mbuji Mayi, 1980–1983+.

Appendix P—Industrial Missionaries (Construction and Maintenance)

Altenbernd, David William, *Congo/Zaire*, IMCK, 1974–1980; *Haiti*, 1981.
Anderson, William James, Jr., *Congo/Zaire*, Bulape, Lubondai, 1919–1961.
Burns, Lawrence J., *Korea*, Chonju, 1971–1973.

DeLand, Lawrence Grover, *Congo/Zaire*, Bulape, 1924–1961.
Dobyns, Robert, *Congo/Zaire*, IMCK, 1976–1978.
Donaldson, Paul Everett, *Congo/Zaire*, IMCK, Bulape, 1961–1974.
Elkes, Raymond Willard, *Congo/Zaire*, IMCK, Tshikagi, 1961–1974.
Goodrum, Garland, *Congo/Zaire*, IMCK, Tshikagi, 1949–1970.
Gutzke, John, *Congo/Zaire*, IMCK, Bulape, 1982–1983+.
Hillhouse, W. Laurens, *Congo/Zaire*, Luebo, 1913–1925.
Kinder, Donald L., *Korea*, Kwangju, 1971–1973.
King, Earl Spottswood, Sr., *Congo/Zaire*, Mutoto, Bibanga, 1923–1960.
Longenecker, J. Hershey, *Congo/Zaire*, Bibanga, 1917–1951.
Ray, Joe, *Congo/Zaire*, Mutoto, 1945–1949.
Shive, Alexander Morgan, *Congo/Zaire*, Luebo, Mutoto, 1920–1960.
Spooner, Joseph Harper, *Congo/Zaire*, Moma, 1944–1977.
Stegall, Carroll Richard, *Congo/Zaire*, Luebo, Lubondai, 1915–1951.
Stockwell, William Foster, *Congo/Zaire*, Mutoto, Lubondai, 1945–1966.
Vandegift, Frank, *Congo/Zaire*, Bibanga, 1948–1960.
Worth, William Chadworth, *Congo/Zaire*, Mutoto, 1926–1966.

Bibliography

General

Annual Reports of the Executive Committee of Foreign Missions and the Board of World Missions of the Presbyterian Church, U.S., 1867–1983.

Barrett, David B., ed. *World Encyclopedia*. Oxford & New York: Oxford University Press, 1982.

Bordley, James III and A. McGegee Harvey. *Two Centuries of American Medicine: 1776–1976*. Philadelphia: W. B. Saunders, 1976.

Brown, G. Thompson. "Overseas Mission Program and Policies of the PCUS: 1861–1983: A Brief Chronology." Atlanta, Ga.: Division of International Mission, PCUSA, typescript, 1985.

Cheung, Yuet-wah. *Missionary Medicine in China: A Study of Two Canadian Protestant Missions in China Before 1937*. New York: University Press of America, 1988.

Christoffer, Grundmann. "The Role of Medical Missions in the Missionary Enterprise: A Historical and Missiological Study." *Journal of the International Association for Mission Studies*, vol. II-2, 1985.

Crane, Paul S. *Korean Patterns*. Seoul, Korea: The Royal Asiatic Society, 1967.

Dietrick, Ronald B. *Modern Medicine and the Mission Mandate: Thoughts on Christian Medical Missions*. Woodville, Tex.: Medical Benevolence Foundation, 1984.

Magazines of the Presbyterian Church, U.S.: *The Missionary, The Mission Survey, The Presbyterian Survey*.

471

Minutes of the Annual Meetings of the American Presbyterian Congo Mission (APCM).

Seel, David J. *Challenge and Crisis in Missionary Medicine*. Pasadena, Calif.: William Carey Library, 1979.

Sprinkle, Patricia Houck. *The Birthday Book: First Fifty Years*. Atlanta, Ga.: PCUS Board of Women's Work, 1972.

Thompson, Ernest T. *Presbyterians in the South*, vol. III. Atlanta, Ga.: John Knox Press, 1973.

Tucker, Ruth A. *From Jerusalem to Irian Jaya*. Grand Rapids, Mich.: Zondervan Publishers, 1983.

Van Reken, David E., M.D. *Mission and Ministry: Christian Medical Practice in Today's Changing World Cultures*. Wheaton, Ill.: A Billy Graham Center Monograph, 1987.

Walls, A. F. "The Heavy Artillery of the Missionary Army: The Domestic Importance of the Nineteenth-Century Medical Missionary." *The Church and Healing*. W. J. Sheils, editor. Oxford: Basil Blackwell, 1982.

China

Bear, James E. *The Mid-China and the North Kiangsu Missions*, vol. II. Richmond, Virginia: typescript in the Union Theological Seminary Library.

Brown, G. Thompson. *Christianity in the Peoples Republic of China*. Atlanta, Ga.: John Knox Press, 1983.

———. *Earthen Vessels and Transcendent Power: American Presbyterians in China, 1837–1852*. Maryknoll, New York: Orbis Books, 1997.

Bullock, Mary Brown. *An American Transplant: The Rockefeller Foundation & Peking Union Medical College*. Berkeley, Ca.: University of California Press, 1980.

Cheeloo University. *Bulletins of the School of Medicine*. Tsinan, China: 1925–26, 1930–31, 1934–38.

Corbett, Charles Hodge. *Shantung Christian University (Cheeloo)*. New York: United Board of Christian Colleges in China, 1955.

Eberle, Edith. *Macklin of Nanking*. St. Louis, Mo.: The Bethany Press, 1936.

The Elizabeth Blake Hospital. Report. 1933.

Fergerson, Mary E. *China Medical Board and Peking Union Medical College.* New York: China Medical Board of New York, Inc., 1970.

Gieser, P. Kenneth. *Ken and Kay Gieser, 1930–1981.* Privately printed, 1984.

Jiaxing Hospital: Celebration of Forty Years. Locally printed, 1934.

Kessler, Lawrence. *The Jiangyin Mission Station: An American Missionary Community in China, 1895–1951.* Chapel Hill: The University of North Carolina Press, 1996.

Little, Lacy. *Rivershade: Historical Sketch of Kiangyin Station, China,* c. 1925.

Nelson, Henry S. *Doctor with Big Shoes.* Franklin, Tenn.: Providence House Publishers, 1995.

"Octavia: Her Life As She Remembers It." Typescript by family of Octavia Howard Price, c. 1984.

Patterson, Craig Houston. *My China That Was.* Privately printed, 1990.

Pollack. John. *A Foreign Devil in China: The Story of L. Nelson Bell.* Minneapolis, Minn.: World Wide Publications, 1938.

Price, P. Frank. *Our China Investment.* Nashville, Tenn.: Executive Committee of Foreign Missions, c. 1927.

Prince, Eva Jane. *China Journal, 1889–1900: An American Family During the Boxer Rebellion.* New York: Charles Scribner, 1989.

Spence, Jonathan D. *The Search for Modern China.* New York: W.W. Norton & Co, 1990.

Tsingkiangpu General Hospital Annual Reports, 1929, 1932, 1938, 1939, 1940.

Korea

Boyer, Elmer T. *To Build Him a House: Missionary Memories.* Seoul, Korea: The Posung Press, 1972.

Brown, G. Thompson. *Mission to Korea.* Seoul, Korea: Presbyterian Church of Korea, Department of Education, 1984.

———. *Not By Might: A Century of Presbyterians in Korea.* Atlanta, Ga.: General Assembly Mission Board, PC(USA), 1984.

Bryceson, Anthony and Pfaltzgraff, Roy E. *Leprosy.* New York: Churchill Livingstone, 1990.

Clark, Allen D. *A History of the Church in Korea.* Seoul, Korea: Christian Literature Society, 1972.

Clark, Charles Allen. *The Nevius Plan for Mission Work*. Seoul, Korea: Christian Literature Society, c. 1936.

Crane, Paul S. *Korean Patterns*. Seoul, Korea: Royal Asiatic Society, 1967 (4th ed., 1978).

Huntley, Martha A. *To Start a Work*. Seoul, Korea: Presbyterian Church of Korea, 1987.

Lew, Joon. *A Korean Model for the Healing of Leprosy*. Seoul, Korea: Lew Institute for Biological Research, 1993.

————. "Leprosy in Korea, Past and Present: A Model for the Healing of Leprosy in Korea." Seoul Korea: Paper presented at the International Seminar on Leprosy Control, Nov. 1991.

Macdonald, Donald Stone. *The Koreans: Contemporary Politics and Society*. Boulder & London: Westview Press, 1988.

————. *U.S.-Korean Relations from Liberation to Self-Reliance: The Twenty-Year Record*. Boulder, Colo.: Westview Press, 1992.

Manning, W. H., Jr. and Manning, Edna A. *Our Kin*. Augusta, Ga.: Walton Printing Co., 1958.

Paik, L. George. *History of Protestant Missions in Korea, 1832–1910*. Seoul, Korea: YMCA Press, 1929.

Pritchard, Margaret. "The Life Story of Margaret Frances Pritchard." Typescript, 1980.

Sterling, Marian. "And They Twain: A Family Chronicle for My Grandchildren." Typescript at the Department of History, PC(USA), Montreat, N.C.

Talmage, J. V. N. "A Prisoner of Christ Jesus." Typescript in the Department of History, Montreat, N.C., 1942.

Congo/Zaire

Anderson, Vernon A. *Still Led in Triumph*. Nashville, Tenn.: PCUS Board of World Missions, 1959.

————. "Witchcraft in Africa. A Missionary Problem." Louisville, Ky.: Ph.D. monograph in the Presbyterian Theological Seminary, 1942.

Bedinger, Robert Dabney. *Triumphs of the Gospel in the Belgian Congo*. Richmond, Va.: Presbyterian Committee of Publication, 1920.

Crawford, John Richard. *Protestant Missions in the Congo: 1878–1969.* Zaire, Kinshasa, c. 1970.

Dabney, Mary. *Light in Darkness.* Knoxville, Tenn., 1971.

Lamb, David. *The Africans.* New York: Vintage Press, 1984.

Longenecker, J. Hershey. *Memories of Congo.* Johnson City, Tenn.: Royal Publishers, Inc., 1964.

Morrison, John. *Mission to Africa.* Nashville, Tenn.: by John Morrison, 1979.

————. *Thomas T. Stixrud of Congo: Beloved Physician.* Nashville, Tenn.: PCUS Board of World Missions, c. 1943.

Nelson, Henry S. *Doctor with Big Shoes.* Franklin, Tenn.: Providence House Publishers, 1995.

Nelson, Kathryn Wolff. *Child Rearing Patterns in a Lulua Village of South Central Congo.* Ann Arbor, Mich.: University Microfilms, Inc., 1969.

Phipps, William E. *The Sheppards and Lapsley: Pioneer Presbyterians in the Congo.* Louisville, Ky.: Presbyterian Church (USA), 1991.

Pruitt, Virginia Gray. "New Nation, New Church: Congo 1960–1970." Typescript, 1970).

Rule, William. *Milestones in Mission.* Knoxville, Tenn.: privately published, 1991.

Shaloff, Stanley. *Reform in Leopold's Congo.* Richmond, Va.: John Knox Press, 1946.

Sheppard, William. *Presbyterian Pioneers in Congo.* Richmond, Va.: Presbyterian Committee of Publication, c. 1910.

Unger, Sanford J. *Africa: The People and Politics of an Emerging Continent.* New York: Simon and Shuster, 1978.

Vass, Winifred Kellersberger. *Doctor Not Afraid: E. R. Kellersberger, M.D.* Austin, Tex.: Nortex Press, 1986.

Vass, Winifred K. and Lachlan C., III. *The Lapsley Saga.* Franklin, Tenn.: Providence House Publishers, 1997.

Washburn, Hezekiah M. *A Knight in the Congo: God's Ambassador in Three Continents.* Bassett, Va., 1972.

Wharton, Conway T. *The Leopard Hunts Alone.* New York: Fleming H. Revell Co., 1927.

Wharton, Ethel Taylor. *Led in Triumph.* Nashville, Tenn.: PCUS Board of World Missions, 1952.

Mexico

Boyce, Marguerite P. *Captain Brenton's Heritage: The Gospel Message for Southwest Mexico*. Franklin, Tenn.: Providence House Publishers, 1994.

————. *I Heard the Donkeys Bray*. Franklin, Tenn.: Providence House Publishers, 1992.

Coppedge, Llewellyn J. "Twelve Years in Congoland." Typescript in the Department of History, Montreat, N.C.

McClelland, Alice J. *Mission to Mexico*. Nashville, Tenn.: Board of World Missions, PCUS, 1960.

Ross, Hervey L. (completed by daughter Jean Ross Everhart). "Sixty-four Years Making Old Mexico New: 1905–1969." Morelia, Michoacan: typescript, 1972.

Brazil

Bear, James E. *Mission to Brazil*. Nashville, Tenn.: PCUS Board of World Missions, 1961.

Japan

Cogswell, James A. *Until the Day Dawn*. Nashville, Tenn.: Board of World Missions, PCUS, 1957.

Moore, Lardner C. and Mollie. "Yodogawa Christian Hospital." *The Japan Christian Quarterly*, Spring 1991.

Bangladesh

Laure, Jason. *Bangladesh: Enchantment of the World*. Chicago: Children's Press, 1992.

Smith, Melanie S. "CHAPA History." Typescript, March 1986.

Haiti

Bessinger, C. D. Jr. and David F. McNeeley. "A Cooperative Model for Provision of Regional Health Services in a Developing Nation." *Journal of the American Medical Association*, vol. 252, 1984.

Franciscus, John Allen. *Haiti: Voodoo Kingdom to Modern Riviera*. Puerto Rico: Franciscus Family Foundation, Inc., 1980.

Michelmore, Peter. *Dr. Mellon of Haiti*. New York: Dodd, Mead & Co., 1964.

Acknowledgments

The following persons deserve special thanks. Their help through interviews, letters, telephone calls, comments, and/or review of the material made this work possible. Copies of oral histories have been placed in the Department of History, Presbyterian Church (USA), Montreat, North Carolina.

China

G. Thompson Brown
Mary Price Coulling
Elizabeth Woods DeCamp
Lalla Iverson, M.D.
Alexander S. Moffett, M.D.
Kirk T. Mosley, M.D.
Henry S. Nelson, M.D.
Kathryn W. Nelson
Mildred Hutcheson Rouse
Henrietta Hutcheson Schwartz

Elizabeth Seecombe (grand-
daughter of Richard Fishburne)
Randolph T. Shields Jr., M.D.
Virginia Bell Somerville
Felix B. Welton, M.D.
Joseph L. Wilkerson, M.D.
Estelle I. Wilkerson
Margaret P. Wood
James B. Woods Jr., M.D.
Ruth Worth

Korea

Albert H. Bridgman, M.D.
Florence C. Bush (Mrs. Ovid)

Martha H. Cope
David B. S. Chu, M.D.

Herbert A. Codington Jr., M.D.
Page L. Codington
Paul S. Crane, M.D.
Virginia K. Cumming
Elizabeth Woods DeCamp
Ronald B. Dietrick, M.D.
Clarence G. Durham
Ruth H. Folta
Virginia Brand Francis
Louise Daniel Gamble
Merrill H. Grubbs
C. Betts Huntley
Janet T. Keller (Mrs. Frank)
John M. McBryde

Sally W. McBryde
John V. Moore
Katherine Boyer Moore
Dick Nieusma Jr., D.D.S.
Margaret Frances Pritchard
David J. Seel, M.D.
Mary B. Seel
Laurence W. Simpson, M.D.
Virginia B. Somerville
John E. Talmage
Ane Marie A. Topple, M.D.
Stanley C. Topple, M.D.
James S. Wilson, M.D.
John Knox Wilson, M.D.

Congo/Zaire

Richard C. Brown, M.D.
Blanche W. Carper
Gertrude H. Cousar (Mrs. George)
Mary B. Crawford
Sam Ediger
Hugh L. Farrior, M.D.
James A. Halverstadt
Nancy R. Hull
Walter B. Hull, M.D.
Ngoyi Kadima, M.D.
Virginia C. King
B. Annette Kriner
Lukusa, R.N.
Sandy C. Marks, D.D.S.
Kenneth H. McGill, M.D.
Nancy T. McGill
Aurie M. Miller
David V. Miller, M.D.
Elizabeth Miller

John K. Miller, M.D.
John Morrison
Mary P. Morrison
Badibanga Mukole, R.N.
Henry S. Nelson, M.D.
Kathryn W. Nelson
Nancy Norman
Mark K. Poole, M.D.
Margaret G. Rambo
V. Birch Rambo, M.D.
William Rule, M.D.
Ralph E. Shannon, M.D.
Jean S. Shive
J. Tinsley Smith Jr., M.D.
Mildred Eliza Coppedge Thomas
Winifred Kellersberger Vass
William C. Washburn
Ruth Worth

Mexico

James R. Boyce, M.D.
Marguerite P. Boyce
Ann S. Dixon

W. Rion Dixon, M.D.
J. Hervey Ross, M.D.
Mildred Eliza Coppedge Thomas

Brazil

Alan G. Gordon, M.D.
Mary Elizabeth Long
Edna Quinn

Jule C. Spach
Margaret P. Wood

Japan

Ann V. Brown (Mrs. Frank)
Florence C. Bush (Mrs. Ovid)
June Lamb

Mollie B. Moore
Lyle W. Peterson

Taiwan

Allen L. Haslup, M.D.
Eva C. Haslup
William E. Rice

Estelle I. Wilkerson
Joseph L. Wilkerson, M.D.

Bangladesh

Herbert A. Codington, M.D.
Patricia L. June, M.D.
Charlotte L. Mack

John T. Nonweiler, M.D.
William E. Rice

Haiti

Irma N. A. de la Torre
J. Salvadore G. de la Torre, M.D.
Dorothy L. Descieux
Ann S. Dixon

W. Rion Dixon, M.D.
David F. McNeeley, M.D.
William E. Rice

Index

483

W